Strength and Conditioning for Sport: A Practical Guide for Coaches

sports coach UK is the brand name of The National Coaching Foundation (The NCF) and has been such since April 2001.

ISBN: 978-1-902523-85-7

Coachwise Business Solutions

sports coach UK
114 Cardigan Road
Headingley
Leeds LS6 3BJ
Tel: 0113-274 4802 Fax: 0113-275 5019
Email: coaching@sportscoachuk.org Website:
www.sportscoachuk.org

Patron: HRH The Princess Royal

The ideas in this text are based on the concepts in
Fitness for Games Players by The NCF
© The National Coaching Foundation and the
Sports Science Education Programme, 1996.

Produced on behalf of sports coach UK by

Coachwise Business Solutions
Chelsea Close
Off Amberley Road
Armley
Leeds LS12 4HP
Tel: 0113-231 1310 Fax: 0113-231 9606

Email: enquiries@coachwisesolutions.co.uk
Website: www.coachwisesolutions.co.uk

Author
Clive Brewer

Editor
Joanne Chapman

Cover photos courtesy of www.actionplus.co.uk and Alan Edwards. All other photos throughout the book are courtesy of the author, unless otherwise stated.

sports coach UK would like to sincerely thank the following for their help in reviewing and developing this resource:

Prof. Michael Stone (Sports Performance Enhancement Consortium, East Tennessee State University, USA)

Mike Favre (United States Olympic Committee)

Ian Jeffreys (UK Strength and Conditioning Association)

Linda Low (**sport**scotland coach education and training).

Author Profile

A director of the UK Strength and Conditioning Association (UKSCA) and leading **sport**scotland's athlete development programme, Clive Brewer is also the national strength and conditioning coach for Scottish Athletics. He is registered as a British Olympic Association strength and conditioning specialist coach, as well as being accredited by the UKSCA and the NSCA (USA) as a strength and conditioning specialist. He is also accredited as a British Association of Sport and Exercise Science sports scientist and has worked with international performers from a diverse range of sports, including rugby, athletics, tennis, soccer and bobsleigh. A member of the sports coach UK expert resource group for participant development (with responsibility for physical conditioning inputs) that advises the UK coaching steering group, Clive also advises a number of national coaching and performance development initiatives. Happiest when  coaching physical conditioning, he is also a widely published author, with a number of peer-reviewed papers and invited presentations at conferences worldwide (representing organisations in both the UK and the USA). He works on national coach education programmes for sports coach UK, UK Strength and Conditioning Association, UK Athletics and various governing bodies of sport.

Foreword

Coaches are constantly challenged to devise new methods of improving performance in their athletes. One important method of raising performance at all levels of sport is by increasing the fitness of the athletes involved. Fitness refers to specific physical and physiological attributes directly related to a specific type of performance. On a very basic level, fitness deals with specific strength, speed, power and endurance capabilities. For example, the appropriate fitness attributes for a tennis player are quite different from those of a rugby player. Strength and conditioning (the process of achieving fitness for sport) is a multifaceted process requiring great creativity on the coach's part. Indeed, it is possible that fitness is the single most important attribute separating winning and losing.

In recent years, recognition of the importance of fitness parameters has led to an explosion in various strength and conditioning resources and methods (as well as myths!) dealing with exactly what constitutes appropriate fitness training. It is important the coach/athlete is able to separate scientifically founded resources from those that are not evidence based.

This book lays out the basic principles underlying strength and conditioning theory, as well as detailed information on how to use the theory in practical applications. Furthermore, there are excellent explanations as to why different training programmes can produce different results. The information provided in this book challenges some older ideas, creates new answers to old problems and is a very practical aid for the coach/athlete in pushing the boundaries of sports performance.

Michael H. Stone

Prof. Michael H. Stone (Fel. UKSCA, FNSCA, ASCC)

Former Director of Sports Physiology, US Olympic Committee
Laboratory Director, East Tennessee State University
Inaugural Fellow of the UK Strength and Conditioning Association

Foreword

Physical conditioning is a central pillar of sports performance. At any level of performance, all other factors being equal, the best-conditioned athlete will win.

Strength and conditioning methods have developed significantly over recent years. However, sports coaches have not always been kept abreast of the latest developments. Clive Brewer makes amendment for this in his book by providing examples of training methods together with coaching points for the use of coaches in any sporting context.

Accredited Members of the UK Strength and Conditioning Association have been assessed in their practical competency to coach athletes in their physical performance development.

It is, however, also a key responsibility of every coach to have an understanding of the physical conditioning needs of athletes in their charge and the ability to deliver improvements in related performance.

Clive's experience as a coach educator is evident in the content and quality of the information presented in this book, which has largely a practical emphasis. He bridges the gap between best practice in coaching and underpinning science by engaging the reader with basic scientific principles and the training process. Thus, he provides the wise coach, athletes, other members of the professional team, parents and teachers with an explanation of his methods, and encourages them to be inquisitive.

This book is an excellent practical resource for both 'sports specific' and 'strength and conditioning specialist' coaches. It makes extensive use of pictures and annotated diagrams to demonstrate correct technique and progressions.

Gil Stevenson (ASCC)

Chair of the UK Strength and Conditioning Association

Contents

Chapter 4
Developing Strength and Power

Chapter 9

Recovery Training for Optimal Performance

Chapter 10

Planning for Peak Performance

Chapter 1
Introduction to Fitness Training: The Principles of Training

Introduction

There are many recognised definitions of the concept of fitness, many of them relating to a healthy lifestyle and a person's ability to meet the demands of their environment without undue stress. In a sporting context, fitness relates to the ability to bring specific physical qualities to enable optimal performance. Typically, this is characterised by the athlete's* motor capacity: the ability to perform physical movements at any time. Strength and conditioning provides specific methodologies and knowledge for coaches to utilise within their sport-specific programmes, with the aim of improving the physical (motor) capacities of their athletes. In the sporting arena, where teams and individuals are constantly seeking to better themselves at all levels of performance, physical conditioning is one of the most influential and changeable elements of performance a coach can effect. There are many approaches to developing physical conditioning in a performer. Modern sports require athletes to have high levels of speed, agility, strength, power and endurance in order to be effective at the top levels. These are traditionally thought to be the major components that must be developed in any sport, in order for the player to be able to perform to a reasonable level of fitness. In simplistic terms, the relationship between these major fitness components is demonstrated in Figure 1 below.

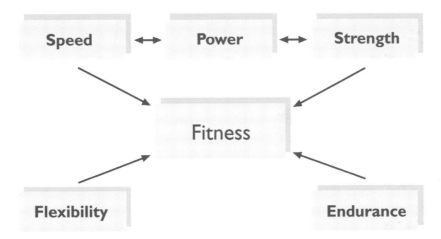

Figure 1: The major fitness components

The practical definitions of these components are outlined in Table 1 overleaf. A glossary of terms can be found at the back of this resource to help in the overall understanding of the main concepts discussed throughout. Notes can be found on page 255.

---

*Readers should note, during this book, the terms 'athletes', 'performers' and 'players' will be used interchangeably. The author is using these terms to refer to the sports performer in a generic context, rather than in a single sport. For example, 'athlete' does not mean a performer in track and field, but in any sport, at any level.

Table 1: Defining the basic components of fitnesss

Component	Definition
Endurance	The ability to sustain performance. Within multiple sprint-based activities, this means the ability to work repeatedly at a high intensity, recover rapidly and keep producing maximal efforts throughout the performance. Conversely, in activities such as long-distance running, the ability to sustain performance will be needed over much longer periods of time, at lower (relative) intensities. As later chapters will demonstrate, endurance is made up of: • **neuromuscular endurance** – the ability of the neuromuscular system to sustain the production of forces to maintain the required intensity of performance • **metabolic endurance** – the ability of the cardiovascular (heart and lung) and circulatory systems to keep producing sufficient energy to fuel the work done to maintain the required intensity of performance.
Flexibility	The range of movement possible about a joint or a series of joints.
Power	The product of work done, per unit of time, or the ability to exert a large force quickly. Work = Force x Distance Power = $\dfrac{\text{Distance}}{\text{Time}}$ or Force x Velocity Power is dependent upon the magnitude of the strength (force) component and the rate at which peak force can be developed (velocity component).
Speed	The ability to move the body, or part of the body, quickly.
Strength	The ability of a muscle to exert a force against a load.

This is a very simplistic view, however, as all sports require different types of speed, strength and endurance in order for athletes to be successful. This is demonstrated in Figures 2 and 3.

Figure 2: Specific fitness components of rugby union

The major fitness components of a rugby union player are power (speed x strength or force x velocity), acceleration and anaerobic endurance. This contrasts with badminton, where the major fitness components are reactions, acceleration over five metres, total body agility and a combination of aerobically and anaerobically produced energy.

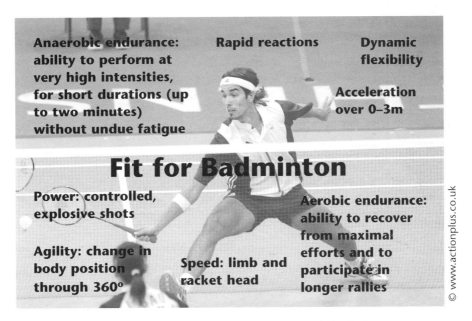

Figure 3: Specific fitness components of badminton

We can also see a difference in the training requirements within specific sports that are dependent upon a specific position demand (eg in soccer, a goalkeeper versus an outfield player, in rugby a forward compared to a back), or specific event demands within a particular track and field discipline (sprints, endurance, jumps and throws).

Regardless of what ages of performer the coach is working with, when a coach puts together a training and competition programme, at every stage of an athlete's career, the athlete's overall programme will comprise each of five elements. Without the developmentally appropriate input at each stage the programme will not be optimal for the individual (for more details, see Collins, Brewer and Martindale, 2007).

The five major elements of preparation are: technical and tactical, psychological, lifestyle management, movement skills (physical literacy) and physical conditioning (motor capacity). The physical conditioning or physical preparation component is one that can make or break a performer: there is much evidence to suggest in top-level sport it is the fittest and most powerful individual or team that usually wins. This may be due to the ability to perform skills more forcefully, or it may be due to the fact that during a performance, performers with better sport-specific endurance are able to replicate high-intensity performances successively and keep producing enough energy to enable effective decisions to be made for the duration of the competition.

As highlighted on page 3, the fitness components for rugby union and badminton are different. Indeed, these components are sports specific in application. Therefore, the training for each of these sports must be approached in a slightly different manner in order for the benefits of physical preparation to be transferred into competitive performance. Prior to establishing any training programme to improve a player's fitness, coaches should always ask themselves the following questions:

- What is the nature and type of strength, speed and power required in this sport?
- What particular energy systems (aerobic or anaerobic) need to be trained?
- What muscle groups need to be trained and in what order should they be recruited by the athlete?
- Which muscle-fibre types should training be geared towards (ie slow-twitch [Type I], fast-twitch intermediate [Type IIa] or fast-twitch [Type IIx])?
- What type of muscle actions (concentric, eccentric or isometric) should be used?
- What would be the most appropriate strength-, speed- and power-training methods for the sport/player, from the range available (eg free-weights movements, bodyweight exercises, plyometrics)?

Many of these questions may not seem to make much sense at the moment. However, after reading the following chapters, the coach should be able to answer each of them and begin to identify how to put together a training programme for a particular sport (and position/event discipline), using the principles outlined to design some sport-specific practices.

It is important to remember that, when designing training programmes, there are several key principles a coach should follow in order to allow training to be successful and progressive. The principles (outlined below) allow the coach to progress training effectively. These principles should be applied to each and every form of training that the coach devises.

These training principles are based on a theoretical model known as the *overcompensation cycle*. This model is central to the idea of training-programme design to maximise competitive performance and demonstrates that only through recovering appropriately from training sessions, can the athletic potential of a player actually improve.

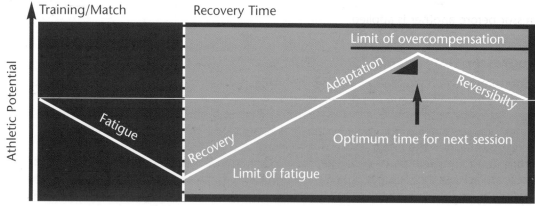

Figure 4: The overcompensation cycle

This is a theoretical model and there are no hard and fast rules for how long each individual will take to reach the point of overcompensation after a specific session. It is best illustrated by nature's principle of repairing a broken bone: once it has fully mended (given time and assuming no medical complications), the bone will be stronger than prior to the break. In terms of training, the training stimulus will be designed to disrupt and stress (fatigue) a particular system (energy system, neuromuscular system, musculoskeletal system, etc) within the body. This system will then repair (given time) to a position of improvement compared to where it was previously (shown in Figure 4 as the limit of overcompensation). The amount of disruption depends on the nature of the training session (the stimulus) and the fitness levels of the individual player concerned (explored in more detail in Chapter 10). It can take the neuromuscular system up to six days to fully recover from some very intense plyometrics sessions, whereas the aerobic and anaerobic metabolic systems may recover within 24 hours from some sessions.

What is certain is that time to achieve overcompensation can be accelerated by facilitated recovery training/activities (as outlined in detail in Chapter 9). The sooner players recover from fatigue, the fresher they will be for training and the better the chances of improving (the aim of coaching). Indeed, the ability of the player to recover from intense training may be a good indicator for coaches to use as a measure of the success of their training programme. It should also be borne in mind that, while the overcompensation model was originally thought of as a physiological model, it also applies to other performance variables, such as psychology. Reduced psychological drive is very much a direct result (not a side-effect) of fatigue.

The Training Principles: Guiding Training Development

The training principles that guide training development are as follows.

Overload

The overload principle states that training programmes should sufficiently stress the athlete's physiological mechanisms to effect an improvement. This means working on the same programme for a long period of time will not cause the athlete to improve: this is because the body will adapt to the training load over time. Therefore, training status will only be improved by gradually increasing the training load the player's body is subjected to. This can be achieved by progressively altering one or more of the following:

- The **intensity** of the session (how hard the work is) – ie the work time, the rest time, the mass lifted etc.
- The **volume** of the session (how much work is done) – ie the number of repetitions done within a set or the number of exercises or sets performed.
- The **frequency** of training – ie how many sessions per week are undertaken.

Coaches should remember training stressors are cumulative: athletes need to recover from one stressor before another is applied.

Progression

Progression is a continuation of the overload principle. As the body's physiological mechanisms adapt to the training stimulus applied, there is a need for the training to be advanced. The player will otherwise remain at a plateau and will not respond to further training efforts. This progression has to be gradual, however, so as to prevent a player becoming injured by overexertion (or, in the longer term, overtraining) and possibly demotivated when participating in further training because targets are not achieved. Optimal learning/training effects are achieved by advancing from general to specific movements and from extensive (typified by high volume, low intensity) to intensive (low volume, highest intensity) workouts, over the course of a planned training cycle (detailed in Chapter 10).

Specificity

Young sports people need to have good all-round athletic skills and physical literacy, prior to specialising in a specific sport (Collins, Brewer and Martindale, 2007). As physical preparation levels improve, all training routines need to be increasingly tailored to the specific demands of the sport, the position being trained for and the individual needs of the athlete, so as to maximise the transfer of training benefits to competitive performance. The underlying factors needed to be taken into account relate to the bioenergetics of metabolism (how energy is created and supplied to the player) and the mechanical factors (neuromuscular and musculoskeletal requirements) involved in specific movements. Further consideration is given to each of these factors in the following chapter, where their importance in understanding performance and designing appropriate training methods is explained.

Coaches should realise, however, this principle is only applicable to a point; training movement patterns that are biomechanically and metabolically similar are the goals of the coach. Using exactly the same movements is not always beneficial. For example, giving a golfer a 30kg golf club will not produce a stronger swing if they practise with it. Indeed (assuming that they don't become injured), it is more likely they will adapt their normal golf swing to cope with the additional club weight, thus interfering with the learnt skill. Similar situations of a negative transfer of training could arise with overuse of weighted tennis rackets, or through sprinters towing sleds that are too heavy, causing them to change their optimal technique. However, if the athlete gets stronger using **biomechanically similar movements** (see Chapter 4), and the coach programmes a 'lag time' to allow for skill to become more forceful (applying the strength gained through learned technique), then strength gains can be very successfully converted into skilful (skill – the forceful application of technique under pressure) performances.

The aim of a physical conditioning programme is to produce better performances, through a positive transfer of training to benefit performance. It is important for the coach to understand that, not only is inappropriate training a waste of time and resources, it can be detrimental to performance (it has a negative transfer of training effect).

Recovery–Adaptation

This training principle also has its origins in the overcompensation cycle (Chapters 9 and 10). Physical training only provides the stimulus for physical development. The recovery period is the time when the body's physiological mechanisms for improvement are implemented and the body can recover from, then adapt to, the training stimulus. Insufficient recovery time will ultimately lead to the body becoming over-trained. This in turn will lead to poor performance and an increased risk of injury. If the recovery period is over-sufficient, then the training effect will be lost. Chapter 9 focuses on methods that can be applied to aid recovery and therefore optimise training and performance potential. It is important both the coach and player realise training/playing only provides a stimulus for improvement: it is only through rest that the body can actually improve.

Training is a stimulus that fatigues the body; it disrupts the body's normal, balanced resting state. As illustrated previously, the human body is designed to repair itself and when damage occurs it will often repair itself to a point where it is stronger (or more efficient) than it was before. Because of this, future training stimuli need to be more stressful, otherwise the player's system will not be sufficiently stressed to need repairing. This is where overload and recovery integrate with one another as training principles. Adaptation and improvement can only result in improved performance if:

a) the training stimulus is sufficient to disrupt (overload) the player's normal homeostatic level (the normal balance of the body); and more importantly:

b) recovery is sufficiently adequate to allow overcompensation (the technical term for the recovery of athletic potential beyond that which existed prior to the stimulus being delivered). This is explored in more detail in Chapters 9 and 10.

Therefore, if the coach allows sufficient recovery time for each physiological component in the athlete (eg muscles, aerobic/anaerobic system, joint structures) that was trained in a session to recover (or sufficient recovery time from a game/performance, which stresses all the body's systems) the athlete's capabilities will be enhanced. Conversely, if athletes train too soon, they will not allow their bodies to recover sufficiently and the next session will commence from an excessively fatigued state. If this pattern continues, the result is likely to be a state of overtraining (more recently thought of as under-recovery) and burnout.

Variation

Variation in training is a key principle that is often overlooked and it is where the art of coaching becomes important. It relates to how the coach manipulates when fitness training moves from general to specific in nature; how much overload to subject the player to, which methods to use and how recovery is promoted within the player. This concept is explored in more detail in later chapters, but some general issues that need to be considered in planning variation are presented below:

- Too little progressive overload results in the player never improving.
- Too little variation in training methods or intensity will mean it becomes very difficult to cause the performer to become overloaded in training. It is also easy for a performer to become stale and bored with repetitive training routines.
- Too much variation means that the performer never has the opportunity to learn, or become consistent.
- Too much overload results in the player never recovering sufficiently to perform to their best potential and risks injury through overtraining.
- Too little emphasis on active recovery training and time to recover within the programme may also lead to the player underperforming and/or becoming over-trained.

The best training effects are realised through a planned distribution or variation in training methods and workloads (volume, intensity, frequency) on a cyclic or periodical basis.

Reversibility

Once the coach has mastered these training principles, the biggest challenge is to develop the training goals and the programme design. The best way to achieve this is to make the training goals all relate to testable variables. These can be monitored on a regular basis to determine whether or not a programme is working. Guidelines for testing all of the major components of fitness are found at the end of Chapters 3–7. These implications revolve around the *use it or lose it* phenomenon. If a training load is inappropriately removed or reduced too much (eg the athlete becomes inactive or injured), then training gains that have been acheived will be lost. Coaches therefore need to plan and control training schedules (ie around holidays or injury) so that a sufficient level of general activity is maintained to prevent detraining (reversibility) from a trained state occurring.

Implications for Coaching

Coaches need to obtain baseline data prior to commencing a training programme, as this will enable them to have a picture of where the player is currently. Means for collecting this data (in the form of testing/monitoring methods) are suggested in following chapters. Training goals relating to the level of the player's skill development, and a time frame for that development to be achieved in, can be planned from here. The next step is to take all of the scientific information that underpins effective training and this, together with the coach's knowledge of training methods, will help develop a training programme that is effective in improving the sport-specific fitness of the games player.

References

Collins, D., Brewer, C. and Martindale, R. (2007) *'Towards a New Model for Athlete Development'*. sports coach UK seminar on Athlete Development, Leeds.

As with all of the concepts applied within this book, coaches can adapt the following science, drills and practices to develop all fitness components, for athletes who use a wheelchair or athletes with other disabilities. For example, agility drills can be performed in sports-specific movement patterns for wheelchair sports, and acceleration drills be adapted for pushing distances, rather than running distances.

Chapter 2
The Science Underpinning Training

Introduction

If coaches are to effectively train their performers, there are a number of important areas they need to have a working understanding of. These are the energy systems of the body, how energy is supplied and used in particular performances (bioenergetics), and the musculoskeletal and neuromuscular systems of the body; how nerves and muscles are structured and how they respond to different training stimuli in order to produce movement.

Anatomy and physiology are the areas of study that combine to give the coach an understanding of the factors contributing to performance. Anatomy relates to the structure and organisation of the body, while (sports) physiology is concerned with how the body functions and responds to the demands of training and competition. Knowledge of human anatomy and the physiological processes underlying exercise allows coaches to become better at one of the most important jobs of the coach; evaluation of both the physical capacities and responses of an individual athlete, and the physiological demands of their chosen sport/performance. This knowledge will assist in the planning and implementation of improved training programmes, giving a higher quality preparation of the athlete for competition.

Coaches frequently ask: 'Why do I need to understand sports science before working on physical conditioning?' A simple analogy relates to the medical profession. Doctors undertake five years of study into the science of medicine (learning the theories) before going away and practising the art of medicine. Coaching is the same: it is those who can better practise the art of applying the scientific principles who will produce the most athletically developed players. It should be remembered the human body can be thought of as a highly complex living 'machine' and athletes come in all shapes and sizes, have different skin colours, and many different living conditions, but their bodies work and respond to exercise and training in a similar way.

Although the human body has eight systems that can be identified as separate, they all work together. Nerves send signals to the muscles to cause them to contract. Therefore, skilled movement is the result of the coordinated activity of the nervous and muscular systems, which is referred to collectively as the **neuromuscular** system. Contractions of the muscles move the bones to produce movement and are collectively referred to as the **musculoskeletal** system. Any drill that assists the athlete in the development of coordination can be referred to as a neuromuscular exercise, or part of neuromuscular conditioning. The circulatory and respiratory systems work together transporting oxygen to where it is needed and are known collectively as the **cardiorespiratory** system. This is crucial in allowing the body to produce energy **(bioenergetics)** to allow the required work to be done.

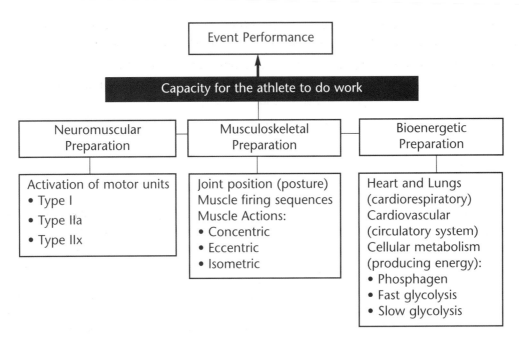

**Figure 5: Improving the physical capacity of the athlete –
preparing for athletic performance**

The purpose of this chapter is to provide coaches with a working knowledge of these aspects of the body's functioning. As the following methodological chapters are digested and further related concepts are introduced, the coach will have an understanding of how to adapt each of the methodologies for their particular sport.

The Neuromuscular System

The purpose of this section is to:

* identify the characteristics and structure of skeletal muscle and how this influences its function

* recognise the importance of the *all or nothing* principle of motor unit recruitment and the implications of this for force development

* identify the three types of human skeletal muscle fibre and understand the role that each of the fibres plays in sports performance

* identify the principles that govern which types of fibres are recruited and when, and the implications of this for the coach in designing a sport-specific training programme.

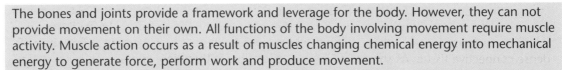

The bones and joints provide a framework and leverage for the body. However, they can not provide movement on their own. All functions of the body involving movement require muscle activity. Muscle action occurs as a result of muscles changing chemical energy into mechanical energy to generate force, perform work and produce movement.

Information about how the musculoskeletal system operates can be found within Chapters 4, 5 and 6.

The Skeletal Muscle

Skeletal muscle is so called because it is attached to bones and moves parts of the skeleton. Skeletal tissue is also called *striated* because of its alternating light and dark bands. It is a voluntary muscle tissue as it can be made to contract under conscious control.

Skeletal muscles can not actively relax; they are either contracted or they are not. Through sustained contraction and the ceasing of contraction, muscle tissue has three key functions:

• **motion** – this relies upon integration of the muscles, bones and joints
• **stabilisation** – skeletal muscle contractions maintain body (or body segment) position in a number of dynamic (changing) and static (non-moving) situations
• **thermo-regulation** (ie the regulation of body heat) – heat is a by-product of skeletal muscle contractions.

General Characteristics of Skeletal Muscle

Muscle tissue has four main characteristics enabling it to carry out its function. Firstly, it is excitable, which means it has the ability to respond to certain stimuli physiologically, with messages being sent from the central nervous system (the brain and the spinal cord) to the muscles. These messages are sent via the motor neurons, which in turn stimulate a movement response from the muscles. This signal causes the muscles to contract, meaning the stimulated muscle fibres have the ability to shorten and thicken, thus generating force to enable work to be done and movement to occur. Sometimes, in performing this movement, muscle fibres are stretched beyond their normal resting length (an eccentric action, investigated in more detail in Chapter 4). In order to achieve this, muscle fibre tissue has to be extensible, which means it can be stretched without damaging the tissue. Muscle fibres must also have elasticity. This is the ability of the fibre to return to its original shape after contraction or extension.

These latter principles allow the stretch reflex to occur in muscles. Imagine the muscle fibre as an elastic band; if you stretch it, it stores potential energy until it reaches a critical point. In muscles, this critical point is sensed by stretch receptors detecting how far and how fast a muscle fibre is being stretched. This is a safety mechanism; if the muscle is stretched too far, then, just like an elastic band, the fibre will cease to be extensible and will tear. Once the stretch receptors sense this point is being reached in the muscle fibres, then a very strong reflex contraction will be initiated in the muscle. This stretch-reflex contraction is the basis of plyometric exercise, which will be introduced in Chapter 5.

Arrangement of Skeletal Muscles

Skeletal muscles are arranged in opposite pairs about a joint. This allows one muscle to contract and flex and an opposing muscle to extend the joint. This opposing arrangement of muscles (or groups of muscles) allows locomotion to occur. For example, in bending (flexing) the elbow, the *biceps brachii*[1] muscle is contracted. To extend (straighten) the elbow, the contraction in the biceps brachii is stopped and the *triceps brachii*[2] is contracted. The same principle can be observed at the knee joint, where the *quadriceps* group[3] contracts to extend the knee and the hamstring group[4] flexes the knee. How this applies to training specific muscles around a joint is explored in more detail in Chapter 4.

Skeletal Muscle Gross Structure

Each of the skeletal muscles in the body consists of thousands of muscle fibres. These generally run in parallel with each other, which means the force of contraction can pull along the axis of the fibre. Each individual fibre is wrapped and separated from its neighbour by a fine layer of dense connective tissue. As shown in Figure 6, each fibre is then part of a bundle of up to 150 fibres (known as a *fasciculus*), which are held together by another layer of connective fibrous tissue (the *endomysium*). There is a number of these bundles within a muscle, each of which is surrounded and bound together by another layer of connective tissue. All of the connective tissue is tapered at both ends and blends together to form the dense, strong connective tissue known as a *tendon*. The tendons connect both ends of the muscle to the outer covering of the bone that it attaches to. This allows the force of muscle contraction to be transmitted directly from the muscle and tendons, which in turn pull on the bone at the point of attachment causing the joint and, therefore, the bone to move.

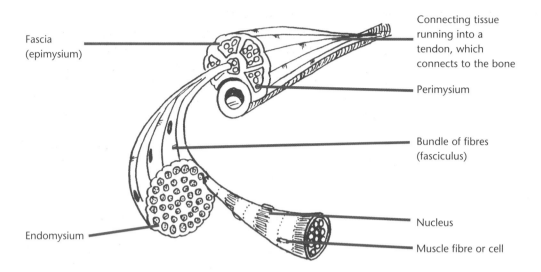

Fascia (epimysium)

Connecting tissue running into a tendon, which connects to the bone

Perimysium

Bundle of fibres (fasciculus)

Endomysium

Nucleus

Muscle fibre or cell

Figure 6: Muscle cross-section[*]

Motor Units – How Muscle Fibres are Activated

A motor neuron (nerve) delivers an electrical stimulus to a muscle, which causes it to contract. The collective term for a motor neuron and all the muscle fibres that it innervates is a *motor unit*. One motor neuron can make contact with an average of 150 muscle fibres. This means one motor unit will cause all the muscle fibres it supplies to contract. Muscles that control precise movements have one motor unit supplying small numbers of fibres (maybe as low as two or three). Muscles responsible for powerful, gross movements have one motor unit supplying approximately 2000 muscle fibres.

It is important for coaches to realise that adjusting the number of motor units activated varies the strength of the resulting muscle contraction. The more force required, the larger the number of motor units needing to be activated.

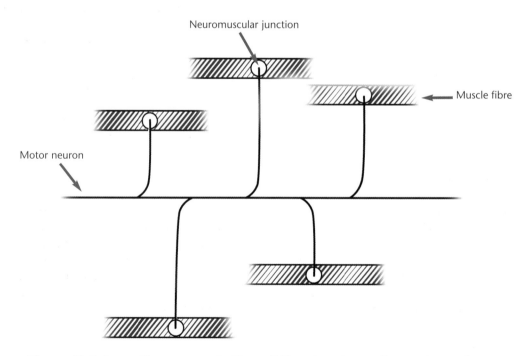

Neuromuscular junction

Muscle fibre

Motor neuron

Figure 7: Schematic representation of the structure of a motor unit

[*]Source: Farrally, M. (1995) *Introduction to the Structure of the Body*. Leeds: Coachwise Business Solutions. ISBN: 978-1-850601-69-2

The *All or Nothing* Principle of Muscular Contraction

As previously identified, when the central nervous system requires a movement to be carried out, an electrical signal is sent along the length of a motor neuron. However, at the end of the neuron there is a small gap between the neuron and the connective tissue surrounding the muscle fibre. The electrical signal can not jump directly from the nerve to the muscle; it can not cross this gap. Instead, the neuron and the muscle communicate with each other through a chemical substance called *acetylcholine* that transmits the message from the nerve cell to the muscle cell (fibre). When a signal reaches the end of the neuron, acetylcholine (known as a *neurotransmitter*) is released and this crosses the gap between the nerve and the muscle. The amount of acetylcholine released is directly proportional to the strength of the neural signal; the stronger the electrical signal that travels along the nerve, the more acetylcholine is released.

Along the muscle fibre membrane are specific receptors that allow neurotransmitters to bind to them. When enough neurotransmitter binds to muscle fibre membrane, it changes the electrical potential of the membrane, giving it a positive electrical charge. There is a threshold effect in this process; if insufficient neurotransmitters are present, the electrical signal will not pass on to the muscle fibre. Until this threshold value is reached, the muscle fibre will not contract. As soon as the threshold level is reached, then the electrical impulse travels along the length of the muscle fibre and initiates the muscular contraction. This is known as the *all or nothing* principle of muscular contraction (ie motor units are either activated or they are not).

The Three Types of Skeletal Muscle Fibre

There are three types of human skeletal muscle fibre. These are characterised according to their speed of contraction and, therefore, function in human movement. This is predominantly determined by the enzyme profile of protein chains within the individual fibres, which in turn determines how fast the fibres contract, how the fibres produce energy (aerobically or anaerobically) and how well they tolerate fatigue. A motor unit can only consist of one type of muscle fibre (ie all fibres attached to one nerve will be either Type I, IIa or IIx in nature).

Type I Fibres

These fibres are predominantly known as *slow-twitch* or *endurance* fibres. Muscles required to be fatigue resistant are predominantly made up of slow-twitch fibres (eg the *gastrocnemius* and *soleus* – the calf muscles – are predominantly slow-twitch in nature as they allow humans to stand and walk for relatively long periods of time without the muscles fatiguing). Because of the endurance nature of these fibres, they rely predominantly on energy produced aerobically (a process known as *slow glycolysis*, which is explained later in this chapter). As such, these fibres have a relatively slow speed of contraction. Type I fibres need a very good supply of oxygen, which in turn requires a good supply of blood. These fibres consequently have a high blood-capillary-to-fibre ratio, causing Type I fibres to appear red when viewed through an electron microscope. These fibres also have a large number of *mitochondria* (where ATP is produced via slow glycolysis – explained later in this chapter) that are larger in size than other muscle's fibres.

Type IIa Fibres

These are intermediate muscle fibres and are known as *fast-twitch oxidative-glycolytic* (FOG) fibres. These fibres are suited to fast, repetitive and low-intensity exercise. As they contain large numbers of mitochondria (the organelle responsible for the aerobic production of energy), they tend to be reasonably resistant to fatigue and can recover very quickly from bouts of intense exercise. Some authorities believe these to be fast-twitch fibres that are adapted for endurance activity. This makes Type IIa ideal fibre types for athletes in multiple high-intensity sports, or events such as slalom skiing or the 800–1500m, who require explosive actions for longer periods of time. In the case of multiple-sprint athletes, with intermittent periods of recovery between.

Type IIx Fibres

Some texts will refer to these as *Type IIb fibres* but, technically speaking, these IIbs are only found in rodent tissue. Type IIx muscle fibres have a very fast speed of contraction (ie they are *fast-twitch* fibres and react up to 10 times faster than slow-twitch fibres) and are responsible for very powerful, high-intensity movements. This means they have an enzyme profile designed to produce energy via anaerobic glycolysis. As such, they are not very resistant to fatigue and can only operate maximally for very short periods of time. Because Type IIx do not require oxygen to produce energy, they have a relatively poor blood supply and therefore will appear white when viewed under an electron microscope. These fibre types also have fewer, smaller mitochondria than in slow-twitch fibres. Relatively speaking, athletes who excel in explosive movements (eg sprinters, throwers, lifters), can have very high numbers of Type IIx muscle fibres. Motor units that have predominantly fast-twitch fibres are characterised by large numbers of fibres to each motor neuron, so that large forces can be achieved very quickly by recruiting relatively small numbers of motor units.

The Size Principle of Motor Unit Recruitment

Motor units tend to be recruited by size, from small to large. Type I muscle fibres are the smallest of the muscle fibre types. These are the fibres that are recruited first in any activity. As soon as the activity requires more than approximately 25% of maximal strength, Type IIa fibres are recruited. As the activity reaches near maximal strength (power levels) or the Type I fibres fatigue (ie glycogen is no longer available as a fuel source), then the largest of the muscle fibres, the Type IIx fibres, are recruited. Force production is related to the recruitment sequence of fibres, which is dependent upon the intensity of exercise – see Figure 8.

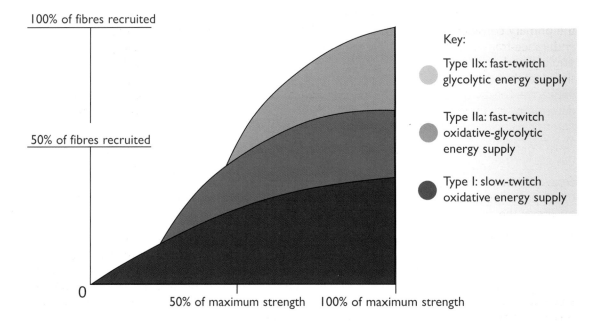

Figure 8: The size principle of muscle fibre recruitment

 Coaches should note fibre size is a relative term. Bodybuilders, who have very large muscles, are not necessarily going to have very much explosive fibre. Much of bodybuilding training is based upon developing large muscles with a good blood supply; this is not explosive muscle. Conversely, there are many very powerful sports players who do not have very big musculature. The Olympic and World Champion triple jumper, Jonathan Edwards, is a classic example of this; at a bodyweight of 68kg, he jumped a world record of 18.29m and could clean 2.23 x bodyweight (150kg) and snatch 110kg (1.6 x bodyweight). Both of these lifts are detailed in Chapter 4.

Are Sprinters Born and Not Made by Training?

Maximal power output and the potential for explosive activity are strongly determined by the proportion of fast-twitch fibres that make up an athlete's muscle. The ratio of fast-twitch to slow-twitch fibres a person has, is predominantly determined by genetics (hence the saying a sprinter is born and not made) and the nature of activity undertaken by children in the very early years. Coaches can influence an athlete's ability to be more powerful by maximising the recruitment of fast-twitch fibres by an individual, through appropriate training activities, and by making the player's technique much more biomechanically efficient (eg in running). However, it is currently thought that it is very difficult, if not impossible, to create more fast-twitch fibres in an athlete by training. 'The coach can not put in what God left out'; phrased differently, you can take a donkey and make it faster but, at best, it will only be a fast donkey – it will never be a thoroughbred racehorse!

Training can influence how effectively an athlete is able to recruit and utilise their explosive fibres. For this reason, it is important for coaches of children under the age of 14 to be able to inspire their athletes to have a movement vocabulary based upon speed development, so that an athlete's neuromuscular system is as well developed as possible.

The Influence of Training on Muscle Fibres

Training influences muscle fibres and motor units in a number of different ways. One of the primary considerations for coaches of athletes is the realisation that inappropriate endurance-training methods can alter the enzyme profiles of muscle fibres. Long-distance, single-paced, low-intensity running will utilise aerobic energy delivery mechanisms and slow-twitch muscle fibres. Overexposure to training of this nature causes the enzyme profiles within the fast-twitch fibres to alter, so the characteristics of the muscle become slow twitch in nature. This can be detrimental to the athlete who relies on intermediate and/or fast-twitch fibres in order to produce explosive power.

Fortunately, with the adoption of appropriate training methods this change is reversible over time, but prevention is better than cure. Although appropriate training can increase the total cross-section of fibre type, there is, unfortunately, little evidence to support the theory that training can increase the number of fast-twitch fibres an athlete has. It is a case of training to maximise the ability to utilise the existing fibres.

The size principle of muscle recruitment illustrates to coaches that if they want to develop fast-twitch muscle fibres in their athletes they need to be working at, or near to, maximum intensities (either in terms of movement speed or weight to be lifted) in order to develop these fibres appropriately. The ability to exert power is the objective of all athletes. **In any sporting situations where skill level is relatively equal (ie in normal competition), it is the most powerful team/player who will always win.**

Power is the ability to exert a force quickly (strength x speed). Training at maximal strength loads with an individual will not necessarily produce more power. For example, let's assume a rower has a maximal squat of 100kg. If this is lifted slowly (as maximal lifts always are), they will produce less power than if they lift 70kg very explosively. Both a moderate load lifted explosively and a heavy load accelerated slowly will recruit fast-twitch fibres.

It should also be recognised that it is the intention of the athlete to move a weight quickly that is the key to generating power, regardless of the weight lifted. All weights should be lifted with maximum effort and with maximum velocity if power is to be developed.

Training at these intense loads will not necessarily cause the muscles to get bigger. In beginners, the initial gains in strength occuring as a result of an intense strength-training programme are the result of the changes in the neural recruitment of motor units. Therefore, athletes are able to recruit more motor units more quickly, hence they are able to exert more force. Training to increase the size of muscle fibres is a specific type of strength training that will be explored more fully in later chapters.

Summary of the Muscular System

- Skeletal muscle is excitable, contractible, extensible and elastic.

- Skeletal muscle can be voluntarily contracted and contractions can be voluntarily ceased, but the muscle can not actively be relaxed. An opposite force has to be applied to return the muscle to its resting length.

- Connective tissue runs throughout the collection of individual muscle fibres that come together to make a muscle. This connective tissue forms the tendons, which join muscle to bone.

- A motor unit is formed from a motor neuron (nerve) and all of the muscle fibres stimulated by that neuron. Fibres within a motor unit are either contracted or not, at any given time. This is because of the all or nothing principle of muscle contraction.

- There are three different types of human muscle fibre. These are commonly known as Type I (slow-twitch, oxidative), Type IIa (fast-twitch, oxidative-glycolytic) and Type IIx (fast-twitch, glycolytic). These fibres are classified according to the enzyme profile of the muscle fibre, which determines the speed of contraction of the fibre and the predominant energy supply the fibre will utilise.

- The coach should design endurance-training sessions to ensure the appropriate fast-twitch fibres are recruited and fibres are not, over time, encouraged to adapt to a profile more closely resembling slow-twitch fibres. This is unless the athlete performs in an endurance (long-distance) event (eg 3000m marathon running) where slow-twitch muscle fibres are a performance requirement.

- Efforts requiring less than 25% of maximal strength will primarily recruit slow-twitch muscle fibre. For fast-twitch muscle fibres to be recruited and trained, exercises must be performed at either near-maximal strength or near-maximal speed.

The Energy System

The purpose of this section is to:

- identify the characteristics of each of the pathways that supply energy to the body
- recognise the importance of each energy system for training, in terms of developing sport-specific training methods for performers
- recognise the importance of the energy supply to a sports performer from a dietary perspective.

The energy currency (the factor limiting the rate at which work can be performed) of the body is called *adenosine tri-phosphate* (ATP). This is made up of an adenosine molecule chemically bonded with three phosphate molecules. These chemical bonds store energy and, when they are broken, this energy is released and used by the body to perform work.

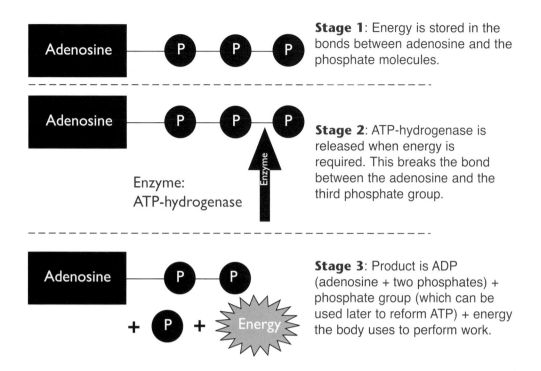

Stage 1: Energy is stored in the bonds between adenosine and the phosphate molecules.

Stage 2: ATP-hydrogenase is released when energy is required. This breaks the bond between the adenosine and the third phosphate group.

Enzyme: ATP-hydrogenase

Stage 3: Product is ADP (adenosine + two phosphates) + phosphate group (which can be used later to reform ATP) + energy the body uses to perform work.

Figure 9: Energy is released by breaking down ATP

The body can only store a very small amount of ATP. This is used almost immediately (within seconds). ATP, therefore, has to be created by breaking down the body's energy stores. The major stores of energy in the body are in the form of blood glucose, glycogen (the muscular store of glucose) and fat. These energy stores are built up from the dietary intake of the individual.

The food we ingest is processed and energy is taken into the body. For example, sugars enter the bloodstream then the muscle cells, where they are either used immediately, or are converted into glycogen, which is the muscles' energy store. What is not used or stored in the muscle, is converted into fat (a high-density calorie store) within the body's adipose tissue.

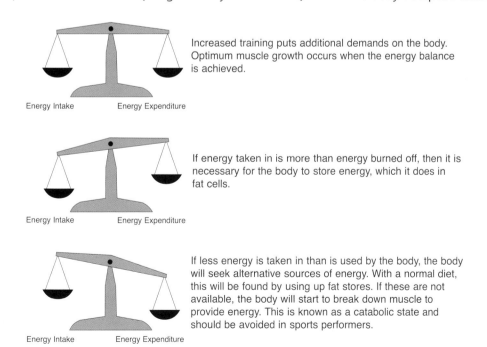

Increased training puts additional demands on the body. Optimum muscle growth occurs when the energy balance is achieved.

Energy Intake   Energy Expenditure

If energy taken in is more than energy burned off, then it is necessary for the body to store energy, which it does in fat cells.

Energy Intake   Energy Expenditure

If less energy is taken in than is used by the body, the body will seek alternative sources of energy. With a normal diet, this will be found by using up fat stores. If these are not available, the body will start to break down muscle to provide energy. This is known as a catabolic state and should be avoided in sports performers.

Energy Intake   Energy Expenditure

Figure 10: The dietary–energy balance

It should be noted that starvation-type diets would not result in the fat stores being broken down in a sports performer. Under such a regime, the body will conserve its high-energy storage (fat) and begin to break down muscles to provide energy. This should be avoided at all times. The safest way to lose body fat, particularly in sports players, is to increase the energy expenditure (through training) and maintain a healthy, balanced diet (see Figure 11).

It can therefore be seen that maintaining the correct energy balance is essential for an athlete if they are to have sufficient energy to perform their sport and be able to maintain low body-fat levels and avoid carrying around useless excess weight in the form of fat. While fat is a high-density energy store (as will be demonstrated later in this chapter) and can provide an alternative source of energy within a normal diet, it is not a useful energy source for the majority of sports people during performances, due to the intensity of activity being performed.

But what is considered to be a normal diet? There are several sources of dietary information available to the coach, many of them driven by fashion or commercial companies advertising their products. Figure 11 illustrates a dietery composition the majority of experts would consider to be reasonable for a sports performer.

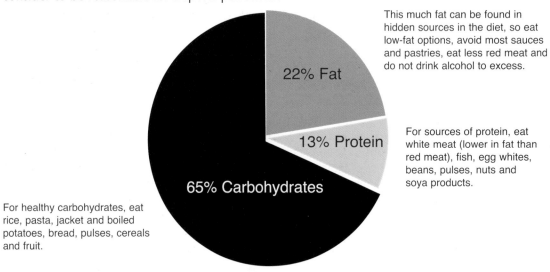

Figure 11: Recommended typical nutritional intake for sports performers

When athletes train for sport-specific endurance, they need to be training the metabolic pathways that deliver energy to the performing muscles. Therefore, it is important for a coach to understand a little about how each of these mechanisms work and the potential impact on the athlete.

There are three energy systems responsible for the production of ATP from the body's stores of chemical energy. These are:

• **the phosphagen system** – sometimes referred to as the *phosphocreatine* or *creatine phosphate* system[5]

• **fast glycolysis** – sometimes referred to as *anaerobic* (without oxygen) *glycolysis*

• **the aerobic metabolism** – energy produced using oxygen.

These three energy systems are not independent of each other. **Indeed, they are integrated with one another and, in any activity, energy is supplied by a combination of these systems**. How they combine and which energy supply mechanism predominates in any given activity depends upon the intensity of the exercise. The more intense the exercise (ie closer to maximum intensity for an individual at any given time), the greater the contribution fast glycolysis will have.

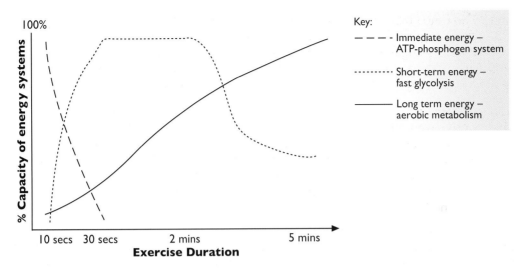

Figure 12: Energy for exercise

There is very little ATP stored in the body's cells – only enough for exercise lasting about 1–3 seconds. To compensate for this, the body is able to produce ATP via a number of different methods. As can be seen in Figure 12, very intense exercise (for durations of up to approximately 10–12 seconds) can be produced by breaking down creatine-phosphate stores in the body to produce ATP and fuel performance. However, after this duration, these stores become exhausted and energy is produced by glycolysis.

Glycolysis is the process whereby glycogen (the muscular and liver store of glucose) or glucose (if it is available in the muscle cell) is converted into a substance known as *pyruvate*. This requires 12 enzymatic reactions in total and produces a net gain of three molecules of ATP (if glycogen is broken down) or two molecules of ATP (if glucose is used) plus hydrogen (which is accepted by a carrier molecule and used at a later stage to produce more ATP in the presence of oxygen). The combined actions of the ATP-PCr (phosphagen) and glycolytic systems allow muscles to generate force when the demand for energy exceeds the rate at which energy can be supplied aerobically. In this way, these two energy systems are the major energy contributors during the early minutes of high-intensity exercise (Figure 12).

The next stage of the process depends upon the rate at which the electron transport system proceeds. In low-intensity exercise[6], where the demand for oxygen can be met by the supply, then oxygen-dependent (slow) glycolysis allows pyruvate to be transported into an organelle within the muscle cell known as a *mitochondrion*. In the mitochondria, a series of chemical reactions occur, which ultimately produces up to 36 molecules of ATP (thus the potential total production of ATP from one molecule of glycogen is 39 molecules). This series of chemical reactions begins with the Krebs cycle, which breaks pyruvate down into a number of hydrogen atoms and electrons. These electrons then pass along an electron transport chain (a series of chemical reactions), producing ATP along the way. The by-products of this series of reactions are water and carbon dioxide, which are removed from the muscle cells by the blood and exhaled through the lungs. This process (known as *oxidative phosphorylation* or the long-term energy system) can occur for as long as the athlete is able to deliver glycogen and oxygen to the working muscles.

When the intensity of exercise exceeds that at which there is sufficient oxygen supply[7], then oxygen-independent (fast) glycolysis becomes largely responsible for creating ATP. The end production of ATP is the same (two or three molecules), but it is the fate of the pyruvate molecule that changes at the point where the intensity of work demands the athlete produce ATP anaerobically. Instead of being transported into the mitochondria, pyruvate is reduced to lactate in the muscle cell.

During medium-intensity exercise, lactate is formed[8] and has two uses. When sufficient oxygen is available, lactate is transformed back into pyruvate, transported into the mitochondria and converted into 36 molecules of ATP (as described above). Alternatively, it is removed from the muscle cell, taken by blood to the liver and converted back into glucose for use as an energy store at a later stage. Following this process, it is easy to see why low- to medium-intensity exercise can be kept going for much longer periods of time. **Thus, it can be seen that lactate, rather than being a toxin (as many coaches think of it) is actually a useful fuel source for the body, particularly in slow-twitch muscle fibres, which have a high number of mitochondria in them.**

High-intensity work (which forms the major components of the majority of games-based sports and all sports where the performances last less than three minutes), can not, however, be kept up for long periods of time. This can produce immediately available energy for up to two minutes in very fit players, but is associated with a significant fatigue component limiting how long the player can keep working anaerobically. This is because the build-up of lactate in the muscle cell is also accompanied by an increase in hydrogen ions (H+). High concentrations of these positively charged particles make the muscle cell more acidic. Higher levels of acidity interfere with the muscle contraction mechanisms and the efficiency of the enzymes involved in ATP production, therefore causing fatigue.

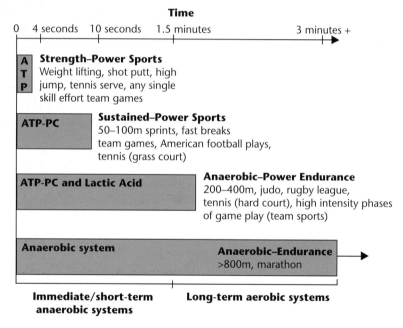

Figure 13: The predominant energy systems that underpin performance requirements in different sports

Delayed Onset of Muscle Soreness (DOMS)

It is a common assumption among many coaches and players that a lactate build-up is responsible for the feeling of stiffness experienced by many players 12–48 hours after performing intense exercise activity. This is not the case. It is much more likely the stiffness is caused by microscopic damage to the muscle tissue and the tendons/fibrous tissue that runs through muscles and connects them to bone. The feelings associated with DOMS may be exacerbated by the player performing too much static stretching, following high-intensity exercise. This is contrary to many practices, whereby coaches insist on static stretching following a training session. This concept is explored in more detail in Chapters 8 and 9.

Once lactate (and H+) levels reach a critical value (known as the onset of blood lactate accumulation or OBLA point), then the player has no choice but to reduce the intensity of exercise performance if activity is to be continued.

Replacing the Oxygen Debt

In activities where the athlete needs more energy than they can produce aerobically (ie work intensity exceeds the ability of the cardiovascular system to deliver oxygen to the muscles) the body builds up an oxygen debt. This can be recognised by the very heavy breathing that follows intense work periods (ie heavy breathing for up to several minutes following a maximal 100m sprint). During this time, the body is taking in more oxygen to be delivered to the working muscles to enable more ATP to be produced using slow glycolysis, processing the pyruvate and lactate that has accumulated during the intense work periods, when fast glycolysis was the predominant energy supply.

Figure 14: After a maximal effort, an oxygen debt is built up that will be recovered through the aerobic energy system (as illustrated by Ashley Cole, following a sprint in a game and Leyton Hewitt, following an intense point).

Many of the training sessions recommended for (intermittent) high-intensity sports (as illustrated in Chapter 3) will target specifically the fast glycolysis energy pathway. However, during the recovery periods in between work efforts, the athlete will be working to replace the oxygen debt built up during the work periods. Therefore, there is definitely an aerobic training component to this form of training that occurs during the recovery (time between work) interval (leading to the term interval training).

The Implications for Training

As with all training adaptations, the mechanisms supplying energy to the working player adapt to the type of training the athlete is subjected to. Generally speaking, an athlete's success in any sport depends upon their ability to perform the high-intensity components of the activity. The component an athlete contributes to a winning performance is based on how often the athlete is able to perform at the highest levels of intensity. High-intensity activities are those with the greatest significance to performances, therefore the number of times that the individual reaches high-intensity activity is what normally characterises an individual's effectiveness in performance, rather than the amount of low-intensity work an athlete performs between the high-intensity bouts, especially in team sports.

Since the mid-1970s, exercise physiologists have promoted the idea that the only games to have a significant component of energy requirements (produced by **oxidative phosphorylation** – the oxygen-dependent long-term energy system) are badminton (which relies on this system for 10% of energy delivery), tennis (20–30%), soccer (30%) and lacrosse (20% for midfield players). This is something often misunderstood by coaches. For example, tennis coaches often state players must be able to perform on court for up to three hours and therefore undertake endurance training to help the player reach this goal. However, if the tennis player is not able to perform high-intensity activities repeatedly, then the coach need not worry about the game going to three hours, as the player will be beaten long before then!

It is easy for an athlete to try to pace themselves, or reduce the intensity of their performance, in order to make sure they can go the distance. This is a mistake. Firstly, opponents gain a psychological advantage, as they can see their opponent is not firing on all cylinders and they know that, by increasing the intensity of their own performance, they can win. Secondly, in a team-sport scenario, the player who is unable to contribute to the high-intensity components of the game will leave their team a player down. This can lead to scores and points being conceded and there is little point in a player being able to finish a game if, at the end, their team is three scores down.

This concept is discussed more when we move on to endurance training in Chapter 3, where specific methods for achieving the desired training effect will be introduced.

However, it is important to realise the player must be able to work at, or near, maximal levels, recover quickly and repeat the maximal efforts for the entire duration of the performance. It is also important to realise that, as will be expanded in Chapter 4, the more effective the neuromuscular and musculoskeletal systems are at producing force, the less energy will be expended for the athlete to do a given amount of work (ie the athlete will be more energy-efficient).

Training must therefore reflect the physiological needs of a sport. In physiological terms, the sports performer needs:

- to be able to produce energy efficiently through the phosphagen system
- to be able to efficiently produce ATP through fast (anaerobic) glycolysis. Training at high intensities will enable the enzymes that are important in glycolysis to become more efficient at creating pyruvate and to lactate from that pyruvate very effectively
- the muscle cells (fibres) to become proficient at contracting and maintaining the rate of enzyme reactions in an acidic environment (the result of a build-up of lactate and hydrogen ions (H+) known as lactate tolerance)
- efficient mechanisms for removing lactate from the muscle cells and transporting it back to the liver for conversion back into glucose, which can then be recycled when oxygen is available
- to have an efficient slow glycolysis mechanism, with an aerobic capacity suitable for the demands of the sport (very high in engine sports such as road cycling, distance running and rowing, significantly lower in other sports)
- to be able to use slow (aerobic) glycolysis and oxidative phosphorylation to produce ATP efficiently and effectively during recovery periods. These training benefits can not be achieved by sub-maximal training efforts that occur at one pace over long distances. Training needs to be undertaken for intensities and durations allowing energy to be delivered predominantly through anaerobic pathways, with recovery periods that will facilitate the training of aerobically produced energy.

Summary of the Energy System

- The ATP-PCr and glycolytic systems produce small to moderate amounts of ATP anaerobically and are the major energy contributors in the early minutes (typically up to two minutes, depending on the training state of the individual) of high-intensity exercise.

- The oxidative system uses oxygen and produces more energy than the anaerobic systems, but the delivery mechanism of the ATP is much slower.

- Carbohydrate oxidation involves glycolysis, the Krebs cycle and the electron transport chain to produce up to 39 ATP per glycogen molecule.

- When an athlete works anaerobically, the build-up of H+ and other charged particles may cause a decrease in the efficiency of the glycolytic enzymes and interferes with the muscular contraction process. This may be a major cause of fatigue in multiple-sprint activities and/or high-intensity exercise that is 1–30 minutes in duration (or when the athlete can not maintain oxygen delivery during distance events).

- Glycogen depletion can be a major cause of fatigue in activities that last longer than 30 minutes. Optimum nutrition and recovery protocols (see Chapter 9) can aid the recovery process for this.

- Coaches need to train the predominant energy systems used in their sport in order to develop effective athletes. This means training at high intensities, for short, intermittent durations, in order to fully develop the effectiveness of the anaerobic energy delivery mechanisms and tolerate the by-products of this method of energy delivery.

Further Reading

Baechle, T. and Earle, R. (eds) (2000) *Essentials of Strength Training and Conditioning*. Illinois: Human Kinetics. ISBN: 978-0-736000-89-5.

Bean, A. (2003) *The Complete Guide to Sports Nutrition*. London: A and C Black. ISBN: 978-0-713667-41-7.*

Byrd, R., Pierce, K., Reilly, L. and Brady, J. (2003), 'Young weightlifters' performance across time'. *Sports Biomechanics*, 2: 133-140. This is available from www.coachesinfo.com/category/strength_and_conditioning/245

Crosland, J. (2005) *Fuelling Performers*. Leeds: Coachwise Business Solutions/The National Coaching Foundation. ISBN: 978-1-902523-23-1.*

Farrally, M. (2003) *An Introduction to the Structure of the Body*. Leeds: Coachwise Business Solutions/The National Coaching Foundation. ISBN: 978-1-850601-69-2.*

Farrally, M. (2005) *An Introduction to Sports Physiology*. Leeds: Coachwise Business Solutions/The National Coaching Foundation. ISBN: 978-0-947850-96-8.*

Pierce, Brewer, Ramsey, Sands and Stone (in press 2008): Opinion Statement and Literature Review: Youth Resistance Training, *Professional Strength and Conditioning (UKSCA Journal)*, Spring 2008.

Siff, M. (2003) *Supertraining*. Supertraining Institute. ISBN: 978-1-874856-65-8.

Thompson, C.W. and Floyd, R.T. (eds) (2003) *Manual of Structural Kinesiology*. New York: McGraw-Hill Education. ISBN:978-0-073028-73-6.

* Available from Coachwise 1st4sport. For a full range of sports education and training equipment, please visit www.1st4sport.com or call 0113-201 5555

23

Notes page

Notes page

Chapter 3
Endurance Training

Introduction

Sport-specific endurance is defined as the ability to sustain performance at a high intensity, recover rapidly and keep producing maximal efforts throughout the game. A well-developed cardiorespiratory system is also important in allowing the removal of waste products that build up during periods of high-intensity activity (when the body will work without oxygen, ie anaerobically). High levels of endurance allow the athlete to:

- continue producing maximal efforts throughout a performance (whether this is in competition or training)
- continue reproducing coordinated and powerful skill execution throughout a performance
- continue making the best decisions throughout a performance (as fatigue interferes with concentration, increasing the likelihood of unforced errors)
- recover quickly from bouts of intense effort within a performance
- recover more quickly after competitions and training, thus increasing effectiveness in subsequent training sessions and performances.

Recent debates between sports scientists, strength and conditioning specialists and coaches within British sport have centred on the need for coaches to recognise the training methods employed to reflect the specific demands of each individual sport. This applies to the bioenergetic components of training as well as the neuromuscular and musculoskeletal elements. While specificity of training is recognised as a basic scientific requirement of any training programme, an overview of practices among those in the field would indicate there are many players and coaches at all levels who are not applying this principle to their competitive preparation, particularly when it comes to endurance training, where the objective is to create sufficient ATP to enable performances to be sustained. This means training the bioenergetic pathways that deliver energy at the required intensity for performance in a sport/event.

One of the easiest ways to determine what form endurance training should take for a particular sport is to profile the needs of training for optimum competitive preparation, by analysing the physiological performance requirements of a sport and relating these analyses to endurance-training requirements. Once this performance analysis has been undertaken, specific training ideas, designed to target the energy systems required by, for example, elite tennis players, can be introduced. This is achieved by manipulation of the mode (type of training), volume and most importantly, the intensity of the work undertaken.

A coach can fairly easily undertake performance analysis of a particular sport. Indeed, in many cases, the published data already exists and can be accessed either through an academic library or, more typically, the sport's governing body. If such information is not readily available, the coach simply needs to spend some time analysing a video of a performance for their sport and complete the information in Table 2, following the instructions therein.

Table 2: A suggested method for the simple analysis of performance

Total Playing Time of Event	No. of Episodes (tally)	Duration of Each Episode	Average Duration (total duration divided by total no. of episodes)	Shortest and Longest Distances Covered at this Pace
Average time spent in competition (eg how long the ball is in play)	Square A: Insert in here one tally bar for each time the ball (for example) is in play.	Square B: Insert in here the number of seconds the ball is in play each time. For each tally in Square A, there needs to be a duration in Square B.	Insert in here the total no. of episodes (ie sum total of entries in Square A) divided by the total amount of time the ball was in play (ie sum total of entries in Square B).	Insert in here the shortest and the longest duration from Square B.
Working at 90–100% (maximal effort/sprinting)	Square C: Insert in here a tally bar for each time the player is working at 90-100%	Square D: Insert in here the number of seconds the player is working at 90-100%. For every tally in Square C, there needs to be a duration in Square D.	Insert in here the total no. of episodes (ie sum total of entries in Square C) divided by the total amount of time the ball was in play (ie sum total of entries in Square D). This gives an average duration for which the player is working above 90%.	Insert in here the shortest and the longest duration from Square D.
Working at 70–90% (eg fast running)	Square E: Insert in here a tally bar for each time the player is working at 70-90%.	Square F: Insert in here the number of seconds the player is working at 70-90%. For each tally in Square E, there needs to be a duration in Square F.	Insert in here the total no. of episodes (ie sum total of entries in Square E) divided by the total amount of time the ball was in play (ie sum total of entries in Square F). This gives an average duration for which the player is working at 70-90%.	Insert in here the shortest and longest duration from Square F.
Working at 50–70% (eg jogging)	Square G: Insert in here a tally bar for each time the player is working at 50-70%.	Square H: Insert in here the number of seconds the player is working at 50-70%. For each tally in Square G, there needs to be a duration in Square H.	Insert in here the total no. of episodes (ie sum total of entries in Square G) divided by the total amount of time the ball was in play (ie sum total of entries in square H). This gives an average duration for which the player is working at 50-70%.	Insert in here the shortest and longest duration from Square H.
Working below 50% (walking, being stationary)	Square I: Insert in here a tally bar for each time the player is working at below 50%.	Square J: Insert in here the number of seconds the player is working at below 50%. For every tally in Square I, there needs to be a duration in Square J.	Insert in here the total no. of episodes (ie sum total from Square I) divided by the total amount of time the ball was in play (ie sum total of entries in Square J). This gives an average duration for which the player is working at below 50%.	Insert in here the shortest and longest duration from Square J.

From the table to your left, calculate the average work:rest ratio over the duration of a game/competitive event. Broadly speaking, this can be demonstrated as:

Work = Above 70%:Rest = Below 70%

This information, combined with subjective analysis of the sport (based on the coach's knowledge) will form the basis for the development of an endurance-training programme. For example, most game-based sports will require performers to repeatedly reproduce high-intensity (maximal) bouts of activity (eg rallies, sprints, contact episodes/wrestling-related activities). Engine sports (for example, rowing, endurance running, cycling) require the ability to prolong the body's capability to produce ATP aerobically while being able to increase performance speeds as required and tolerate the metabolic by-products of this increased intensity (ie as described in Chapter 2, move from slow to fast glycolysis as a predominant energy supply, while being able to tolerate the metabolic acidosis resulting from this).

By relating the intensity and duration of work to the mechanisms of energy supply, the coach can get an idea of the predominant energy supply pathways that need to be trained for a particular sport or event. This is a very important concept, as a performer who has a well-developed aerobic metabolic pathway will not necessarily be able to cope well with periods of high-intensity work. Surprisingly, however, there is a crossover in the opposite direction, in that athletes (especially from multiple-sprint-/high-intensity activity sports) who are trained to tolerate high anaerobic workloads will not necessarily have a very high VO_2 max[9] but they will be able to sustain a high percentage of that VO_2 max for a long period of time and work using aerobically produced energy. VO_2 max[*] is calculated by (heart rate x stroke volume) x (the amount of oxygen extracted from the blood by the muscles)[**]. Even in sports/events typically associated with the need to have a very high VO_2 max (often referred to, appropriately enough, as engine sports) such as endurance running, it may not be as crucial as first thought once it reaches a certain level. For example, data presented by Professor Andy Jones at the 2005 BASES (British Association of Sport and Exercise Science) Annual Conference indicated that Paula Radcliffe's VO_2 max has not significantly increased over the last 14 years but, in that time, the velocity at which she can achieve VO_2 max has increased significantly (indicating more work done for less energy cost).

Prior to looking at what methods should be applied in order to produce such an endurance-training profile, there is one more factor that needs to be taken into consideration. This relates to the effect of endurance training on muscle fibre characteristics. Most game-based sports (often referred to as invasion games) and combat sports require rapid accelerations, agility[10] and speed over distances of up to 100m (although more frequently over distances of 5–20m). These sports (eg football, rugby, hockey, cricket, tennis, badminton, squash, judo, karate, boxing) are also characterised by the requirement for lower- and upper-body power (force x velocity)[11] as a must for elite levels of performance. Such requirements mean the player must be able to recruit maximum numbers of fast-twitch (Types IIa and IIx) muscle fibres (refer to Chapter 2). Other sports requiring single maximum efforts (ie sprinting, jumping, throwing, lifting) also rely on these IIx fibres to facilitate performance. As detailed earlier, these fibres are characterised by their contractile speed, which is in turn, enabled by their enzyme profile. Training can alter that fibre profile. Research indicates prolonged exposure to traditional endurance training (ie sub-maximal exercise that does not involve maximal speed/force production in training) will result in the changing of fibre characteristics from Type IIx fibres to Type IIa, and Type IIa fibres to a profile more similar to Type I (slow-twitch, aerobic fibres). These Type I fibres have little use in power/speed development and would therefore not be desirable for multiple-sprint/single maximum-effort performers.

* Defined as the maximum amount of oxygen that can be uptaken when breathing at sea level.

** Heart rate is measured in beats per minute. Stroke volume is a measure of the blood volume, in litres, pumped per heartbeat.

Athletes in longer duration activities (eg running, rowing) that do not have such multiple-sprint requirements may have different considerations, depending upon the duration of the event and the importance of having the ability to change pace at different stages during the performance.

This information should direct the coach of a multiple-sprint/single maximum-effort sport to avoid exposing athletes to endurance-training routines comprising of long-duration, low- to medium-intensity activities. While such activities may have been thought of in the past as being beneficial to the increase of maximum oxygen uptake in players, it should be recognised that there are other means of doing this, which limit potentially adverse alterations in fibre characteristics. In many cases with sport, and particularly in multiple sprint activities, it is not the level of VO_2 max that is important for multiple-sprint performance, but rather the highest percentage of the maximum an athlete can sustain.

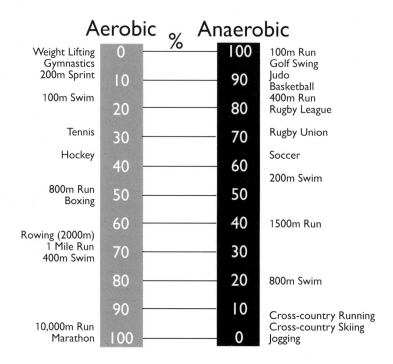

Figure 15: The energy continuum and various sports

Example 1: Tennis

Tennis is a sport characterised by intermittent exercise bouts of varying intensities requiring immediate bursts of energy (eg a powerful serve), periods of intense activity lasting less than 10 seconds (a typical three- or four-shot point) or up to a minute (eg a 10-shot rally on a slow surface, such as clay). The nature of the tennis match is for numerous repetitive bursts of high-intensity activity, interspersed with recovery periods that, between points, must not exceed 20 seconds (Rule 30: ITF, 2000). Longer recovery breaks (maximum of 90 seconds according to rule 30) are taken between every second game and between sets.

Due to its influence on the bounce of the ball, the court surface has a big influence on the duration of the played points, with faster surfaces (eg grass) having a lower, faster bounce[12] than the slower surfaces (eg clay). Duration of played points on the faster surfaces will therefore be shorter. This analysis would indicate that training methods should reflect an intermittent period of high-intensity activity with a series of short rest breaks, with additional longer breaks reflecting performance demand.

By relating the intensity of tennis activities to the energy supply, it can be noted the tennis player needs to be able to produce energy via both creatine-phosphate breakdown and anaerobic fast glycolysis. Similarly, capillary lactate measurements, which indicate the build-up of toxins from anaerobic energy supply, (as undertaken by Reilly and Palmer, 1995), suggest the major energy contributions in singles tennis are from the creatine-phosphate system and aerobic metabolism of carbohydrate. Given the short duration of activity in the tennis shot and, the relatively short duration of points, it would seem that training the creatine-phosphate system and the ability to regenerate creatine-phosphate supplies (which can only happen once recovery begins), would be an important component of endurance training in tennis.

Christmass et al. (1995) demonstrated that, following the sixth change of ends, blood lactate levels reached a peak of 5.86 millimoles and these levels remained elevated until the end of the game. This would imply that there is a significant energy contribution from anaerobic metabolism[13]. While we need to accept playing style, opponents and court surface all significantly influence the intensity and pace of a match, it would seem apparent that endurance training should be designed to target all of the body's energy systems. Anaerobic training would need to form a significant contribution to the comprehensive preparation of players for singles tennis competition. As well as being able to produce energy anaerobically, the player must also be able to tolerate the fatiguing by-products resulting from this for the duration of a match, which may last between 1–4 hours.

Therefore, sessions must be devised to combine high-intensity activities with recovery periods. But how long should these work and recovery periods be? This is indicated by the work:rest ratio, which can be determined by looking at some match analysis research. Reilly and Palmer (1995) found that in a three-set male tennis match there was an average of 23 (±7) games, with the ball in play for approximately 28% of the total match time. Similar results were found by Christmass et al. (1995), who found the ball to be in play for 21 minutes (23%) of a 90 minute match on a hard court surface. Further analysis by these authors revealed that, in state-level matches, the work:rest ratio was 1:1.7. Elliott et al. (1985) found a similar ratio to this, with work:rest being 1:1.8, although this changed significantly when the time it takes to change ends was built into the equation (work:rest ratio of 1:3). From these results, it would appear that endurance-training sessions need not exceed 30 minutes, with high-intensity periods of activity interspersed with rest periods on a ratio of one work unit to two rest units (an example session is outlined in Figure 16).

Figure 16: Tennis player Anna Fitzpatrick (Monte Carlo Tennis Academy) completes 15 x 200m runs (target time 38 seconds with 60 seconds recovery between reps) to improve her match endurance

Example 2: Rugby League

It has been shown that, during an 80 minute match, forwards can cover approximately 10,000m; much of this is at high intensity and, as an indication of the amount of high-intensity work carried out and the time available for recovery, the work:rest ratio is 1:10 or 1:7 for the prop or hooker. Backs, on average, cover approximately 8500m, with a work:rest ratio of between 1:12 and 1:28 (Meir et al., 2001). This is reflected in patterns of play that coaches are familiar with. Forwards are expected to be able to break defensive lines in the first few phases of the six-tackle possession and be able to play the ball quickly enough to exploit the disrupted defence or cause an overlap for the outside backs to exploit at pace. On average, it can be seen that every four seconds of high-intensity activity is followed by between 30–80 seconds of low- to medium-intensity activity (eg moving up and back in the defensive line). Forwards work for shorter periods but are involved in the action more, whereas wingers have longer recovery periods, as they are on the fringes of the attacking/defensive line, but are expected be quicker and run further when they do get the ball.

When questioned, nearly 50% of Great Britain internationals listed breaking/being tackled as the most fatiguing aspect of the game. Similarly, making tackles is also a major aspect of the game and, unsurprisingly, approximately 30% of international players would list making tackles as the most demanding aspect of the game.

Therefore, as well as incorporating the work:rest patterns into endurance training for rugby league, its is important for the player that other intensely fatiguing activities such as tackling and running backwards to the offside line following a tackle are incorporated into endurance-training activities.

Determining Exercise Intensity

The easiest means of determining how hard an athlete is working is to monitor their heart rate. Figure 17 indicates a common method of manual palpation used to record heartbeats, using the first two fingers to feel the pulse. It is important to note the thumb should not be used, as this digit has a pulse of its own. It should also be noted heart rates are very hard to count manually when an athlete is working hard and there is a usual error of +10% using this method. An alternative method is to use a heart-rate monitor that uses telemetry to record heart rate on a wristwatch display. These watches make the monitoring process very easy and convenient for the performer. They enable heart rate to be checked throughout a training session and provide instant feedback. Athletes do not necessarily all need to be using one at the same time. It is an educational process and players quickly become familiar with the level of effort and intensity required to achieve particular heart-rate training zones.

Figure 17: Manual palpation of the pulse

Maximal heart rate can only be determined by working at maximal levels. Once this is known, a training percentage can be calculated. Alternatively, a formula for calculating the theoretical heart-rate maximum can be used:

220 – age = heart-rate maximum

For example, a 25-year-old who wants to train at 75–85% of heart-rate maximum would calculate:

220 – 25 = (195) x 0.75 = 146 beats per minute (bpm)

220 – 25 = (195) x 0.85 = 166 bpm

Training heart-rate range = 144–166 bpm

This is only an estimate, however, as the fitter an individual becomes, the higher their maximum heart rate. As an indicator, an athlete should be struggling to hold a conversation when working at 75% or above.

Endurance Training and Children

It should be remembered that children are not miniature adults and they are often less economical in their movement. Prior to puberty, children have a less-developed ability to support anaerobic metabolism. This is because they do not have significant levels of an enzyme called *phosphofructokinase* (more simply PFK) which allows fast glycolysis to operate.

Table 3: The difference in pre- and post-puberty endurance

Child (pre-puberty)	Early adulthood (post-puberty)
Working maximally, ATP needs to be produced aerobically, therefore when an oxygen debt is present, a child will work harder to try and produce ATP aerobically.	As the ability to deliver oxygen becomes challenged, the adult will increasingly rely on ATP produced anaerobically (moderated by PFK).
With no natural fatiguing mechanism, heat (the by-product of the hard work) needs to be dissipated. However with a decreased skin surface area, and an increased skin surface temperature, heat stress becomes a potential problem to watch out for.	Metabolic acidosis provides a natural fatiguing stimulus, limiting the subsequent activity the performer does.

Prior to puberty, the preferred means of a child producing ATP are through the ATP-CP and slow glycolysis pathways. As well as other crucial qualities (confidence, technical skill, decision making etc), these metabolic pathways are easily developed through the playing of small-sided (or modified conditioning) games. Details (and examples) of the importance of playing small-sided games as a means of developing both ATP-CP energy systems and aerobic fitness (particularly with children, but equally appropriate with adults) will be presented later in this chapter, within the examples.

PFK levels have been shown to significantly increase during puberty. Another substance (a hormone) that significantly increases during puberty is testosterone. It is often not realised this has potential implications for the metabolic (energy producing) pathways of a child. Firstly, it has been demonstrated that the pubertal increase in testosterone is associated with both an increase in the number of red blood cells available and an increase in the slow-glycolytic enzymes within the mitochondria, making aerobic metabolism more effective. Therefore, **if the sport requires it** (eg the engine sports: distance running, cycling, rowing), there is an opportunity here to begin to maximise aerobic capacity and power through appropriate training.

Children also have a less-efficient cardiovascular system, as would be anticipated. Their smaller lungs mean they need to have a higher respiratory rate (take more breaths per minute) than adults (eg 60 breaths per minute v 40 breaths per minute for the equivalent level of exercise). Children also have a smaller cardiac output (blood pumped per minute). This is because they have smaller heart chambers, and therefore pump less blood per heartbeat (known as the stroke volume). This is somewhat compensated by having a higher maximum heart rate. The VO_2 max of a child will, however, be significantly less than an adult, as they are also less efficient at extracting oxygen from the blood from the working muscles. Smaller muscle cells in children (relative to adults) will also mean they have decreased stores of muscle glycogen and also lower creatine-phosphate stores, meaning they are limited in terms of the fuel that they have to supply the phosphagen and slow-glycolytic energy pathways.

Children are also obviously smaller in stature and less strong physically than adults, meaning they are often less economical in their movement. This provides a biomechanical disadvantage that leads to an increased (compared to adults) oxygen consumption at a given pace, meaning they can do less work for the same energy expenditure.

Endurance Training for Multiple-sprint and High-intensity Sports

Figure 18: Training decisions chart

Endurance training can take different forms (see Figure 18); each of them can be developed to suit both the sport and the time of the competitive year.

Decisions about the nature of an endurance session can be based upon the following variables that can be manipulated, as will be demonstrated throughout the chapter:

- The mode of exercise (swimming, rowing, cycling, swimming, game-based, resisted etc)
- Type of terrain or environment (hills, sand, water, cross-country etc)
- Duration or distance of each repetition
- Intensity of the activity
- Number of repetitions
- Number of sets (if any)

- Duration of recovery
- Recovery activity (nature, duration, intensity).

As previously identified, one of the best ways of developing an athlete's endurance is to work through the use of high-intensity, recovery-interval methods of training. Training at 75–85% of maximum heart rate will help to improve a player's VO_2 max. This is because it improves the efficiency of the respiratory and cardiovascular systems and also leads to adaptations within muscles, resulting in better use of the available oxygen. However, as has been identified, it is the athlete's ability to cope with higher intensity workloads that becomes important in sports performance and, at such workloads, it becomes harder for the athlete to continue to produce oxygen aerobically and delay the onset of anaerobic work. Delaying this onset avoids the production of toxic by-products associated with anaerobic work, which interfere with muscular contraction and contribute to fatigue in high-intensity exercise (as outlined in Chapter 2, the cells of the body become increasingly acidic). One of the aims of endurance training must be to delay the onset of the accumulation of anaerobic by-products by increasing both the relative intensity of exercise that a performer can sustain aerobically, and by training the body's ability to deal with (and utilise) the metabolic by-products of anaerobic exercise more efficiently. Therefore, a lot of training needs to be done at a level close to, and above, the intensity at which these by-products of anaerobic metabolism begin to accumulate.

It is not only the improvement of VO_2 max that will lead to improved performance, but the relative intensity an athlete can work at, for a sustained period of time that will enable them to be more effective in competition.

This will enable the athlete to work at higher percentages of their maximum load without the fatigue associated with metabolic by-products of anaerobic work. An example of this would be lactate generation leading to acidosis in the muscle cells (refer to Chapter 2). Coaches should be aware that lactate generation can be achieved through near-maximal intensity activity with a work:rest ratio of 1:5. Tolerance for anaerobic by-products is achieved with sessions based on work:rest ratios of 1:1 to 1:3 (ie 80–100% work for between 10–90 seconds) (see Table 4). By manipulating the interval intensity (making it less intense) and the recovery intensity (making it more intense) the athlete can develop the ability not only to produce lactate, but to utilise it as a fuel source (described later).

Interval sessions are designed to separate periods of work and periods of active recovery. This allows the body to work more intensely (ie harder and with more quality) than is possible when working continuously. Although the work efforts in an interval are predominantly of the intensity to utilise fast glycolysis to produce ATP (although this can change depending upon the intensity of the work effort and the work:rest ratio), there are many aerobic benefits to such exercise in terms of both aerobic capacity and power. This is because, in the recovery intervals, the athlete is working hard aerobically to replace the oxygen debt (see Chapter 2) built up during high-intensity workloads. Such training can easily be manipulated to develop the high-intensity anaerobic fitness required in competition.

By prescribing endurance exercise as a percentage of a maximum, a coach is able to individualise a training session. A group/team of performers may all do the same session, but the individuals within the group can all work at their own pace, making the training session maximally beneficial for all athletes, and allowing the coach to achieve their objective for the session in all their athletes.

Table 4: Prescriptions for interval training

Major Energy Systems	Exercise Duration (seconds)	Work:Rest Ratio	Number of Repetitions per Set	Suggested Sets per Workout	Intensity of Effort (determined by a % of maximum effort)
Phosphagen	<10	1:5–1:3	7–10	4–6	Maximal
ATP-PCr/ upper-end fast glycolysis	10–90	1:5–1:2	6–8	2–5	Maximal
Lower-end fast glycolysis/ slow glycolysis	90–180	1:2–1:1	4–6	2–3	Sub-maximal (85–95%)
Aerobic	180–300	1:1–1:0.5	3–4	1–2	Sub-maximal (65–85%)

In between work intervals, it is important the athlete's recovery is not static, but active. This usually involves walking, but a light jog is also an option to be considered. Active recovery serves to maintain circulation within the working muscles, ensuring a constant oxygen supply and promoting the removal of fatiguing by-products (such as lactate, H+ etc) accumulated during the work stages.

However, if the work interval is reduced in intensity (for example, from 90% of maximal to 75%, and the recovery intensity is increased (from, for example, 90 seconds of walking recovery to 90 seconds of jogging at 40%), it may be the athlete is able to begin to utilise lactate as a fuel. This results in increasing the body's ability to shuttle the lactate from the muscle cells where it is produced (predominantly the fast-twitch muscle fibres), to the slow-twitch muscle fibres, where the mitochondria in the cells can utilise it to produce energy using the slow glycolysis pathway (it effectively becomes recycled). To be really effective, the athlete needs to know the pace or intensity at which lactate begins to accumulate in the muscle cells (ie lactate production exceeds lactate removal known as OBLA, refer to Chapter 2) and to base the intensity of repetitions upon this. If this is not known, using the 75% of maximum pace as an indicator may suffice as a guideline. While this may not be a primary objective for multiple-sprint sports where there is relatively long recovery between work intervals (for example, 11-a-side football), sports where the performance is continuous may find this is essential for the athletes at some point within the planned training programme.

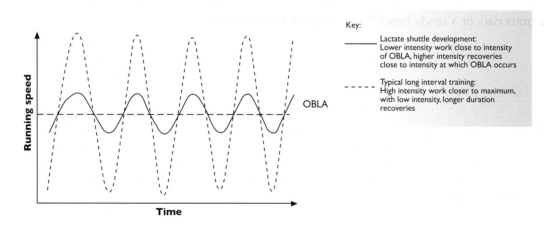

Figure 19: Manipulating interval training for different objectives*

* Modified from Thompson, P. (2007) for UK Athletics coach education material.

Fartlek Training

Some sports do not have a defined duration of play, for example, tennis and squash. Matches can take 1–4 hours to complete. Given that many players have a psychological need to feel they can undertake longer-distance efforts (the need to be confident in meeting the challenge of playing three-hour matches), coaches may want to intersperse sprint-based training with longer-distance work. This should, however, follow the principles outlined here and be based upon the fartlek (speed play) formula for training runs. Examples of fartlek training are outlined below.

Example 1

Following a **dynamic warm-up** (refer to Chapter 7):

* three minutes steady-state running, incorporating one 10 second sprint every 60 seconds.
* three minutes steady-state running, incorporating one 40m sprint every 60 seconds.
* three minutes steady-state running, incorporating one 20 seconds fast, sustained running, followed by one 10 seconds maximal pace running.
* Repeat above three steps x two or three sets.
* Cool down/stretch.

Example 2

Following a **dynamic warm-up**:

* Run at an easy pace for five minutes.
* Increase pace for three minutes (eg 75% maximum).
* Sprint for 15 seconds, followed by one 45 second recovery jog.
* Repeat previous step (ie sprint/jog set) for seven repetitions (reps).
* Jog for three minutes.
* Sprint for 10 seconds, followed by one 20 second recovery jog.
* Repeat sprint/jog cycle for five reps, with a 20 second recovery between sprints.
* Jog for three minutes.
* 75% pace for one minute, jog for one minute (x 3).
* Cool down/stretch.

Long-interval Training

Long-interval training consists of running a specified number of distances, from 300–400m, in a given time, at about 90% maximal effort level, with short walk back recoveries or rest periods of up to two minutes. During this form of training, it is best to work on an athletic track where the running surface is good and the distance can be measured accurately, but running around a grass park or a sandy beach[14] can be used as alternatives.

The intervals are set according to a pace dictated by maximum time over a given distance. Therefore, prior to commencing and, at regular intervals during training (in order to accommodate adaptation), it is important to record the athlete's maximal times over these distances. The intensity of such sessions can be increased by running more intervals or by reducing the length of the rest interval.

There are many variations possible in developing an interval training session. If the basic principles are followed, the limitations correspond to the need for the training medium to reflect the nature of the sport on a regular basis and for the coach to introduce imaginative and useful variation to the training. Three examples of long-interval training are outlined overleaf.

Example 1

Dynamic warm-up and mobilisation drills then:

Distance:	400m
Pace:	75% maximum
Repetitions:	4
Sets:	3
Recovery between reps:	two minutes (walk 100m slowly)
Recovery between sets:	four minutes

Example 2

Dynamic warm-up and mobilisation drills then:

Distance:	300m
Pace:	85%
Repetitions:	5
Sets:	3
Recovery between reps:	90 seconds (walk 100m)
Recovery between sets:	two to three minutes

Example 3 (specifically designed for the 'endurance/engine sport' athlete):

Dynamic warm-up and mobilisation drills then:

Distance:	400m
Pace:	3000m race pace
Repetitions:	8
Recovery between reps:	300m easy jog

Followed by 10–15m active rest then:

Distance:	150m split, 100m at 75% and a 50m sprint at 100%
Repetitions:	4
Recovery between reps:	250m walked recovery

Short-interval Training

Short-interval sessions that consist of high-quality speed-endurance work (not speed development: this never has an element of cardiorespiratory fatigue involved, although neuromuscular fatigue will probably be a result of this type of work) can be carried out over distances of 10–150m. This will improve the athlete's ability to work at near-maximal speeds (important for training the fast-twitch muscle fibres and anaerobic energy systems) with specific recovery intervals. During recovery periods, the aerobic system will be trained, as the body works to replace the oxygen debt built up during the high-intensity work intervals.

High-intensity work is carried out at 85–100% of maximum effort (the shorter the distance, the more intense the effort needed) and is interspersed with periods of active recovery. In order to accurately calculate the correct running pace (running at a certain percentage of the maximum) 100m and 200m time trials should be used. It is important to maintain an appropriate working pace, to avoid premature fatigue.

Coaches should ensure such sessions are scheduled for cushioning surfaces such as an athletics track or grass. These surfaces provide the advantage of allowing markings enabling distances to be measured accurately. Sand is an effective training medium for running (and is actually great at training the stabilising muscles in and around the ankle joint), but coaches will need to relate intensity to a percentage of maximum effort, not a percentage of quickest time, as running on sand is much harder and much slower.

Option 1

Distance	Reps	Sets	Recovery between Reps	Intensity
200m	6	1	2 minutes	80%
150m	4	1	90 seconds	85%
100m	5	1	60 seconds	85%

Option 2

Distance	Reps	Sets	Recovery between Reps	Intensity
130m	4	2	90 seconds	80%
180m	6	1	90 seconds	85%
120m	4	1	90 seconds	85%

Option 3

Distance	Reps	Sets	Recovery between Reps	Intensity
100m	8	4	45 seconds	80%

Option 4: The glory grid

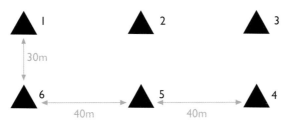

Figure 20: The glory grid

To conduct the glory grid drill you will need six cones and a 40m measuring tape.

How it works:

• set up cones as indicated in Figure 20.

• on lap one the athletes run past the cones in the sequence shown, at 70%.

• on lap two the athletes sprint from cones 1 to 2, then at 65% around the rest of lap.

• on lap three the athletes sprint from cones 1 to 3, then at 65% around the rest of lap.

• on lap four the athletes sprint from cones 1 to 4 (via 3), then at 65% around the rest of lap.

• on laps five and six the athletes sprint to cones 5 and 6 respectively.

• on lap seven the athletes sprint from cone 1 all the way around and back to 1.

• on lap eight the athletes do a two minute recovery walk.

• on lap nine the athletes repeat lap seven.

• on lap ten the athletes repeat lap six.

• After this, the athletes repeat laps five to one in descending order.

Notes:

• You need to ensure the athlete has a definite change of pace at the start of the sprint on all laps.

• Such sessions can also be done over very short distances with the players running at 100% of their maximum.

Alternative Short-interval Training

Examples of shorter distance sessions (very definitely geared towards speed endurance work in a games-based context, where most repeated accelerations are between 5–40m in length) are outlined below. Coaches should remember that, although target times based upon a single maximum best performance for the distances run can be set, with fatigue, athletes will not be able to maintain the same time. Therefore, they should adjust their target times as the session progresses, or work using 100% effort, without a defined time indicator:

40m at 100%

• three to four sets of six lots of 40m in six to seven seconds.

• 40 seconds active recovery between reps.

• two minutes active recovery between sets.

20m at 100%

• two to three sets of 10 lots of 20m in three to four seconds.

• 20 seconds active recovery between reps.

• one minute active recovery between sets.

© Brandon Malone/Action Images

Figure 21: Chelsea players perform multiple sprints during training

Alternative Training Mediums

Most sports are based on running or activities where the player is on their feet (with the obvious exceptions being riding and water-based sports). Continually training in this fashion places impact strains on the feet, ankle and leg joints, as well as the back. Therefore, a cross-training medium is beneficial in developing endurance in an athlete who is predominantly performing on their feet. Two such cross-training activities are outlined, with example sessions, below.

Rowing

This is a sport that utilises the whole body and, therefore, provides an ideal cross-training benefit for endurance training within most sports (sport is a total-body activity). An example of such an activity is the rowing ergometer (Figure 22), which requires the cardiorespiratory system to deliver oxygen to all major muscles in the body in order to maintain workload.

© John Storey/Action Images

Figure 22: Rowing machines are an excellent way to develop endurance in any sports performer by challenging the entire body in a non-load-bearing manner

Examples of rowing sessions that can be undertaken are detailed below:

Example 1: Long interval

• three sets of 10 minutes at 75% intensity.

• two minutes active rest between sets.

Example 2: Short interval

• five minutes at 65% intensity.

• four lots of five minutes at 85% intensity.

• two minutes active rest between sets.

Example 3: Short interval

• five minutes at 65% intensity.

• four minutes at 75% intensity.

• three lots of (two minutes at 80% intensity, two minutes at 90% intensity, two minutes at 65% intensity).

• 90 seconds active recovery between sets.

Example 4:

• six to eight lots of 500m inside target time (for example, 100 seconds for a powerful male athlete with good endurance background, 115 seconds for a female athlete of a similar standard).

• 60 seconds recovery between each set.

Example 5:

• 20 lots of 100m at maximum pace, starting the effort every 60 seconds (ie the quicker the work interval, the longer the recovery time).

Swimming

One of the problems associated with continually using running to develop endurance is that there is a repetitive stress load being applied to the musculoskeletal structures in the legs and feet. One way of overcoming this problem, apart from the use of ergometers, is to utilise swim belts (floatation belts fitted around the player's waist) in deep water. These devices allow the player to remain upright in the water and run through a session without being subject to the impact forces associated with running. The sessions also have a therapeutic benefit, as the hydrostatic pressure of the water will aid muscular recovery from competitive and training stresses in a manner that no other training session can achieve. An example of such an interval session performed in the pool is detailed below.

© Chris Helgren/Action Images/Reuters

Figure 23: Scotland's Rob Dewey undertakes an endurance session in the pool during the 2007 Rugby World Cup

Example 1: Running (with swim belt) interval session in the pool

- five minutes warm-up (jogging at 65% – this will also allow the player to get used to the feeling of running in the water).
- this should be followed by ten lots of 30-second sprints (with 45 seconds recovery between each repetition).
- two minutes active recovery.
- ten lots of 30-second sprints (with 30 seconds active recovery between each sprint).
- two minutes active recovery.
- ten lots of 15-second sprints (10 seconds recovery between each rep).
- cool-down.

If no swim-belt is available, and the player is a competent swimmer, then a swimming programme can also be an effective way of introducing variety into an interval-training programme.

Example 2: Swimming as an interval training session

- warm-up: 200m freestyle.
- ten lots of 75m (three lengths) freestyle (at 100%) with 30 seconds rest between sets.
- two minutes active recovery.
- ten 50m (two lengths) 100% pace with 2:1 work:rest ratio (good swimmers should be aiming for 40 seconds work to 20 seconds recovery).
- two minutes active recovery.
- ten lots of one length freestyle (100%) going every 30 seconds (or 1:1.5 work:rest ratio).
- cool-down: 100m of individual's choice of stroke.

The nature of the sessions described to the left is based on the manipulation of work intensity, in intermittent activities to achieve high levels of match-specific endurance capabilities for the games-based sports. They all have a basis in the scientifically devised principles governing multiple-sprint activities.

Using Bodyweight Circuits

Many sports have traditionally used bodyweight circuits to improve strength in athletes. However, this training method is not really designed to increase strength in an individual as it involves performing multiple repetitions and, as will be detailed in Chapter 4, anything an athlete can perform more than 10 repetitions of, will not sufficiently overload the individual to develop strength. These sessions are, however, excellent for developing cardiovascular endurance in athletes from all sports, particularly those where the performers may not have access to swimming pools, rowing machines etc, or where running is not the preferred means of developing cardiovascular endurance.

Circuits provide coaches with an enormous potential number of options in terms of the nature of the session design. Common variations on the theme include a sequence of push exercises followed by pull exercises; or an upper body exercise followed by a leg exercise followed by a trunk exercise, for example. Exercises can be progressed from one to the next according to how many repetitions have been done or performed for a designated period of time with a fixed work:rest ratio. Exercises can be substituted according to the specific needs of the sport (for example, 30 seconds of wrestling activity for a rugby player, 30 seconds of jumping onto/down from a high box for a hurdler, climbing a rope for a judo player, slalom jumps for a skier etc). The options are really only limited by the coaches imagination. Table 5 below is an example of how such a typical circuit training session might be organised (all exercises detailed are presented within the following pages of this book).

Table 5: Circuit times and recovery

Exercise	Time	Recovery
Press-ups	30 seconds	100m stride
Sit-up with twist	30 seconds	100m stride
Step-up with barbell on shoulders	30 seconds	100m stride
Dips	30 seconds	100m stride
Springboks	30 seconds	100m stride
Multi-directional jumps over low hurdle	30 seconds	100m stride
Pull-ups	30 seconds	100m stride
Crunches	30 seconds	100m stride
Alternate leg squat thrust	30 seconds	100m stride
6 x 20m shuttle sprints	–	–
Active recovery	3 minutes	Jogging
Repeat the above sequence x 3	–	–

Using Conditioning Games

There are many team or group activities that can be modified to develop endurance in sports performers. Such games bring additional variety and movement challenges to an athlete's training routine, as well as being adaptable for the specific endurance needs of a particular sport. Again, the potential variations of the themes (determined by the required work duration, work intensity and work:rest ratios) are limitless, depending upon the imagination of, and resources available to, the coach.

Playing 30 minutes of water polo in a swimming pool is one such challenge, especially if those playing are able to play without touching the floor of the pool. With five players on each side, a game can be played across the width of a standard swimming pool, with goals scored by touching (being in contact with) the ball against the side defended by the opposition. The ball should not be allowed under the water, and possession is lost if it goes onto the poolside. Coaches should take care though that the enthusiasm of the players does not compromise the safety of the activity.

Killer rectangles is another such modified conditioning game combining anaerobic conditioning with agility, balance, coordination, reactions, decision-making and teamwork. It can be played with eight or more players (it works better with 12 players or more), and requires some marker cones, open space and 8–12 foam or soft rubber balls to play. The playing area (size determined by numbers involved) is set up as shown in Figure 24, with four equal playing zones, with each of the two teams split between alternating areas.

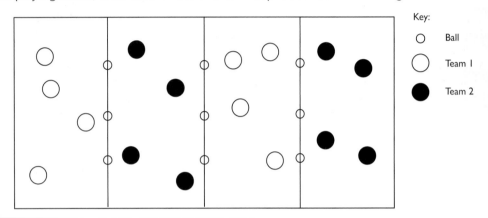

Key:

○ Ball

◯ Team 1

● Team 2

Figure 24: Killer rectangles

On the referee's starting whistle, the athletes collect the balls as quickly as possible and throw them at opposing team members. If an athlete is hit, they must run to the sidelines (coaches can manipulate which one) and perform an exercise (eg 15 down and ups* perform a maximum vertical jump, land and return to the start position = one rep). After doing this, the player rejoins their team. If an athlete catches a flying ball or hits an opponent with a ball, their team receives a point. If a player throws a ball that is caught, they must go to the sideline and perform a different exercise or sequence (eg 10 sit-ups into 10 press-ups) before rejoining the game. When a player is exercising on the sideline, they are out of the game and can not be targeted. Resting players can be around the outside to retrieve any stray balls. Play up to four quarters of five minutes, with the winning team being the one with the most points. Variations in the playing side numbers, playing area, having four separate teams and more/fewer balls are all means of providing variation to the game.

*A down and up involves the following: lie face down on the floor, stretch arms out to the side with legs straight and together (forming a crucifix position), then stand up.

Endurance Development Using Skill and Match-play Practices

Efficient use of training time is important for both the coach and the athlete, and combining elements of training is an ideal way to achieve this, particularly if a coach has limited time with athletes. Therefore, introducing endurance training to a technical coaching session is an ideal training method. If this comes at the start of the session, be aware that the player will be fatigued during later practice, which may interfere with skill/technique development. However, if the endurance training is always done at the end of training, the player will never learn to perform skills (or skills will never be tested) when fatigued, so variation on this is required within the long-term programme.

Example 1: On-court endurance training for tennis

From match analysis, it is understood that within a match players will get a maximum rest of 25 seconds between points and 90 seconds every other game. Coaches should also bear in mind that points between well-matched players last, on average, 5–10 seconds. Therefore, if a player is forced to return 15 fed balls to an identified target area of the court, at a ratio of 1.3–1.5 seconds per fed ball, then a 20-second work interval will be established. The player should not know how many points they will be forced to play during the interval, nor will they know how or where the next shot will be played or what the next shot will be. In this way, the conditioned practice replicates game play very closely; every shot should be played with maximum intensity.

Heart-rate monitors are excellent ways to monitor how hard a person is working. A coach can monitor a player's heart rate (HR) and compare it to a known maximum HR to see how much time a player is spending working at different percentages of the maximum.

Such sessions can last for 60 minutes, with the player being forced to take a 90 second break every 10 minutes or so.

Example 2: Defensive re-alignment development and endurance training for rugby

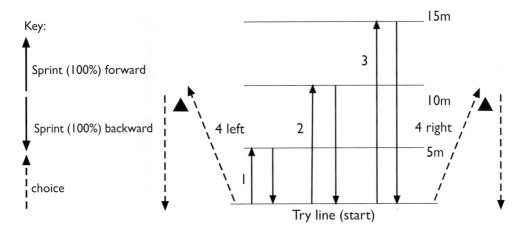

Figure 25: The defensive re-alignment development and endurance training drill for rugby union

To conduct the above endurance drill, the coach will need a 15m measuring tape and two cones.

How it works:

- Start on the try line (start), lying on their back.
- Sprint to the 5m line, touch with the feet, and sprint backwards to the start (point 1 in Figure 25).
- At the try line, lie on the floor so that the chest touches the ground, and get up as soon as possible.
- Sprint to the 10m line, touch with the hand, turn and sprint back to the start line (point 2).
- At the try line, lie on the floor so the chest touches the ground and get up as soon as possible.
- Sprint to the 15m line (point 3), stop and do three down and ups.
- Sprint back to the start line.
- Here, the coach calls 'left' or 'right', or a code word, and the player has to sprint to the diagonal cone on the 10m line, turn around it, and sprint back to finish (point 4).

Notes:

- The drill can be made harder by putting a tackle bag at each of the lines and making the player make a tackle at each line.
- This can also be done as a communication drill, by making a line of players move through the tackles at the same time, as long as the slowest ones do not make the fastest ones lose the endurance benefit of the drill's intensity.
- Perform three sets of 4–6 reps with 20 seconds between reps for elite players and up to 40 seconds between reps for club players.
- Include two minutes between sets for both levels of participant.

Example 3: Football

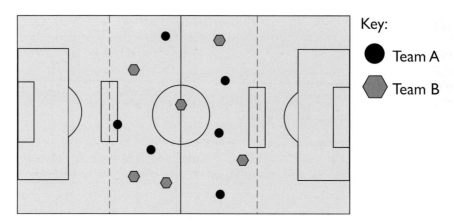

Figure 26: Six-a-side fitness game for football

- This is a six-a-side game on a modified pitch, with no goalkeepers.
- To score, all players must be in the attacking half (or another attacking area that the coach can specify to make the players work harder).
- Two of these players must be in the goal (dark grey) areas.
- The ball is passed into the grey area and controlled by an attacking player for a goal to be scored[15].
- The smaller the attacking area, the higher the intensity of the game.
- If one member of the defending team is not in the defending zone when a goal is scored, it is counted as double.

Example 4: Small-sided games

Without manipulating anything other than playing pitch size and numbers in the teams, playing small-sided games has been shown to have particular conditioning and skill development benefits. For example, research published in *Insight* (the Football Association coaches' journal) in 2003 demonstrated that playing 4 v 4 games had a number of benefits (demonstrated in the box below) that are great for, in particular, a young child's development in the game of football. These findings have been recently supported by a study at the University of Abertay in Scotland (Small, G, 2006). In a conditioning sense, because the child has more involvement in the small-sided game, and this revolves around 1–5 seconds of speed-based work, followed by short recovery periods, small-sided games are excellent for developing both slow-glycolysis and more important ATP-CP energy supply pathways. This makes them particularly important for the pre-pubescent athlete, who can not effectively utilise fast glycolytic energy pathways, as outlined earlier. Evidence from male professional players demonstrated average heart rates above 200 when playing such small-sided games, so this principle does not simply apply to children.

A study at Manchester United (*Insight*, 2003) found players involved in small-sided games (4 v 4 compared to 7 v 7) increased:

- passes by 135% (585 more passes)
- scoring attempts by 260% (481 more attempts)
- goals scored by 500% (301 more goals)
- 1 v 1 encounters by 225% (525 more 1 v 1s)
- tricks demonstrated (an obvious marker of player-confidence) by 280% (436 more dribbling skills).

Testing Endurance Levels

As with other elements of an athlete's physical conditioning, it is important the coach is able to assess the endurance capabilities of their performer(s). At the start of a programme, this information will provide the coach with baseline data that can be used to set the parameters for the subsequent programme and set realistic SMARTER[16] goals for the player. Tests can also be used periodically within a programme in order to determine how well an athlete is progressing on the training schedule set by the coach. All fitness tests must meet two criteria: they must be valid and reliable.

Validity relates to the ability of the test to measure exactly what it is supposed to. This is important for measuring sport-specific endurance, as there are many testing protocols that exist and can be used, but the extent to which they measure sports-specific endurance needs careful consideration.

Reliability refers to the repeatability of the test. If a test is not repeatable, in that the athletes can undergo exactly the same procedure, under the same conditions, with the same scoring methods etc, then no direct comparisons can be made between one test and the next. The coach will therefore have no idea if any progress has been made.

The gold standard means of measuring a player's endurance capability (whether this be VO_2 max or anaerobic power) is to take the player to an accredited sports science laboratory. This is impractical for all but the elite, as testing of this nature is complicated, time consuming and expensive to complete. Therefore, coaches should use field tests to obtain an objective (ie data-based) analysis of their athlete's endurance capabilities.

One of the best-known tests for gaining a reasonably accurate estimate of an athlete's VO_2 max (maximal aerobic capacity) is the multi-stage fitness test* (commonly referred to as the bleep test). This involves an athlete running between two markers placed 20m apart, at specifically timed intervals and with progressively increasing levels of difficulty. This commences with level one, where the individual has eight seconds to complete the 20m and goes up to level 21, where the speed required makes it difficult for many to complete the distance in the time given, even if they were starting the 20m distance afresh. This test has been very popular for a number of years. However, it has several limitations for sports performers. Firstly, it has

---

* Available from **Coachwise 1st4sport**. For a full range of sports education and training equipment, please visit www.1st4sport.com or call 0113-201 5555.

been validated to estimate VO$_2$ max, which as previously explained, is not a requirement for many sports performers who fall out with the 'engine' sports (and even then it is less important than previously thought). It is especially not valid for the multiple-sprint performer who needs to be able to make repeated maximal efforts without fatiguing. Secondly, the majority of the bleep test is spent running at sub-maximal paces at artificially controlled speeds, which are alien to the sportsperson and influence the efficiency of their movement. Therefore, the validity of the bleep test as a measure of the endurance capability of the athlete is very questionable.

A test does not have to produce a specific estimate of the players VO$_2$ max or other scientific measurement. A test should be simple to set up, simple to implement and record a number that a coach can use to evaluate how the player is progressing in relation to previous tests. The test should incorporate as many sport-specific elements as possible (eg movement patterns), as long as these can be controllable by the coach.

Example 1: Anaerobic endurance shuttle test

This test has been used to assess the endurance capacities of rugby players but it is suitable for many high-intensity intermittent sports. It involves short sprints of between 5–25m, with turning[17], running at maximal speeds and getting up and down from the floor. In order to keep the surface constant, the test will ideally be set up inside. The coach will need a 25m tape measure (or similar measuring device), cones, a stopwatch, a pen and the scoring sheet (Figure 27b) shown on page 47.

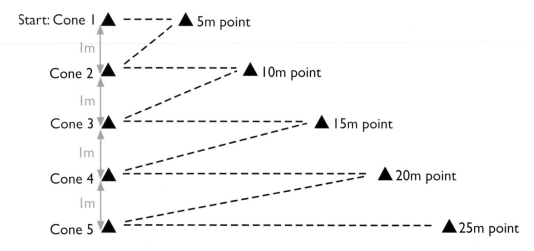

Figure 27a: The anaerobic endurance shuttle test

How it works:

- The course should be marked out as illustrated in Figure 27a.
- Begin at the start line (Cone 1), in a prone position (lying down on front) facing forwards.
- On the 'Go' command (start stopwatch) sprint to the 5m point (hand touches the cone).
- Turn, sprint to Cone 2 then sprint to the 10m point.
- Turn, sprint to Cone 3, lie prone, get up, and sprint to the 15m point.
- Repeat sets to 25m point.

Notes:

• The player goes down onto the chest at the start, at Cone 3 and Cone 5.

• The player does a simple turn and sprint at Cones 2 and 4.

• The aim is to work at 100% and go as far as possible in 30 seconds. Players must not pace themselves; this will reduce the validity of the test.

• After 30 seconds, the whistle is blown and the point the player reaches is marked on the score sheet (see Figure: 27b) with a '1'. The set is repeated and the point the player reaches is marked with a '2', etc.

• In the example provided (Figure 27b) the player manages to achieve 135m in the first trial.

• If the player manages to complete the whole 150m course in 30 seconds, they sprint back to Cone 1 and start again.

• The stopwatch is kept running and the player walks back to the start.

• After 60 seconds the whistle is blown again and the player begins Trial 2.

• The 30-second work:30-second rest pattern is followed for 5 minutes 30 seconds, by which time the player has completed six trials and has distances recorded for each.

• Total distance is calculated by adding up all the individual trial distances.

The fatigue index is calculated as a percentage of the fastest effort, as follows:

$$100 - \left(\frac{\text{Distance of shortest trial*}}{\text{Distance of furthest trial**}} \times 100 \right)$$

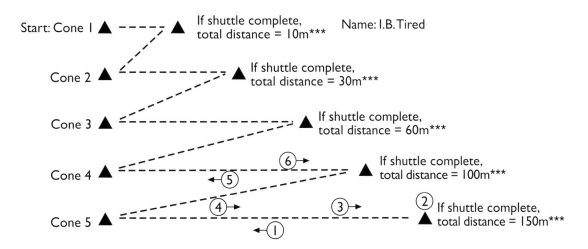

Trial	1	2	3	4	5	6	Total distance	Fatigue index
Trial distance (m)	135	125	120	110	90	75	655	44.5%

Figure 27b: Example of the anaerobic shuttle test score sheet

*   Should be Trial 6
**   Should be Trial 1
***   For the purposes of this exercise, total shuttle distance will disregard the slight increase caused by the diagonal return run.

Example 2: The 40m sprint test

This test is less intensive and is more suited to sports such as soccer, where periods of action are more intermittent. Match analysis indicates the longest sprint a player would normally undertake in a game is 40m (average 17m), with sprinting or high-intensity action occurring once every 70 seconds. To conduct this test, a coach will require a 20m measuring tape, two stopwatches, two testers, a scoring chart (as below) and a pen.

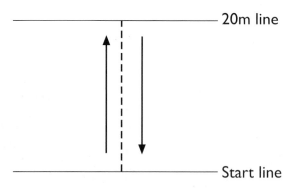

Figure 28a: The 40m sprint test

Sprint	1	2	3	4	5	6	7	8	9	10	Total sprint time
Time											

$$\text{Fatigue Index} = 100 - \left(\frac{\text{Time of slowest sprint*}}{\text{Time of fastest sprint**}} \times 100 \right)$$

Figure 28b: The 40m sprint-test score sheet

How it works:

- Set the course up as illustrated in Figure 28a.
- After a thorough warm-up, the players go to the start position.
- Tester 1 shouts 'Go' and immediately starts the stopwatch.
- Tester 2 immediately starts the other stopwatch, which will act as a running clock.
- Players sprint from the start line to the 20m line, touch it with a foot, turn and sprint back to the start line (total distance 40m) in the fastest time possible.
- The time for Sprint 1 is recorded.
- When 50 seconds show on the running clock, the players are called back to the start line.
- When 60 seconds show, Tester 1 shouts 'Go' and players begin Sprint 2.
- This process is repeated, with the player starting a sprint every minute until 10 sprints have been completed.

Notes:

- The coach should record total sprint time and the fatigue index, and use these to compare athlete improvement between tests.

*should be Sprint 10
**should be Sprint 1

Example 3: The 4000m fartlek test

With some imagination, the coach can devise other testing methods that allow a whole squad/group to be measured while performing simultaneously, making the process more easily adaptable for a group coaching session. The fartlek test (Figure 29) illustrates how this can be achieved. This is a continuous test that can be employed to see how quickly players can cover a 4000m distance (approximately half the distance recorded for backs in rugby union or outfield players in soccer). It is important to note this is not a test that measures how quickly an athlete can run 4000m, as this would not represent the stop–start nature of intermittent sport. Because it is self-paced, this test (and others of a similar nature) also provides the coach with an indication of how much motivational drive the athlete has to push themselves in endurance-training sessions.

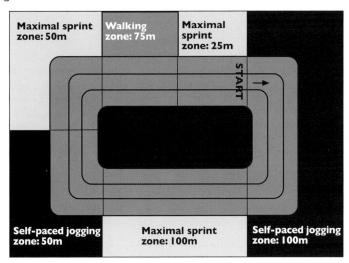

Figure 29: The fartlek test

How it works:

- Mark out a 400m athletics track, as identified in Figure 29.
- Following a thorough warm-up, the squad all start together on the start line.
- On the coach's 'Go' command, the athletes run around the track (in the direction indicated by the arrow).
- In the areas marked for maximal sprints, the athletes must run as fast as they possibly can.
- In the self-paced areas, they can choose how quickly they wish to go.
- In the walking zone, the athletes are not allowed to overtake squad members. They can go as slow as they want to, but can not overtake someone else who is in front of them (in this zone only). This means that, as in a game when they are required to work sub-maximally off the ball, they are forced to work a bit harder to get the best result (ie the best possible time).
- The coach should record the total time taken for 10 laps (ie 4000m).

Notes:

- The objective is to complete the 4000m in the fastest possible time, applying the above, zoned conditions.
- As a result, in the first part of the test they work as hard as they can, in the middle part they work as hard as they want to, and in the final part their work rate is determined by someone else.
- The coach can record, with one stopwatch, the total amount of time it takes each athlete to complete the test.

Example 4: The Kosmin Test

The Kosmin test is an example of a sports-, indeed event-specific, test of anaerobic power and endurance that coaches can use to predict the 800m performance of their athlete. Similar predictive tests exist for the 1500m, but also for a range of other sports-specific performances.

The 800m Kosmin test involves the athlete running around a 400m track for two maximal efforts of 60 seconds at a time, with the coach observing and marking where the athlete completes the 60 seconds. There is a three-minute rest period between the efforts of 60 seconds and the athlete starts again on the track where the first 60 seconds expired. This might, for example, be at 420m. Should the athlete then cover another 405m in 60 seconds, the total distance covered is 825m. This figure is then compared to the predicted table produced by the British Milers club (Table 5) to achieve an estimate of the athlete's 800m performance that may reflect competitive performance, but will certainly provide a motivational goal for the athlete and also a measure of progress on a test–retest basis.

Table 5: The Kosmin test

Kosmin Test					
Distance Projected (m)	800m Time (minutes: seconds)	Distance (m)	Projected 800m Time	Distance (m)	Projected 800m Time
500	2:38.0	655	2:19.5	805	2:01.6
505	37.4	660	18.9	810	1.0
510	36.8	665	18.3	815	0.4
515	36.2	670	17.7	820	1:59.9
520	35.6	675	17.1	825	59.2
525	35.0	680	16.5	830	58.6
530	34.4	685	15.9	835	58.0
535	33.8	690	15.3	840	57.4
540	33.2	695	14.7	845	56.8
545	32.6	700	14.1	850	56.2
550	32.0	705	13.5	855	55.7
555	31.4	710	12.9	860	55.1
560	30.8	715	12.3	865	54.5
565	30.2	720	11.7	870	53.9
570	29.6	725	11.1	875	53.3
575	29.0	730	10.5	880	52.7
580	28.4	735	9.9	885	52.1
585	27.8	740	9.4	890	51.5
590	27.2	745	8.8	895	50.9
595	25.6	750	8.2	900	50.3
600	26.0	755	7.6	905	49.7
605	25.4	760	7.0	910	49.1
610	24.8	765	6.4	915	48.5
615	24.2	770	5.8	920	47.9
620	23.6	775	5.2	925	47.3
625	23.0	780	4.6	930	46.6
630	22.4	785	4.0	935	46.0
635	21.8	790	3.4	940	45.4
640	21.2	795	2.8	945	44.8
645	20.6	800	2.2	950	44.2
650	20.1				

Summary

Appropriately designed endurance training for sports performers should facilitate:

- increased cell myoglobin content, increased capillary density and number of mitochondria for improved transport of oxygen to the cell and improved utilisation of oxygen within the muscle
- increased efficiency of the cardiovascular system for increased stroke volume per beat, increased cardiac output and increased waste product removal
- increased muscle glycogen stores
- enhanced quality and function of muscle fibres, particularly fast-twitch fibres
- increased activity of enzymes involved in the process of producing energy aerobically and anaerobically from glucose and glycogen
- improved resistance to fatigue during high-intensity exercise
- enhanced ability to repeat multi-directional speed of movement.

Coaches should base their endurance-training sessions upon an analysis of their particular sport. Objectives determine methods: once the principle energy systems for the sport have been identified and the principle muscle fibres required, the work and recovery intensities and work:rest ratios, can be identified.

Coaches can achieve overload in an interval training session by manipulating any of the following:

- The duration of the work interval.
- The mode (walk, jog) and length of the rest interval (both factors are determined by the predominant work:rest interval).
- The intensity of the work interval (determined by the energy supply mechanism predominant for the individual sport).
- The total volume of work done (remembering that more is not necessarily always better).

Efficient coaching practice involves incorporating endurance drills into training sessions and combining them with skill- and/or situation-specific practices. When designing these practices, the coach should be guided by their imagination and the scientific principles governing the energy supply requirements and work:rest ratios for their sport.

Tests for sport-specific endurance should be repeatable, interpretable, easy to implement and measure, and should test the individuals' capabilities to perform the endurance requirements of the sport in question.

References

Christmass, M.A., Richmond, S.E., Cable, N.T. and Hartmann, P.E. (1995) 'A metabolic characterisation of singles tennis' in *Science and Racket Sports II* (1998) Lees, A., Maynard, I., Hughes, M. and Reilly, T. (eds). London: E. and F.N. Spon. ISBN: 978-0-419230-30-0.

Elliott, B., Dawson, B. and Pyke, F. (1985) 'The ergogenics of singles tennis', *Journal of Human Movement Studies* 11: 11–20.

Fenoglio, R. (2003). The Manchester United 4 v 4 Pilot Scheme for U9's: Part 2: The Analysis *Insight – The FA Coaches Association Resource,* Autumn, 2003.

International Tennis Federation (2000) Rules of Tennis. London: ITF Ltd.

Meir, R., Colla, P. and Milligan, C. (2001) *'Impact of the 10-meter rule change on professional rugby league: implications for training,'* Strength and Conditioning Journal 23 (6): 42–6.

Reilly, T. and Palmer, J. (1995) 'Investigation of exercise intensity in male tennis single/lawn tennis' in *Science and Racket Sports II*, Lees, A., Maynard, I., Hughes, M. and Reilly, T. (eds). London: E. and F.N. Spon. ISBN: 978-0-419230-30-0.

Small, G (2006) *Small-sided games study of young football athletes in Scotland,* Independent consultation paper for the Scottish FA.

Further Reading

Siff, M. (2003) *Supertraining*. Supertraining Institute. ISBN: 978-1-874856-65-8.

Stafford, I. (2004) *Coaching for Long-term Athlete Development*. Leeds: Coachwise Business Solutions/The National Coaching Foundation. ISBN: 978-1-902523-70-9.*

To purchase wristwatch monitors, as mentioned in the Determining Exercise Intensity section of this chapter, please contact **Coachwise 1st4sport** at the points of contact below.

For other resources on LTAD principles, please contact **Coachwise 1st4sport**.

* Available from **Coachwise 1st4sport**. For a full range of sports education and training equipment, please visit www.1st4sport.com or call 0113-201 5555.

Chapter 4
Developing Strength and Power

Introduction

There have probably been more misconceptions about the role of strength training in sport and the products of strength training than any other element of fitness training. This chapter addresses some of the common misconceptions, demonstrates that strength and power training is a fundamental underpinning for all sports programmes and provides coaches with guidelines for specific exercises that will promote sport-specific strength.

Strength

Strength is the ability of the muscle to exert a force against a load. It is a vector quantity, in terms of application, direction of the force and the magnitude of application of that force. The force created is a result of the contraction of specific muscles. Strength gain in the muscles (as a result of appropriate training) is specific to the angle of the joint at which training has occurred.

In sport, forces are required to be exerted externally (eg against the ground, to move the body forward, or against an external object, such as a ball, javelin or opponent) and internally (eg against a bone, to move a limb around a joint).

Strength is important in sports to:

- enhance performance by allowing the more forceful application of skills
- act as a basis for long-term power development
- aid in the prevention of contact and non-contact injuries.

However, before designing a sport-specific strength-training programme, the coach needs to understand the answers to the following questions:

- What is the nature of the strength or power required?
- What joint actions (and therefore what muscle groups) need to be trained?
- What types of muscle actions are involved?
- What is the most appropriate method to use in order to achieve the desired objectives?

Sport-specific technique can be considered to be the result of the appropriate application of the developed force, which is a product of strength and motor control. Such motor control is developed through the nervous system and appropriate strength training has been shown to lead to improved neuromuscular efficiency aiding performance in biomechanically similar movements (Stone, 2000).

Functional strength is therefore related to being strong in the normal movement patterns for an athlete in their particular sporting situation. As will be demonstrated in the following chapter, functional strength can be considered as being where performance outcomes are the result of multi-muscle, multi-joint movements, with muscles co-acting with each other to produce:

- efficient movement
- multi-planar forces
- a stable structure to support that movement.

Power

Strength is also the precursor to power, which is probably the most important characteristic an athlete can develop. Within physics, power is described as the product of work done (or energy expended) per unit of time. As energy can be seen to be the product of force x the distance moved in the direction of force, power can also be seen to be:

$$\text{Power} = \frac{\text{force x distance}}{\text{time}}$$

Velocity is the product of displacement (distance moved from the starting point) divided by the time taken to move that distance. Therefore, we can replace the distance element of the power equation to say that:

Power = force x velocity (so 'powerful' athletes have the ability to exert large forces quickly).

Power is therefore dependent upon the magnitude of the strength component, which may be a primary determinant in contact-oriented sports, such as rugby. It is also dependent upon the speed (velocity) component, which will be the key factor in sports where power is determined by the velocity component, such as tennis (racket-head speed) or soccer (Figure 30).

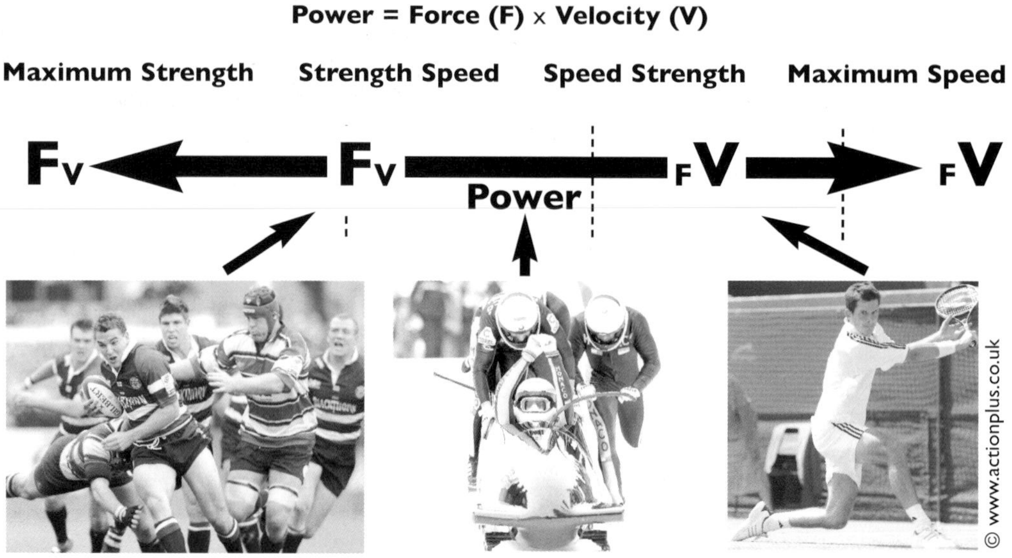

Power = Force (F) × Velocity (V)

| Maximum Strength | Strength Speed | Speed Strength | Maximum Speed |

$$\mathbf{F_V} \longleftarrow \mathbf{F_V} \underset{\textbf{Power}}{=\!=\!=\!=} {}_{\mathbf{F}}\mathbf{V} \longrightarrow {}_{\mathbf{F}}\mathbf{V}$$

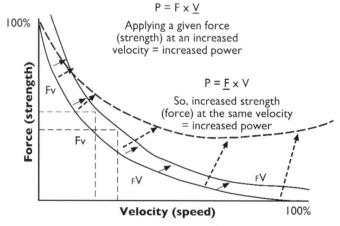

Figure 30: The force–velocity continuum

The relationship between force and velocity needs careful consideration in the context of long-term training plans. The relationship can typically be explained by considering a force–velocity curve. Figure 31 demonstrates that, at any given time, power can be expressed as the product of force x velocity and, by altering the input of either variable, a change in the nature of the power produced can be achieved.

$$P = F \times \underline{V}$$

Applying a given force (strength) at an increased velocity = increased power

$$P = \underline{F} \times V$$

So, increased strength (force) at the same velocity = increased power

100%

Force (strength)

Fv

Fv

ғV   ғV

Velocity (speed)   100%

Figure 31: The force–velocity curve, indicating the role of the strength training to increasing power in an athlete

One thing is certain, the coach needs to correctly understand the nature of power required for performance in their particular sport. It is no good being the strongest, slowest 15m shot-putter in the world if the performance requirement is for sufficient power to throw 18m. Similar parallels can be drawn from any sport. However, as Figure 31 demonstrates, the gradient of the force–velocity curve is constant, and to shift the power line to the right (make the performer more powerful), which is a realistic expectation of training, the coach must improve both the force-producing capacity and the velocity-producing capacity of the athlete. Regardless of the nature of the sport, some time within the programme must be spent increasing the athlete's maximum strength, proportionally to the velocity component of the programme. As Figure 32 (below) demonstrates, nowhere in science is there the ability to alter the gradient of the power curve (ie attempt to raise the speed end without raising the strength end, as shown by the dashed line) by focusing on speed training only. There must be a focus on increasing both maximum strength and maximum speed at different times within the programme (see Chapter 10) in order to functionally increase the ability to produce power.

So, to achieve a long-term goal of learning to produce the necessary force (for the sports performance) in the minimum time required, a series of prerequisite objectives need to be met. Firstly, for the athlete to produce greater force through full range of motion, by improving their absolute strength and/or strength:body weight ratio.

The next objective is to produce this increased force in a decreased time. As strength and now speed are being developed, the athlete will also have been practising technique drills (to reinforce the motor pattern of the skill). Therefore, after a period of time, the athlete will be able to apply their power through skill application, producing increased force in a proper direction to enable optimal skill execution.

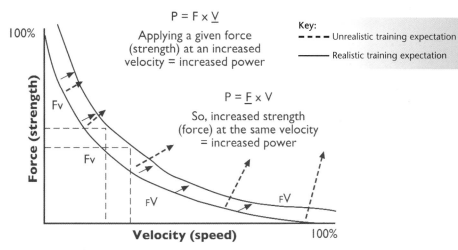

Figure 32: To increase power capability, the athlete's programme needs to focus on maximum strength and velocity components at different stages of the programme

Understanding Force in Sports Performance

Force generation is determined by Newton's second law: Force = mass x acceleration

Acceleration is important as this results in velocity, which is the vital component of power. It is also very important to realise the rate at which force is developed (RFD) is associated with acceleration capabilities in athletes and this can be a determining factor in generating superior athletic performance. Most critical aspects of sports performance occur in very short time frames (<250 milliseconds). If athletes can be trained to produce greater forces within that time frame, then greater accelerations, and therefore velocities, can be achieved.

For example, an elite sprinter has a ground contact time of 0.09 seconds compared with a developmental or non-elite sprinter, who may have a ground contact time of 0.12 seconds (the longer the ground contact time, the less elite the performer will be). It is only during contact with the ground that the elite sprinter is able to exert force against the ground, so that their centre of mass is propelled forward. So, the goal of the elite sprinter is to produce as much force as possible in 0.09 seconds. While ground contact times vary between sports (for example, in long jump the ground contact time is 0.11–0.16 seconds depending upon the athlete; in high jump it is typically 0.18–0.22 seconds), the basic principle still applies: the goal is to produce the maximum amount of force in the minimum amount of time (whether against the ground or an object, such as a racket contacting a ball). Hence, the ability to produce force (strength) and its related component, RFD, is an integral part of power production and, as such, may be a key component in determining athletic success.

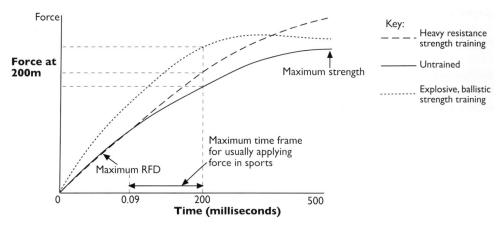

Figure 33: Force production as a result of training type[18]

Figure 33 shows the RFD and force at 0.2 seconds for untrained (solid line), heavy-resistance trained (dashed line) and explosive-ballistic trained (dotted line) subjects.

The Importance of Sport-specific Strength and Power Training

The concept of strength training should be very specific to the nature of the sport the athlete is being conditioned for. Most sports require higher levels of power and acceleration rather than absolute strength or increased muscle bulk. For example, force is applied for 0.09–0.3 seconds during the ground-support phase of running (depending upon the speed), whereas peak force production requires up to 0.6–0.8 seconds in dynamic movements. Even in largely non-ballistic movement activities, such as cycling, rowing or swimming, performance is usually determined by the ability to generate force quickly and thereby achieve a critical force output, more often than not within the 0.2-seconds time frame. Therefore, in order to be effective, training methods need to be based around exercises that develop maximal force in gross muscle structure in minimal amounts of time, because most sports rely on large groups of muscles working together to execute skilful movements.

As illustrated in Figure 33, a performer who is untrained cannot generate a large overall force, particularly when compared to someone who has undertaken resistance training designed to promote maximum strength. However, if you compare the rate of force development that is achievable up to, and at, 200 milliseconds with untrained and maximum-strength-trained performers, there is not much difference between them. In a sportsperson who has been trained using methods designed to promote explosive strength, however, it can be seen that, although the maximum amount of force that can be generated is much less than in someone who has undertaken heavy-resistance strength training, the rate of force production is significantly greater, particularly at the vital 200 millisecond point. This makes explosive-strength training a very real and highly relevant underpinning component of a sportsperson's training programme.

There is significant evidence to indicate the efficacy of using high-force, high-velocity, movement-specific training exercises in order to produce superior performance gains in strength-/power-oriented sports (Stone, 2000). In all sports, the biggest physical training priority (ie factors that primarily influence winning and losing) is strength and speed (power). In any given situation, it is usually the most physically powerful team/individuals that will predominate. This has been backed up by a number of studies in the USA (Stone, 2002), which have compared performance measures with power, both in the short and long term, and which demonstrate a strong positive association between maximum strength, sports performance and related variables. Also, given that stronger athletes tend to be more powerful, it is safe to hypothesize that more powerful athletes are better performers. Therefore, performers should strive to become as strong as possible, and then as powerful as possible, within the context of their sport (Stone, 2002). **As identified earlier, to become more powerful, an athlete has first to become stronger (left hand end of the Fv curve on Figure 32) then this can form the basis of power and speed (right hand end of fV curve on Figure 32)**. Power is a prerequisite physical characteristic underpinning many aspects of sporting performance including acceleration, directional change, jumping actions and sports-specific skills (Hoff et al, 2001; Newton et al., 1997, Wisloff et al., 2004). Imagine being a defender in soccer and trying to mark a centre forward who has the ability to jump one metre off the ground. Alternatively, imagine playing against a netball player who can rapidly explode a pass the length of the court; tackling a rugby player who can efficiently change direction at pace and/or accelerate into contact, or a tennis player who can consistently serve at 145 mph. **Power is a prerequisite physical characteristic for each of these skills, regardless of the sporting context (acceleration, directional change, top speed, jumping, turning and man-on-man play)** [research summarised in Brewer and Stone, 2005].

Understanding the Role of Strength in Endurance Performance

Many sports with large endurance components (such as rowing, cycling and marathon running) have traditionally approached strength training with a view to developing strength endurance. This has meant they have engaged in practices using light resistive loads and many repetitions, with little recovery. However, this is nothing more than a cardiovascular session for the athlete (as will be explained later, performing more than a 10-repetition maximum of any exercise has little effect on developing strength).

Consider this challenge, identical twins that both have a body mass of 70kg. Twin A can bench press (see page 95) 140kg (twice his body weight, meaning he has exceptional levels of upper-body strength). Twin B can bench press 70kg (his bodyweight). If we were looking to measure their upper body strength endurance, who would do the most clap press-ups (see page 147)?

The answer is Twin A. If strength is the ability to exert (maximal) forces, then strength endurance is simply about exerting (maximal) forces repeatedly. Now, if Twin A can bench press double bodyweight x one repetition, then he can do 140 x 1, 135 x 2, 130 x 4, 125 x 6, 120 x 8, 115 x 12, 110 x 15 – 70kg (bodyweight) x 40. However, Twin B can only do this once (allowing for a bit of mechanical difference between doing a bodyweight press-up and lifting body mass on a bar). We can also analyse this from a mechanical efficiency perspective: when Twin B is doing the clap press-ups, he is working at 100% effort. When Twin A is doing the clap press-ups, he is working at 50% maximal effort.

So, by increasing maximal force capacity, sub-maximal work becomes more efficient (ie less energy cost for the same amount of work – the goal for any endurance performance).

What will be a limiting factor in such tests as the press-up is not strength (for Twin A) but cardiovascular fitness. This is being taken care of in all the other sessions the endurance athlete (runner, rower, cyclist etc) takes part in as part of their programme. Therefore, when these athletes go into the gym, they should not spend time doing another cardiovascular session – this will not give them better strength endurance. If they invest their time improving maximal (relative term) strength, the strength endurance will improve proportionally.

© Mark Sheerman

Figure 34: World marathon record holder Paula Radcliffe performs squats to improve her strength and therefore her movement efficiency

Movement Analysis: Sport and Training Movements

Sports are based on the application of strength and power through practice at movement-specific patterns. These patterns of movement can be determined through notational analysis of movement. The result is a stronger and faster athlete; a concept that is obviously beneficial in the explosive, sometimes collision-based, power-oriented world of sports, whatever sport or position the athlete plays.

So, in a strength context, what do we mean by position-specific movement? This relates to two major concepts. Firstly, the nature of muscle action that can occur within sport-specific movements and secondly, the nature of joint actions occuring within sporting actions.

Muscular and Joint Action

There are three major types of muscular action seen during sports performance, as outlined below (refer to Chapter 2 for more information on muscle structure).

Concentric Action
This is where one or both myotendinous ends of the muscle (ie the tendon joining muscle to bone) move towards each other and the muscle is shortened, during the contraction.

Eccentric Action
This is where the muscle is actively lengthened while contracted. A muscle can only be lengthened by a greater opposing force (eg an external load or a force exerted by a different muscle), as it cannot actively lengthen by itself.

Isometric Action
Iso – same, *metric* – length. In this type of contraction, the force generated by the muscle is equal to the resistive mass opposing it and so the muscle remains the same length while contracting.

Figure 35 illustrates the relationship between resistive load and muscular action in concentric, eccentric and isometric muscle action. $9.81 m/s^2$ is the constant force exerted by gravity.

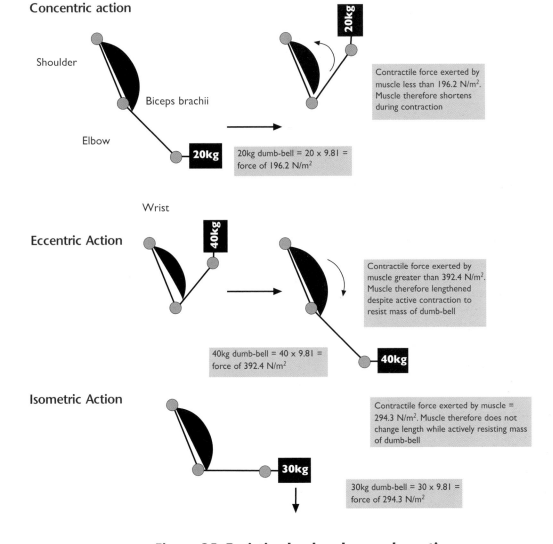

Concentric action

Shoulder

Biceps brachii

Elbow

20kg

20kg

Contractile force exerted by muscle less than 196.2 N/m². Muscle therefore shortens during contraction

20kg dumb-bell = 20 x 9.81 = force of 196.2 N/m²

Wrist

Eccentric Action

40kg

40kg

Contractile force exerted by muscle greater than 392.4 N/m². Muscle therefore lengthened despite active contraction to resist mass of dumb-bell

40kg dumb-bell = 40 x 9.81 = force of 392.4 N/m²

Isometric Action

Contractile force exerted by muscle = 294.3 N/m². Muscle therefore does not change length while actively resisting mass of dumb-bell

30kg

30kg dumb-bell = 30 x 9.81 = force of 294.3 N/m²

Figure 35: Resistive load and muscular action

Stretch-shortening Action

Stretched muscles store elastic energy. Also, as discussed in Chapter 2, the stretch-shortening cycle of muscular contraction involves stretch receptors in a muscle sensing the rate and length of the stretch in a fibre. These receptors initiate a forceful, reflex, concentric contraction in the muscle when the rate of strength reaches a threshold point. Many sporting actions rely on this to enable a muscle to reach maximal strength in a short space of time. This works by stretching a muscle and then relying on its elastic properties to produce greater forces than are normally possible in the reflex contraction (ie as the muscle returns to its resting length). In order to achieve this greater muscular force, the muscle must contract within the shortest possible time after it has been lengthened.

As identified in Chapter 2, muscles are either contracted or they are not. Those muscles responsible for the initiation of a particular movement are called prime movers. As we know, muscles are arranged in pairs and every muscle has an opposing muscle or group of muscles. While it is easy to think that when a muscle is active, its antagonistic/opposing partner is not, in reality this is very rarely the case. The opposing muscle is usually involved in a stabilising role or it is eccentrically working to brake or control the movement created in a joint by the prime mover. Thus muscles can be prime movers in one movement, stabilisers in another, and synergists (muscles indirectly assisting the prime movers) in other movements. This is particularly important when a prime mover crosses two joints. A classic example can be seen in the deadlift in Figure 36 (a full breakdown of this lift can be seen on page 87).

Figure 36: The Deadlift

This exercise involves the simultaneous extension of the knee and hip joints from the starting position shown above. In order to achieve this, the quadriceps muscle group is the prime mover. Of this group, the *rectus femoris* muscle crosses both the hip and the knee joint and is responsible for flexion in the hip and extension of the knee. If both of these actions were to occur simultaneously, the athlete performing the deadlift would not be able to stand straight up from the start position. Therefore, the *gluteal* muscles in the buttock are also concentrically contracted at the same time as the rectus femoris. Broadly speaking, in this activity, the gluteal muscles are responsible for hip extension, and this action counters the hip-flexing actions of the rectus femoris muscle. This then allows the hip and knee to extend and the athlete to perform the full deadlift, ending in a standing position.

Understanding the Nature of Movement-specific Strength Training for Sports

The importance of specificity of training has been highlighted in previous chapters when discussing the principles that underpin effective training. There are many books and training routines published that provide information for aspiring bodybuilders and fitness training participants. However, many of these are not suitable for the development of an athlete or sports performer, as the routines involved do not replicate the force production or movement demands of modern sport. Many routines are based upon training individual muscle groups or particular body parts. As will be illustrated, this does not replicate many sports performance scenarios.

A key phrase to remember when training to enhance sports performance is to train the movements, not the muscles. A strength-training programme needs to reflect the joint involvement and movement pattern, muscle actions and intensity of activity related to the particular sport for which the athlete is training. As such, effective strength training for sports performers begins with a working knowledge of basic movement mechanics. Kinesiological analysis[19] of almost any sporting movement will indicate that the basis of strength–power training exercises for an athlete in any sport should be closed-kinetic-chain exercises[20]. These exercises should also allow maximum force in gross (large) muscle structure (especially around the legs, hips and trunk) to be reached in minimum time. It is well documented that strength (the ability to produce force) and power (the product of force x velocity) gain is specific to the angle of the joint at which training occurs. The training actions and programme design should therefore reflect the total dynamic range of movement an athlete might require in sports performance.

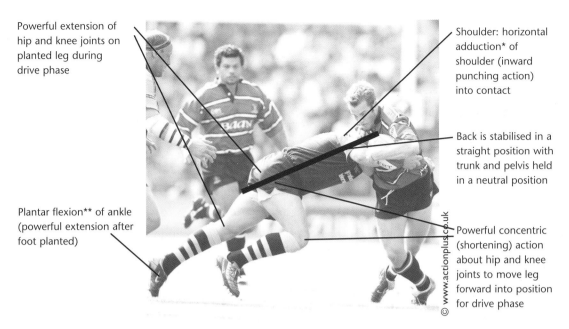

Powerful extension of hip and knee joints on planted leg during drive phase

Shoulder: horizontal adduction* of shoulder (inward punching action) into contact

Back is stabilised in a straight position with trunk and pelvis held in a neutral position

Plantar flexion** of ankle (powerful extension after foot planted)

Powerful concentric (shortening) action about hip and knee joints to move leg forward into position for drive phase

© www.actionplus.co.uk

Figure 37: Basic kinesiological analysis of the head-on tackle in rugby union

(Hidden shoulder) horizontal adduction* of shoulder and powerful extension of elbow into the shot

Horizontal abduction*** (movement away from body) of shoulder and powerful extension of the elbow into the shot

Rotation of trunk about the hip joint

Back is stabilised in straight position with trunk and pelvis held in a neutral position

Powerful triple extension (ankle, knee, hip) as the player stands (from a flexed position) to catch the ball

Powerful triple extension (hip, knee, ankle) from flexed positions as the player moves into the shot

© www.actionplus.co.uk

Figure 38: Basic kinesiological analysis of the hook shot in cricket

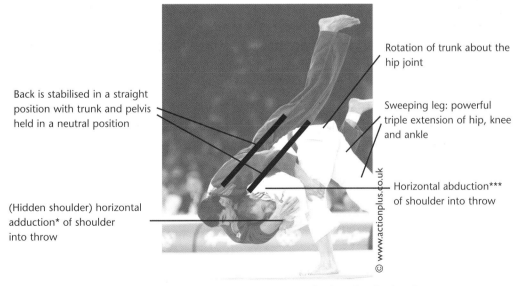

Rotation of trunk about the hip joint

Back is stabilised in a straight position with trunk and pelvis held in a neutral position

Sweeping leg: powerful triple extension of hip, knee and ankle

Horizontal abduction*** of shoulder into throw

(Hidden shoulder) horizontal adduction* of shoulder into throw

© www.actionplus.co.uk

Figure 39: Basic kinesiological analysis of a judo throw

*the movement of a muscle or limb towards the midline of the body
**the movement of pointing toes downwards by extension of the ankle
***the movement of a muscle or limb away from the midline of the body

Powerful extension of elbow into shot

Powerful shoulder flexion from the extended position

Powerful extension of hips, knees and ankles (plantar flexion) to generate vertical and rotational power to give height and speed to serve

Back is stabilised in a straight position with trunk and pelvis held in a neutral position. Very strong position from which to generate power in the limbs

Figure 40: Basic kinesiological analysis of a tennis serve

Powerful extension of the knee

Powerful ankle extension

Powerful extension of the hip

Back straightening to naturally straight position before the swimmer hits the water

© Action Images/Reuters

Figure 41: Basic kinesiological analysis of a block start in swimming

Powerful flexion of the shoulder as throwing arm brought forward

Powerful (eccentric) braking forces at the hip and knee of the front leg

Powerful ankle flexion (dorsiflexion) from extended position

Powerful ankle extension (plantarflexion)

Back straightens as throwing arm is brought forward to impart force into javelin

Pelvis in neutral position

Powerful extension of the knee and hip propels centre of mass forward

© Action Images

Figure 42: Basic kinesiological analysis of the javelin release

Figures 37–42 illustrate the actions of the joints as a function of the prime movers' actions. They do not indicate where, if at all, the joint actions are occurring as a result of gravity or momentum, nor do they indicate any synergistic or stabilising activity occurring in any of the muscles. The purpose of such basic analysis is to enable a coach of a particular sport to calculate the major joint movements involved in that sport and begin to replicate these actions in training movements.

Figures 43–45 show the movement patterns of three major weight-lifting movements (the techniques for which are found on pages 61–62). Comparison between the kinesiological demands of almost any primary sporting movements (ie Figures 37–42) and these training movements indicate many similarities in terms of:

- total body movements
- coordinated triple extensions of the ankle, knee and hip
- coordinated triple flexions of the ankle, knee and hip
- postural control in terms of maintaining a naturally straight back and a neutral position of the pelvic and shoulder girdles, from which to provide a power base for high-velocity limb movements.

Figure 43: The clean lifting technique

Figure 44: The snatch lifting technique

Figure 45: The squat lifting technique

These movement patterns are adaptable to encompass unilateral, rotational and multi-directional movements (ie single-leg lifts, unbalanced bars – more weight on one end than the other etc) in more competent athletes. Further detail of this is provided in the following pages of this chapter.

These kinesiological analyses provide further evidence for basing strength-training exercises for the athlete or sports performers on closed-kinetic-chain exercises (exercises where the body has a point in contact with the ground) allowing maximum force in gross-muscle structure to be reached in minimum time. Similarly, when considering prehabilitation (prevention) of injuries, coaches need to ensure the neuromuscular system is adequately trained to tolerate the strains imposed during functional (as defined earlier) tasks. Particular emphasis on trunk stability (sometimes referred to as core stability) has been a feature in contemporary sports medicine. This stems from the realisation that inappropriate muscular recruitment is the cause of a number of injuries in elite sportspersons, relating to the musculature of the lumbar spine, trunk and groin regions.

Weight Lifting

As sport is about moving the total body and involves few movements isolating single joints, strength-training sessions should focus on multiple-joint lifts that stress the entire body, without focusing on individual body parts (as Figures 43–45 remind us, train the movement, not the muscles). Two to three sessions of such workouts per week also allow every body part to receive two to three quality workouts per week, rather than one. These lifts also facilitate the development of intramuscular (between muscles) coordination, thus providing vital support for skill learning and performance that single-joint/isolated muscle-group lifts do not provide.

As mentioned earlier, strength gain is specific to the angle of the joint at which training occurs. Given this consideration, and the nature of hip action and gross-muscle involvement required in sports, exercises such as the squat, deadlift and derivatives of the clean, snatch and presses form the cornerstone of recommended resistance-training routines. Particular emphasis should be placed on the upward movements of these exercises as, for sports requiring sprinting and jumping, it is the vertical component of force that is the biggest predictor of speed and power.

These exercises also facilitate the incorporation of countermovements[21] in both slow (squat) and fast (squat clean, snatch, press and jerk) movements. They also incorporate dead-stop start accelerations (deadlifts, squat clean, snatch) that involve the overcoming of inertia in order to get a relatively large load moving from a static position (additionally they have been demonstrated as being maximally beneficial to sports performance and muscular growth). Coordinated concentric driving forces and eccentric braking forces are also key components of these exercises, as well as key components of sports performances.

Weight Lifting and Training Technique

As demonstrated, there are many ways in which to use resistance training in order to achieve different objectives. It is important to understand that the lifts presented here may have different versions and uses, particular to an individual context. The exercises and coaching points presented are designed to communicate the most beneficial means of using particular techniques to develop strength/power for sportspeople. Some differences in terminology between disciplines are worth highlighting here. It is recognised that weightlifting (one word, a sport in its own right) and weight lifting (two words) for sports conditioning may be slightly different. The bodybuilding shrug and the power shrug used in sports training also differ.

The coaching/lifting method (explained below) for the weight-lifting movements is known as the double-knee-bend (DKB) or transition-phase lifting technique. This has been demonstrated to be the most powerful method of completing lifts, such as the snatch and clean, and is certainly the most specific for sports training (Stone, 2005). The transition phase allows a greater force to be transmitted more effectively and greater transfer of training effects to other sports, and it is also a safer lift with less potential risk to the back. This method ensures the knees and hips are placed in the optimum position for generating vertical power, similar to that used in many sports movements. The transition phase also ensures a plyometric (stretch-reflex) response can be induced in the thigh muscles, making for a highly effective and powerful training movement (Brewer et al, 2005).

If one looks at the movements for the transition phase during a clean (and snatch) lift, and the movements that an experienced athlete would go through to perform a maximal vertical jump, the transfer of training benefits become obvious (see Figures 46 and 47). Indeed, it could be argued that 'weight jumping' is being taught, rather than 'weight lifting', which may aid the coach in developing a rationale for the use of this training modality.

Figure 46: The transition phase movements in a snatch lift

Figure 47: The movement pattern for a maximal vertical jump (similar to the snatch lift)

The transition phase must occur if the lift is to be optimal (Stone, 2005). It is the optimal technique to derive the benefits these lifts offer. Some coaches may say you cannot teach the transition phase because it is a stretch reflex, but why does this stretch reflex happen? Again, the first pull technique should be executed correctly, thus placing the athlete in the proper position to elicit the stretch-shortening cycle. This technique certainly can, and should, be coached (Brewer et al, 2005 Brewer and Stone, 2006). Waiting for the athlete to stumble upon the technique as an accidental phenomenon will only allow incorrect motor patterns to establish themselves. We are creatures of habit and, as such, proper technique should become a habit rather than an accidental phenomenon.

It is hard to imagine taking the same accidental approach when teaching a squat, where many athletes find a full range of movement difficult while keeping their heels on the floor. Do we just allow them to squat on their toes because they were unable to execute proper technique right away?

It is hard, in fact, to argue a case for any coach not wanting to develop correct technique in performers from the outset of learning a skill. It is most unlikely that an athlete will not be able to execute the correct weight-lifting technique after proper instruction. How quickly they learn the technique depends on the individual as well as on the experience and ability of the coach.

Using the Appropriate Equipment

The lifts in this section can all be done with either an Olympic barbell or a dumb-bell. Barbells are long bars held in two hands, dumb-bells are held in one hand. The use of barbells enables the athlete to move the maximum possible weight in total-body lifts and allows the double-knee bend to be performed. Using dumb-bells allows each side of the body to be moved independently, which means left–right differences that may develop in sports performers (and which may be masked by barbell lifting) can be identified and trained (see Figure 48). It is should be noted, however, that using a dumb-bell to perform many of these lifts is a relatively advanced concept. Therefore, an athlete is encouraged to learn the lifts with a barbell before performing them with a dumb-bell in an adapted movement.

Figure 48: Lifting sequence for a dumb-bell snatch lift (the barbell snatch is highlighted on page 74)

The use of an Olympic barbell is important for most of the major weight-lifting exercises described. An Olympic barbell is one that has free-rotating ends (these come in a range of weights from 10–20kg), whereas a normal barbell does not and is usually a lot lighter than an unloaded Olympic bar.

10kg Olympic bar loaded with 2 x 5kg discs

Unloaded 20kg Olympic bar

Standard 8kg barbell loaded with 2 x 6kg discs

Figure 49: A range of bars all weighing 20kg

When performing a lift such as the clean or the snatch (see pages 74–85), angular momentum is created as the bar is accelerated upwards and the athlete rotates under the bar. With an Olympic bar, the bar will spin, while the discs and bar ends remain relatively still. In a normal bar, where the ends do not rotate, this angular momentum may cause the athlete's wrist to rotate excessively, causing injury to the joint structures. You will notice, in the following figures, that the weight discs are not secured with collars on the bars. This allows the coach and athlete to receive immediate feedback about any left–right imbalances in the technique, as this may cause the disks to move. The following exercise summaries are designed as a guide to the free-weight exercises that should form the cornerstone of any strength-/power-training schedules for any sport. As with any training technique, however, it is imperative that all athletes are sure to develop appropriate technique prior to commencing serious training. With the correct technique, there is no reason why any form of training should promote injury in an athlete.

Breathing During Weight Lifting

There is a common myth in training that, during the effort phase of a lift (ie when it is hardest), the athlete should exhale. In reality, the opposite is true. When the athlete pulls the abdominal muscles tight (known as **bracing the trunk musculature**) and inhales, prior to performing a lift, the combination of tightened musculature and flattened diaphragm significantly increases the pressure within the abdomen. This intra-abdominal pressure provides necessary support to the spine during effort. Exhaling (and relaxing the brace) will release this intra-abdominal pressure and, if this is done during the effort phase (when the lifter needs it most), then the back becomes vulnerable. So, the athlete should breathe in at the start of a repetition, hold the breath during the repetition, and exhale at the end of the lift. In reality, holding your breath during a lift is a natural pattern that most athletes do without coaching, and it is usually not necessary to mention it.

The Major Lifts

Major conditioning lifts should form the cornerstone of any strength-/power-training programme for a sports performer. This section is followed by a supplementary exercises section: these exercises either allow the athlete to become stronger in ways that will enable them to perform the major conditioning lifts in a more powerful and efficient manner, or they may be beneficial to certain sports in aiding the performer to become stronger in specific positions/ranges of motion.

Between them, these major conditioning lift exercises, form the basis of a programme that will work every neuromuscular and joint complex in the body. The following exercise summaries are designed to provide a coach with basic guidelines and coaching tips to follow while carrying out these exercises. They are not a substitute for instruction by qualified and experienced strength and conditioning coaches[22].

The Back Squat

You can do whatever you want to get an athlete strong, as long as they are doing squats! The squat is considered an essential exercise in the stimulation of increased, overall strength, increased ligament and tendon strength, increased bone density, development of large musculature around the lower back, hip and knee and improved neuromuscular efficiency that aids performance in biomechanically similar movements. Sequential photos of this lift are shown in Figure 45 on page 64.

Addressing the Bar (Figure 50)

- Place the bar in the squat rack/stand, at a level slightly below shoulder height. Ensure the athlete always walks into the squat frame.

- The athlete settles the bar across the base of the neck, so that it rests across the top of the *deltoids* and *trapezius* muscles. It is essential the athlete position themselves in the middle of the bar before any movement is attempted.

- The bar is held in an over-grasp grip, with the hands evenly spaced, so the elbows are bent to 90°.

- The athlete pulls the shoulder blades back fully, then pushes the chest upwards and outwards. Maintaining this tight position aids the strength development in the back.

- The athlete fully prepares the body to receive the weight before lifting the bar.

- From this position, the athlete stands straight up and takes 2–3 steps backwards.

Figure 50: Addressing the bar in the squat rack

Start (also Finish) Position

- The eyes should be fixed on a point in front and slightly above eye level. The athlete should keep focused on this point throughout the lift. This will keep the head up throughout the lift, which will in turn aid in keeping the back flat (Figure 51).

- The shoulders and chest are also important in maintaining a normal curve in the lumbar (lower) spine throughout the lift. The athlete should pull the shoulder blades back fully (they should try to imagine that they have to hold a £5 note in between their shoulder blades) and at the same time push the chest upwards and outwards (Figure 51).

- The hand positions described earlier should be maintained.
- The feet should be flat on the floor and shoulder width apart (although those with long legs or poor flexibility may benefit from a wider stance). Most lifters find it more comfortable to have the toes pointing slightly outwards but, equally, they can face forward; it is a matter of individual style.

Figure 51: Start and finish position

Beginning the Descent
- Immediately before beginning the lift, the athlete should take a deep breath.
  This should be held until the very final stages of the lift as it will aid trunk stability by increasing intra-abdominal pressure.

- Prior to moving, the athlete should actively tighten the lower back and the gluteal muscles in the buttocks. Pulling the elbows in towards the body (to engage the *lats* muscles) aids this. It will enable the knees to move in the correct plane during the lift.

- The movement begins by flexing the hips and the knees simultaneously. The trunk should be kept upright throughout the lift, with the back straight (in a neutral position, which means displaying a normal inward (lumbar) curve in the lumbar/lower spine).

- Knees should be moving along a line that points in the same direction as the toes (Figure 52). Common mistakes occur at this stage, with athletes bringing their knees inwards into very weak positions during the descent ('Bambi knees').

- The athlete continues the downward movement until the hip joint passes below the level of the knee joint. This means the knees will bend past 90° (Figure 53). Despite popular beliefs to the contrary, this is fine in any athlete. Indeed, the knee is designed to go through a full range of movement, and will do so in most sporting situations. It is important they are trained in such positions, so the hamstrings and gluteal muscles can be fully activated.

Figure 52: The descent

Figure 53: The bottom position

- The hip joint should now be below the level of the knees (the top of the thighs will have broken parallel with the floor) at this point the athlete should go as low as possible while maintaining the correct technique (see Figure 53: chest high, maintain normal lumbar curve and keep knees in line with the toes). The feet should still be flat on the floor at all times throughout the lift. At this stage of the lift, the centre of pressure of the weight will be towards the rear of the mid-foot. Athletes with poor Achilles tendon flexibility will commonly not be able to get this full range of movement without the heels coming off the floor. This should be avoided at all costs, as it will cause the weighted bar to move forward, tipping the athlete off balance. This also shifts the weight from the prime movers to the lower back, significantly increasing the chances of injury.

- The best way to improve the ankle's range of movement is to work through it, but remedial stretching will help. In the short term, having a wider stance may help, or in extreme cases, a small weights plate can be put under the heels of the athlete. However, the size of this plate should be progressively reduced over time to encourage the athlete to achieve the full range of movement. Weightlifting shoes, which have an inbuilt heel-raise (as worn by the athletes in the illustrations) will help this.

- One tactic to improve things that works very well with athletes who cannot perform full range movements is to have the athletes go as low as they can (maintaining normal technique), then hold this position for a count of 6–8 seconds. This will enable the stretch inhibitors in the muscle (see Chapter 8 on flexibility) to switch off and the athlete can then (without standing up) go lower into the squat. The time spent in the squat position is also beneficial in getting the athlete to become comfortable with (or get used to) the squat position and, therefore, have the confidence to go lower with the bar.

- The trunk should still be upright, with the chest pushed upwards. Eyes should still be focused on the same point and the shoulders should still be pulled back.

Figure 54: The bottom position (rear view)

The Ascent

- The upward movement should be led by the chest, with the torso being kept upright. The hips and knees are extended by a powerful drive from the legs. Standing up should be an explosive action.

- Athletes whose legs are not strong enough at this stage will often seek to take the pressure off the legs by leaning the trunk forward, so the legs drive straight and the trunk comes forward. This means the only part of the body left to lift the weight is the lower back, which is very vulnerable in this position. It is vital that the trunk remains in a stable, upright position.

- At the top of the lift, as the standing position is reached, the athlete should exhale.

For every exercise in which the athlete has his feet flat on the floor, a great coaching point to engage the correct action of the glutes throughout the sequence is to imagine (and action, without moving the feet) that the feet are pushing out sideways, trying to grip and rip up the floor.

The Spotter

Most free-weight lifts do not need a spotter, but the squat is one that generally does. The role of the spotter is to aid the athlete should they get into any difficulty at some point during the lift (this may include aiding the lifter through a difficult/sticking point in the lift).

It is important the spotter does not try to lift the bar. This can tip the athlete sideways or, more frequently, forwards and should be avoided. Communication problems between two spotters on either end of the bar can also have the same effect. The lifter needs to remain in control of the bar.

To spot the squat, the spotter should stay close to the lifter as they ascend and descend. If assistance is needed, the spotter should put their arms beneath the armpits of the lifter, so that the upper arm is resting under the armpit and then lift the lifter as the bar is moved upwards.

Figure 55: Spotting the squat

The Front Squat

The front squat is an important lift for two reasons. Firstly, it is a progressive stage towards the clean; you cannot clean properly until you can front squat (see 'squat clean' on page 83). Secondly, as an exercise in its own right, it moves the line of action of the mass of the bar away from the lower back (as in the back squat) to a position around the middle of the thighs (in front of the body). This takes the pressure off the lower back, but means smaller muscles are utilised in the driving action and so less weight can be lifted compared to the back squat.

With the weight being on the front of the body, if the athlete has any forward lean of the body during the squat movement, they will feel this immediately. This tends to bring the posture into the desired upright position very quickly. For this reason, many coaches use the front squat as the first stage in progressing the teaching of the back squat (where athletes often find the upright torso hard to maintain as they learn the lift).

Start (and Finish) Position
- The athlete should ensure they address the bar so it is evenly balanced and they are in the middle of the bar.
- The bar should be positioned so it rests on the upper-front deltoids and is held in place by the fingers in an over-grasp grip (the bar does not sit in the hands) with hands spaced approximately shoulder-width apart. The bar should actively rest on the shoulders (the platform is made by the elbows coming forward to the high position).
- Elbows should be held high and level with the bar. This will require the wrists to be extended and the grip relaxed. It will not be comfortable at first but athletes should persevere with it. Many people have inflexibility around the shoulders which prevents the elbows from coming high. If this is not worked on and emphasised during the lift, then the shoulder inflexibility will never improve.
- As with the front squat, the athlete fixes their eyes on a point slightly higher than eye level.
- The shoulder blades are pulled back (holding that £5 note) and the chest is held high.
- The feet remain shoulder-width apart, pointing slightly outwards and remaining flat on the floor.

Figure 56: Front squat start (and finish) position

Figure 57: Front squat bottom position

The Lift
The descent, bottom position and ascent of this lift are very similar to the back squat.

• The athlete inhales prior to the start of the movement. With the trunk braced, the descent is from flexion of the hips and knees.

• The back must remain straight and upright throughout the lift, with the head up, shoulders back and elbows remaining high. The elbow position here is crucial. If the elbows drop, the bar tends to move forward, pulling the trunk forward.

• The bottom position of the front squat is very similar to the spot, with the thighs breaking parallel and the knees pointing along the same line as the toes (see Figure 57).

• The heels should remain on the ground throughout the movement, with the weight acting down through the heels into the ground.

• Similarly, the ascent is led by the chest, with the knees and hips driving explosively upwards and the trunk remaining upright (with the natural lumbar curve in the spine).

Overhead Squat

This exercise is sometimes referred to as the snatch squat, as it is a vital component of the squat (full-range) snatch lift. Indeed, an athlete cannot be expected to control a full snatch movement until they can perform the overhead squat lift.

This is one of the best exercises for developing trunk strength and postural control, as the athlete has to control the neutral pelvic position, the trunk position (maintaining the normal curves in the spine) and the shoulder girdle throughout the full range of the dynamic movement. These demands make this an excellent conditioning movement for all sports.

The Start Position
• The athlete holds the bar in a wide snatch grip (refer to Figure 58) above the head, with the elbows pointing along the length of the bar. The narrower the grip, the harder the exercise becomes. Initially, the athlete may just want to perform the movement with the arms as far apart as possible.

• The arms should remain straight throughout the exercise.

• The athlete raises the bar to a position above and slightly behind the head, with the arms staying extended throughout the lift (Figure 58).

• As with other squat movements, the head remains upwards throughout the lift, with the eyes focused on a point slightly above eye level.

• The athlete follows the same trunk, chest and shoulder blade positions as in the back squat. One way to ensure the shoulders remain in a fixed position during the lift is to have the athlete imagine the bar is made of bungee chord and that, once it is overhead, the hands (which are fixed) are trying to stretch the bungee chord. This will set up an isometric contraction around the shoulder girdle, and stop the arms/shoulders from moving.

• The athlete inhales prior to the start of the movement, with the trunk braced and the descent is from flexion of the hips and knees.

Figure 58: Overhead squat start position

The Bottom Position

- The athlete should descend until the thighs break parallel with the ground (Figure 59).

- The trunk should be upright, the head should remain up (eyes fixed on the same point as at the start of the lift), shoulder blades pulled back, chest high.

- The knees should still be pointing out along the same lines as the toes, and not be coming inwards.

- The heels should remain on the ground throughout the movement, with the weight acting down through the heels into the ground.

Figure 59: Overhead squat bottom position

The Ascent

- As with all of the squatting movements, the upward drive should be controlled, explosive and led with the chest, so that the trunk remains upright throughout the movement.

Asymmetrical Loading

As previously identified, the overhead squat is a core exercise for developing postural control through a full range of movement. When an athlete is technically proficient at this lift, one means of further challenging the postural control of the athlete is to load both ends of the bar with different weights (Figure 60). This advanced exercise creates a moment arm, which the athlete has to control in order to maintain an upright and balanced posture.

Figure 60: The asymmetrically loaded overhead squat

The Snatch

The snatch lift is recognised as the most powerful whole-body human movement possible in sport. It is a multiple-joint lift that takes a bar from a static position (either on the floor from the hang position at the knees or the thigh, as demonstrated later in this chapter) to a position above the head. Sequential photos of this lift are shown in Figure 44 on page 64.

The Grip

Grip the bar with an over-grasp grip (hand comes over the top of the bar). The most secure method in which to grip the bar is to a use a hook grip, although this will initially feel uncomfortable when it is first used.

To get the hook grip the athlete should:

- place the flap of skin between the thumb and the index finger along the top of the bar
- position the thumb so that it is running along the length of the bar, pointing away from the body (Figure 61)
- close the remaining four fingers over the top of the bar and around it, so that the thumb is enclosed (as much as possible) by the fingers (Figure 62).

Figure 61: The hook grip stage 1

Figure 62: The hook grip stage 2

Determining Hand Spacing

The snatch lift uses a very wide hand spacing (relative to other lifts). In order to find out how wide the hands should be placed, follow the guidelines below:

- The athlete should stand over the bar with the arms raised to a position parallel with the floor and fingertips outstretched (Figure 63). Some guides will tell you that the measurement from outside of the shoulder to the fingertips in this position should be the width of the grip that you should use in the snatch. If this is comfortable then an athlete can use it. However, there is a means of calculating a more individually-specific grip width.

- Arguably the best means to identify the athlete's grip width is to get the athlete to find their jump position (ie they should imagine they are going to jump as high as they can). This will involve a countermovement (Figure 64). They should go to the position that they would go to for this countermovement. This is the jump or power position for each athlete as an individual). At this point, the athlete should place their hands as far apart along the bar as they need to get the bar to rest against the groove between the thigh and the hips. That will give them the correct grip width for the snatch (Figure 65).

Figure 63: The 'shoulder to opposite fingertip' grip distance

Figure 64: The athlete's jump position at the bottom of the countermovement

Figure 65: The snatch grip width determined by the bar being correctly placed in the jump position

The Start Position

• The athlete starts with the bar close to (1–2 inches, but not touching) the shins.

• The feet are flat on the floor, beneath the bar, which should be directly above the first hole (one nearest the shins) of the laces on the shoe.

• The athlete bends the knees over the bar, with the hips slightly higher than the knees.

• The bar is gripped in an over-grasp grip (hook grip recommended, but a claw grip – thumb around the bar – can be used if preferred).

• The arms should be straight, with the elbows locked outwards and pointing along the length of the bar.

• The athlete holds the back straight (with a normal lumbar curve in the lumbar spine). This is aided by the shoulder blades being pulled back towards each other and the chest pushed out at the same time. Indeed, a coach standing in front of the athlete lifting should be able to see the whole of the chest from the front.

• The head should be up at all times.

• Immediately prior to the lift, the athlete inhales and braces the trunk taking all of the slack out of the system (ie body plus bar). At the start of the lift, the centre of pressure of the bar is acting through the middle of the foot. This will move backwards as the bar begins to lift.

Figure 66: Snatch start position

First Pull

• During this stage, the lifter/bar complex will move up and back **until the bar is just above the knees** (Figure 67).

• The athlete lifts the bar from the floor slowly. A common fault is to attempt to rip the bar straight from the floor, but the first stages of this lift are about overcoming inertia and giving the bar some momentum.

• The bar is moved by extending the knees (ie knees back position), but the athlete should maintain the same angle between the back and the hips as there was at the start position (a common mistake is to extend the knees, so that they extend fully, but also decrease the angle between the trunk and the hips, thus the bar is not raised vertically and the lower back becomes stressed). It is important that the trunk/ground angle does not change (see Figure 67).

- The shoulders remain in front of the bar, with the arms straight (long and loose, as if they are cables on a suspension bridge), elbows pointing along the length of the bar, and the wrists flexed. The head remains up.

- The knees are extended until they are in a position that is slightly behind and underneath the bar. At this stage, the centre of pressure of the bar is towards the heel of the foot, as it is planted on the floor (see Figure 90 on page 85).

Figure 67: Snatch bar knee height

Transition Phase

- From the end of the first pull (bar at the top of the knees – see Figure 67), and **without stopping the upward movement of the bar**, the knees are now re-bent and pushed forwards, under and in front of the bar (Figure 68). Using correct technique, every time the knees and hips are extended during the upward phases of the lift, the bar will be accelerated. However, this does not mean there is a stopping of the upward movement of the bar when this is not occurring.

- At the same time, the trunk moves upwards and backwards into an upright position, with the bar moving to a position close to the hips at the upper-thigh level. This trunk movement is a result of the knees coming forward; moving the trunk without this will result in the athlete not moving into the required position at the end of the phase (see Figures 68–69) but standing up with knees straight, which is not correct.

- The centre of pressure of the bar moves forward to the middle of the foot, in preparation for the following stage (see Figure 90 on page 85).

- The position of the body at this stage is similar to that which would be seen if the athlete were attempting to take off for a maximum vertical jump (Figure 47 on page 66). This indicates the potential power that can be generated from this position.

- It is important the arms stay straight at all times during this phase of the lift.

Figure 68: Power or jump position at the end of the transition phase (side)

Figure 69: Power or jump position (front)

The Second Pull

- It is important to realise the second pull progresses immediately after the transition phase (which occurs immediately after the first pull). They are distinct movements, but there is no time gap between them. It should also be realised that following this sequence (first pull, transition phase) to get to the jump position significantly reduces the tension on the back.

- As the bar reaches the top of the thigh (hips), there is a brushing contact with the upper thigh. At this point, the athlete dives off the floor jumping upwards.

- This occurs as the athlete moves through the jump position: the feet remain flat, with the centre of pressure moving forwards to mid-foot. The hips are behind the bar, over the ankles, and the knees are in front of the bar, bent to an angle of 130–140°. The trunk is nearly vertical and the shoulders have moved directly over the bar. The arms remain straight, with the elbows pointing along the length of the bar and the wrists flexed (Figure 69).

- As the athlete moves through the jump position, the ankles, knees and hips are powerfully and fully extended simultaneously (the triple extension), which is followed by a violent shoulder shrug (see Figure 70). Although this is the realistic sequence that is followed in the lift (a progressive transfer of momentum), this stage is often coached as 'shrug so violently that you pull yourself up onto yourself up onto your toes!' This is because, in reality, there is little difference in timing between the joint extensions and the shrug, and experience shows athletes often find it easier to think of initiating the movement with the shrug than following the extension with the shrug.

- At the start of the shrug, the centre of mass of the bar is towards the balls of the feet as you powerfully extend the ankle. It may be that you are able to generate sufficient power to get your feet to leave the ground completely, which is perfectly acceptable, although not something to be actively encouraged, as this means the ankle extension component of the movement will be lost.

- Note that when watching people lift heavy weights (a relative term), the shoulders may not visibly shrug much or the heels may not leave the floor; this is a function of the weight that is on the bar and it does not mean that the athlete is not performing the same actions.

- This sequence of actions is completed with the arms straight and the wrists slightly flexed. Wrist flexion, combined with an aggressive shrug, will help to keep the bar very close to the trunk as it is raised. It is important to realise, if the bar comes away from the trunk, it will start to pull the athlete forward at the upper stages of this lift (Figure 71).

- The second pull stage is completed with the arms straight, the elbows still pointing along the length of the bar.

There is a simple mantra that can be repeated by the athlete to aid performance of the lift and sequence the stages appropriately:

Start position -> knees back -> knees forward -> jump and shrug

Figure 70: Jump and shrug (side view): The top of the second pull

Figure 71: Jump and shrug (diagonal view – often coached as 'shrug and jump')

Figure 72: Dropping under the bar

The Catch

- At the top of the second pull, before the upward momentum of the bar is lost, the body has to drop below the bar (Figure 72). This is achieved by slightly flexing the elbows along the length of the bar (the bar should not move away from its position close to the body) and simultaneously dropping the body quickly under the bar. It is almost as if the bar is the pivot point about which the body is rotated as it moves under (as soon as the elbows bend, the athlete jumps under the bar).

- As the body rotates under the bar, the arms forcibly re-extend, pushing the bar upwards towards the ceiling (as if the bar was being thrown vertically in the air).

- As the body comes underneath the bar, the athlete will land on their heels as the bar is caught at the bottom position of the overhead squat, with the arms fully extended (Figure 73). The elbow extension (locking out of the elbows) and landing on the heels occur simultaneously. The bar should be resting directly over the back of the head, which should be looking forwards.

- If the athlete is performing a power snatch, then the bar will be caught in a higher position, where the thighs have not lowered past a point of being parallel with the floor (Figure 74). This exercise requires the bar to be thrown higher in the air but does not require the same amount of flexibility, speed and eccentric control (all of which are important qualities for the sportsperson to develop) as the squat snatch. (In reality, we require everyone to be able to perform a full squat snatch (Figure 73) it is simply the weight on the bar which will determine how high up the bar is moved and, therefore, how low the athlete needs to move to catch the bar.) **The key thing is that the athlete has been taught to perform both movements and therefore has the athletic and gymastic ability to perform both as required by the load on the bar**.

- From the bottom position, the athlete drives powerfully upwards into a standing position (Figure 75). The upward drive should be controlled, explosive and led with the chest, so that the trunk remains upright throughout the movement.

Figure 73: Squat snatch catch position **Figure 74: Power snatch catch position** **Figure 75: The snatch finish position**

Partial Lifts: Snatch from Hang and Thigh (Jump) Positions

- A lift from the hang position is one that does not begin from the floor, but from either the knees (hang: Figure 76) or the power/jump position (Figure 68) at the end of the transition phase (from thigh or, in some cultures, the high hang).

- From these start positions, the athlete completes the snatch sequence as described above.

- These lifts do not develop the performer through the full range of motion, but they are a stage in the learning process and help to develop high levels of power through a limited range of movement.

Figure 76: Snatch from the hang position

The Pull:Snatch Grip

- The snatch pull involves completing the first and second pull stages of the snatch, finishing with the arms straight and the elbows still pointing along the length of the bar although sometimes (as illustrated in Figure 77), the momentum of the upward movement causes the elbows to bend along the length of the bar. This is a phenomenon of the explosive movement and should not be actively encouraged.

- This lift can be completed from the floor, hang or jump positions (the less distance the bar is moved through, the higher the level of force needed to overcome inertia of the mass to be lifted.

- The catch is not part of this lift, the bar is simply returned to the start position (floor, knee, thigh).

- When utilised within a programme, this exercise allows the athlete to focus on the stages of the lift associated with the development of vertical power.

Figure 77: The Pull (snatch grip) end position

The Clean

The clean is a multiple-joint lift that takes a bar from a static position (either on the floor or in a hang position, as demonstrated in Figure 87 on page 84) to a standing position on the front of the shoulders. The clean is also often used as part of a sequence of exercises in both a conditioning and a sport-specific sense (eg the recognised Olympic discipline of the clean and jerk). Sequential photos of this lift are shown in Figure 43 on page 63.

The Grip

- The athlete places their hands slightly wider apart than shoulder-width – a good guide to use may be one thumb length from the edge of the knurling (the rough bit of the bar).

- The bar is grasped with an over-grasp grip (hand comes over the top of the bar).

- The most secure method in which to grip the bar is to a use a hook grip (see instructions in the snatch and Figure 62 on page 74), although a claw grip (normal grip with the thumb around the bar) can also be used if this is perceived to be more comfortable.

The Start Position

- This is very similar to the snatch start, the major difference being the narrower hand position, which also allows the hips to be in a slightly higher position at the start.

- The athlete starts with the bar close to the shins.

- The feet go beneath the bar, which should be directly above the first hole (one nearest the shins) of the laces on the shoe. The feet should be flat on the floor, with the weight over the balls of the feet.

- The knees are bent over the bar, with the hips slightly higher than the knees.

- The arms should be straight, with the elbows locked outwards and pointing along the length of the bar.

- The back should be held straight (with a normal curve in the lumbar spine). This is aided by the shoulder blades being pulled back towards each other and the chest pushed out at the same time.

- The shoulders should be in front of the bar, and the head should be up at all times.

- Immediately before the lift, the athlete should inhale, brace the trunk musculature and take all of the slack out of the system. At the start of the lift, the centre of pressure of the bar is acting through the middle of the foot. This will move backwards as the bar begins to lift.

Figure 78: Clean start position

First Pull

- As with the snatch, in order to overcome the inertia of the static bar on the floor, the initial movements of the lift are relatively slow. During this stage of the lift, the lifter/bar complex will move upwards and backwards until the bar is above the knees.

- The bar is moved by extending the knees (ie knees back), but the athlete should maintain the same angle between the back and the hips as there was at the start position. It is crucial this angle is maintained as the bar is lifted, to avoid putting pressure on the lumbar spine or pulling the athlete forward. The spine remains flat (displaying the normal lumbar curve), aided by the head remaining up, the chest being pushed forward and the shoulder blades pulled back (holding the £5 note. See Figure 79).

- At all times in this lift, the bar should travel right up the front of the body and never be more than an inch away, otherwise the athlete will be pulled forward, off balance.

- The shoulders should remain in front of the bar, with the arms straight and elbows pointing along the length of the bar.

- The knees are extended until they are in a position that is slightly behind and underneath, the bar (Figures 79 and 80). At this stage, the centre of pressure of the bar should be acting towards the heel of the foot, which remains planted (feet flat) on the floor.

Figure 79: End of first pull bar at the knees

Figure 80: End of first pull (side view)

Transition Phase

- From the end of the first pull (bar at the top of the knees – see Figure 79 or 80), and **without stopping the upward movement of the bar**, the knees are now re-bent and pushed forwards, under and in front of the bar (Figure 79). Using correct technique, every time the knees and hips are extended, the bar will be accelerated. However, this does not mean there is a stopping of the upward movement of the bar when this is not occurring.

- At the same time, the trunk moves upwards and backwards into an upright position, with the bar moving to a position close to the hips at the mid-thigh level (it is the same movement as with the snatch, but the hands are closer together so the bar will contact the thigh at a lower level in the jump position). This trunk movement is a result of the knees coming forward; moving the trunk without this will result in the athlete not moving into the required position at the end of the phase (see Figure 81) but standing up with knees straight, which is not correct.

- The centre of mass of the body (+bar) moves forward to the middle of the foot, in preparation for the following stage (see Figure 90 on page 85).

- The position of the body at this stage is similar to that which would be seen if the athlete were attempting a maximum vertical jump (Figures 46 and 47 on page 66 and Figure 81 below). This indicates the potential power that can be generated from this position.

- It is important the arms stay straight at all times during this phase of the lift.

Figure 81: The jump position – at the end of the transition phase

The Second Pull

- It is important to realise the second pull progresses immediately after the transition phase (which occurs immediately after the first pull). They are distinct movements, but there is no time gap between them. It should also be realised that following this sequence (first pull, transition phase), to get to the jump position significantly reduces the tension on the back.

- As the bar reaches the middle of the thigh, there is a brushing contact with the thigh. At this point, the athlete jumps upwards.

- This occurs as the athlete is in the jump position. The feet remain flat, with the centre of pressure moving forwards to mid-foot. The hips are behind the bar, over the ankles and the knees are in front of the bar, bent to an angle of 130–140°. The trunk is nearly vertical, and the shoulders have moved directly over bar. The arms remain straight. The elbows are pointing along the length of the bar and wrists are flexed (Figure 81).

- As the athlete moves through the jump position, the ankles, knees and hips are powerfully and fully extended simultaneously (the triple extension), which is followed by a violent shoulder shrug (see Figure 82). Although this is the realistic sequence that is followed in the lift (a progressive transfer of momentum), this stage is often coached as 'shrug so violently that you will pull yourself, up onto your toes'. This is because, in reality, there is little difference in timing between the joint extensions and the shrug, and athletes find it easier to think of initiating the movement with the shrug than following the extension with the shrug.

- At the start of the shrug, the centre of mass of the bar is towards the balls of the feet as the athlete powerfully extends the ankle. It may be that they are able to generate sufficient power to get their feet to leave the ground completely, which is perfectly acceptable, although not something to be actively encouraged, as this typically results in the ankle extension component of the movement being lost.

- Note that when watching people lift heavy weights (a relative term), the shoulders may not visibly shrug much or the heels may not leave the floor; this is a function of the weight that is on the bar and it does not mean that the athlete is not performing the same actions.

- This sequence of actions is completed with the arms straight and the wrists slightly flexed. Wrist flexion, combined with an aggressive shrug, will help to keep the bar very close to the trunk as it is raised (see Figure 82). It is important to realise that, if the bar comes away from the trunk, it will start to pull the athlete forwards at the upper stages of this lift.

- The second pull stage is completed with the arms straight, the elbows still pointing along the length of the bar.

There is a simple mantra that can be repeated by the athlete to aid performance of the lift and sequence the stages appropriately:

Start position -> knees back -> knees forward -> jump and shrug

Figure 82: Clean at the top of the second-pull   **Figure 83: Rotate the wrists and elbows then jump under the bar**

Drop under the bar to receive (catch)

- At the top of the second pull, as the bar reaches the top of its ascent (after the completion of the full extension phase and before the upward momentum of the bar is lost), the athlete flexes at the elbows, which are pointing along the length of the bar (the bar should not move away from its position close to the body), then rotates the wrists and elbows around to a position in front of the bar (Figure 83).

- At the same time as this is occurring, (ie the moment the elbows bend) the athlete jumps down under the bar, landing on flat feet with their weight resting on the heels, and catches the bar on the upper part of the deltoids. The contact of the heel on the floor and the bar on the shoulders, should be simultaneous.

- In effect, the bar is caught at the bottom position of the front squat, with the elbows high in front of the bar (Figure 84).

- If performing a power clean, the bar will be caught in a higher position, where the thighs have not lowered past a point of being parallel with the floor (Figure 85). This exercise requires the bar to be thrown higher in the air, but does not require the same amount of flexibility, speed and eccentric control (all of which are important qualities for the sportsperson to develop) as the squat clean. (In reality, we require everyone to be able to perform a full squat clean. It is simply the weight on the bar which will determine how high up the bar is moved and, therefore, how low the athlete needs to move to catch the bar).

- From the bottom (catch) position, the athlete should powerfully drive upwards into a standing position. The upward drive should be controlled, explosive and led with the chest, so that the trunk remains upright throughout the movement (Figure 86).

Figure 84: Catch position squat clean **Figure 85: Catch position power clean** **Figure 86: Clean finish position**

Partial Lifts: Clean from Hang and Thigh (Jump) Positions

- A lift from the hang position is one that does not begin from the floor but from either the knees (hang: see Figure 87) or the power/jump position at the end of the transition phase (from thigh: see Figure 88).

- From these start positions, the athlete completes the clean sequence as described above.

- These lifts do not develop the performer through the full range of motion, but they are a stage in the learning process and are extremely beneficial in the development of high levels of power through a limited range of movement.

- For most sports training, the squat clean is recommended (and all should be able to perform this) as the core version that is used, as the greater range of motion required promotes greater speed, greater eccentric strength development and greater flexibility in a performer than a power clean.

Figure 87: Clean from the hang position

Figure 88: Start position – clean or pull from thigh

The Pull: Clean Grip

- The clean pull involves completing the first and second pull stages of the clean, finishing with the arms straight (although the elbows might bend slightly: this is not a deliberately coached movement) The elbows will still be pointing along the length of the bar (Figure 89).

- This lift can be started from the floor, hang or jump positions (the less distance the bar is moved through, the higher the level of force needed to overcome inertia of the mass to be lifted). Using all of these at different times in an athlete's planned programme is recommended.

- The catch is not part of this lift; the bar is simply returned to the start position. This exercise allows the athlete to focus on the stages of the lift associated with the development of vertical power and is an excellent strength/strength–speed developing exercise for all sports programmes.

Figure 89: High pull (finish position)

During both the snatch and the clean lifts, as the bar travels up the body, the weight distribution through the foot and into the floor can be seen to change as summarised in Figure 90. The weight transfer is important to understand as it demonstrates the dynamic movement of the body around the bar as the lift progresses.

1. Start position (Figures 66 and 78)
2 Bar at knee (Figures 67 and 79)
3 Bar at jump position (Figures 68 and 81)
4 Triple extension (Figures 70 and 82)
5 Bottom position: receiving the bar
 (Figures 73, 74, 84 and 85)

Figure 90: The movement of the centre of pressure through the foot during the snatch and clean lifts

Split Snatch and Split Clean

The split snatch and split clean involve the same basic lifting principles and technique as the normal (squat or power) snatch and clean. The difference between the two lifts occurs after the second pull. The aim of these lifts is to land with the legs split evenly, forming a stable base, rather than landing with legs together. This helps to develop unilateral, eccentric strength and dynamic balance in muscles, as well as leg-drive to the standing position from the legs in a split position. Such unilateral positions are very relevant to many sports. However, the range of movement in this lift is less in the ankles, knees, hips and lower back than in the squat clean or snatch. It also requires less flexibility in the shoulders when compared to the squat snatch. Therefore, it is not recommended that this type of lift is performed exclusively in a programme, in preference to the squat clean or snatch. However, it does provide some variation for the technically proficient athlete.

The Lift

• From the power position, the athlete performs the same explosive upwards jumping movement as in the squat clean/snatch, through the second-pull stages of the lift. The ankles, knees and hips are powerfully and fully extended in sequence (the triple extension), which is followed by a violent shoulder shrug (see Figures 70 and 82).

• This sequence of actions is completed with the arms straight and the wrists slightly flexed. Wrist flexion, combined with an aggressive shrug, will help to keep the bar very close to the trunk as it is raised. Remember, if the bar comes away from the trunk, it will start to pull the athlete forward at the upper stages of this lift.

• The arm action for the catch sequence of the lift should follow that of the snatch/clean, as appropriate, at the end of the second-pull phase.

• At the top of the full extension of the ankles, knees and hips (see Figure 82 on page 82), the athlete simultaneously splits (with flat feet) the legs to land in the split position (see Figures 92–95). This should be done about an imaginary cross, known as a Murray Cross, which can be drawn on the lifting platform if it helps (see Figure 91).

• The front leg (this should be alternated with each repetition) should be planted flat on the floor (the centre of pressure should be on the heel of this foot) at 45° to the centre of the cross (so the foot has moved forwards).

• The centre of mass should be immediately above the centre of the cross (see Figures 92–95).

• Simultaneously, the back foot moves backwards, again at a 45° angle to the centre of the cross. The athletes should land (remembering that this is not a jump, but a flat-foot split) on the ball of the foot.

- After the split position has been achieved and once stabilised, the feet should be moved back to a position shoulder-width apart. This should start with the front foot moving backwards towards the mid-line, then the rear foot moving forwards.

- The lift is completed with both feet level and the bar either at the shoulder (clean) or fully extended overhead (snatch).

Figure 91 illustrates the movement of the foot from the start position (grey) of the lift to the split position (white). (Remember, this could be reversed on alternate lifts, so the athlete leads with the right leg on the next lift).

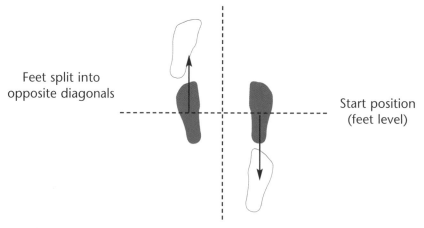

Feet split into opposite diagonals

Start position (feet level)

Figure 91: The Murray Cross: The foot position from the start (grey) of the lift to the split (white) position (NB this could be reversed on alternate lifts, so the athlete leads with the right leg)

Figure 92: Split snatch catch (side view)

Figure 93: Split snatch catch (front view)

Figure 94: Split clean end of pull phase

Figure 95: Split clean catch

The Deadlift

The deadlift is one of the major mass- and strength-developing exercises for the legs and back. It is a pulling movement that involves taking a heavy (individually relative) weight from a static position on the floor to a position near the mid-thigh when standing. Although this lift forms part of the sport of power lifting, the speed component of this lift is normally minimal and it is therefore regarded as a maximal strength, rather than a power, exercise.

Start Position
- The start position is very similar to the power clean, although the weight needs to be further back onto the heels. Therefore, many athletes often do this exercise in socks.
- The athlete should assume a stance with feet shoulder-width apart and flat on the floor.
- The bar should be close to the shins, over the balls of the feet (over the first or second eye of the shoelaces).
- The athlete should squat down so the knees come in front of the bar, pointing along the line of the toes, with the hips slightly above the level of the knee (Figure 96).
- Either a closed, over-grasp grip or an alternate grip (one hand over the bar, one hand under the bar, see Figure 36 on page 60) should be used (whichever is comfortable for the individual).
- The hands should be positioned slightly wider than shoulder-width apart.
- The elbows should be fully extended and remain so throughout the lift.
- The shoulders should be positioned so they are just in front of the bar, with the shoulder blades pulled back and together, and the chest pushed up. This pulls the back into a naturally straight posture (maintaining the lumbar curve), which is maintained throughout the lift. Note, however, the shoulders are not as far over the bar as in the clean or snatch, meaning the starting posture is more upright.
- The head should be up and looking slightly upwards.

Figure 96: Deadlift start position

The Lift
- Immediately prior to moving, the athlete inhales and braces the trunk musculature.
- The lift is executed by the simultaneous extension of the hips and knees to set the bar in motion (see Figure 97).
- The initial movement of the bar takes it back towards the shins, after which it is lifted straight up the front of the legs as they straighten.
- The hips are driven forward and knees pulled back at the same rate (Figure 97), with the trunk–thigh angle increasing at a constant rate. Coaches should note this is different from the clean and snatch techniques.
- The bar is kept close to the body, with elbows fully extended, head looking slightly upwards and shoulders positioned slightly over the bar until the final stages of the lift.
- The athlete should continue until the knees and hips are fully extended, establishing an erect body position to complete the lift (Figure 98).

Figure 97: Deadlift transition   **Figure 98: Deadlift finish position**

Stiff-leg Deadlift (also known as the Romanian Deadlift)

This is a crucial lift for sports performers for three main reasons; firstly, as the primary exercise for developing eccentric strength in the hamstring muscles; secondly, as a strengthening exercise for the supporting musculature in the back and trunk, and thirdly, as an assistance exercise for developing clean-and-snatch technique (the lowest point of this lift is the weakest position during the snatch and clean). Eccentric strengthening of the hamstrings is something that is often poorly developed in many sports training programmes. Indeed, despite the fact many hamstring injuries occur during eccentric contractions or extended positions, most hamstring strength work has traditionally focused on concentric training motions.

Start Position

- The athlete holds the bar in an over-grasp grip (hook or claw, according to their preference).

- The hands should be shoulder-width apart (clean grip), with the elbows straight (Figure 99), unless the focus is on using this to develop snatch technique, in which case a snatch grip can be used. This could also be used in an athlete with greater ranges of hamstring flexibility.

- The trunk should be erect, the head up, the shoulder blades pulled back and the chest up.

- The feet should be shoulder-width apart, knees should be slightly bent (this is not, as commonly thought, a straight-leg deadlift). This knee position is crucial and once the bent-knee position has been established it should not be adjusted at all during the movement of the lift.

Figure 99: Stiff-leg deadlift
(start position)

The Descent
- Maintaining the straight back (with the shoulders pulled back) and knee position, the bar is lowered, under control, directly down the front of the thighs.
- This movement is aided by flexing the hips and moving them backwards as the bar gets lower. There should be no deliberate movement of the knees, although as the hips move backward during the descent, the coach will observe a slight straightening of the knee in its locked position as the thigh angle changes with hip movement. This is an incidental movement; the coaching point is to keep the knee stiff or locked.
- It is important to maintain a straight back (with the normal slight inward curve in the lower spine) throughout the movement. The coach should emphasise the importance of the athlete pulling the shoulder blades back together (again – hold the £5 note) and forcing the chest forwards throughout the movement.
- The descent continues until the hamstrings become fully stretched and tight (see Figure 100).
- Most athletes feel this before the bar reaches the knees. If the athlete has flexible hamstrings and a greater range of movement is needed to feel the stretch, then this is fine, as long as the athlete's back does not become horizontal (which would change the entire focus of the lift inappropriately). If the athlete does not feel the stretch before this point, and the knees are in the correct position and the shoulders appropriately pulled back, progressively add more weight to the bar until the athlete does feel the movement.

Figure 100: Stiff-leg deadlift (bottom position)

The Ascent
- From the bottom position (full stretch on the hamstrings), the trunk is returned to the start position through hip extension and raising the trunk.
- The bar should return along the same path as it descended until the athlete has returned to the start position (Figure 99).

This exercise can also be done as a single leg exercise (described in detail in Chapter 7: Warming Up for Training). The emphasis is on maintaining postural control, keeping the hips high and level throughout the movement, while eccentrically loading the hamstring.

Reverse Hamstring Curls

Often called Russian hamstring curls, this exercise uses bodyweight to develop both eccentric and concentric strength in the hamstring and other postural muscles (ie gluteals in the buttock, trunk, shoulder girdle stabilisers). There are two versions that can be progressively developed. The first version is an eccentric-only exercise:

- The athlete starts by kneeling up, with the coach applying a strong resistive force to the athlete's calf muscles. The athlete should have dorsiflexed ankles, the pelvis should be in a neutral position, with the chest high, shoulder blades pulled back and down (having the athlete clasp their hands behind their back aids this process – although this should not be done in the learning stages of the lift, as will become apparent in the next paragraph). The head should be looking forwards and there should be a straight-line position between the ear, shoulder, hip and knee (Figure 101).

Figure 101: Start position: reverse hamstring curl

• From this position, and maintaining the straight line of the body at all times, the athlete leans forward, using eccentric (lengthening) contractions of the hamstrings to lower the trunk towards the floor. The straight line between the legs and the upper body must not be broken (Figure 102). The athlete continues this movement under control, until reaching a point where they can not control this movement any more, and the body falls (under control, landing on the hands – hence not holding them behind the back) to the floor (Figure 103).

Figure 102: Lowered position: reverse hamstring curl

Figure 103: Fallen position: reverse hamstring curl

Once the athlete is comfortable with this movement, the eccentric–concentric progression involves lowering the body until the point beyond which control would be lost and then using concentric contractions of the hamstrings to raise the **straight line body position** back to the start position.

Push Press

This is an overhead lift that involves the athlete moving the bar from the shoulders to a finishing point with the bar straight above the head and arms locked out. However, the majority of the power in allowing this movement comes from the triple extension of the hips, knees and ankles, with minimal upper body (shoulder and arm extension) work at the end of the lift. This sequential transfer of power makes the lift specific to many sports.

Start Position

• The start position for this lift is the same as the end position for the power clean and front squat (see Figure 104 on page 91).

• The bar rests across the *anterior deltoids* (front of the shoulder), held in an over-grasp grip.

• The elbows should be pointing forward.

• The head should be up, shoulder blades pulled back, chest elevated and trunk straight.

• The feet should be shoulder-width apart.

Figure 104: Push press start position

Alternative Start Position
- This lift can be started with the bar behind your head, resting across the top of the deltoids (the start position for the back squat – see Figure 105).
- This changes the line of action of the mass of the bar from the front of the body to the rear.

Figure 105: Push press alternative start position

The Descent
Prior to any movement, the athlete inhales and braces the musculature in the trunk, groin and buttocks.

- The first movement is for the knees to bend to 130–140° (Figure 106). This is the position an athlete would intuitively adopt if undertaking an explosive vertical jump; it is the optimum angle for generating vertical power.
- At the same time, the elbows can be dropped below the bar, but should not be brought too far under (pointing the elbows towards the floor at this point is a mistake).
- The trunk descends vertically, with no forward lean as the knees flex.
- The rapid countermovement (bending) of the knee is rapidly followed by the ascent.

Figure 106: Push press bottom of descent

The Ascent

- Having dropped the elbows and bent the knees to the bottom position, there is an immediate explosive upward extension of the ankles, knees and hips, which causes the upward movement of the bar from the shoulders.
- This is followed by a coordinated full extension of the arms and the bar is 'thrown' upwards.
- This extension is full and the lift is completed with the arms locked out overhead and the feet flat on the floor (weight through the rear foot).
- The athlete should then exhale as the bar reaches its top position, with the bar held in arms locked directly over the back of the head (Figure 107).
- From here, the bar is lowered slowly to the start position.

Figure 107: Push press finish position

The Push Jerk

The push jerk involves a similar movement to the push press, but the jerk involves a countermovement to come underneath and catch the rising bar. This re-bending action, beneath the bar, adds an additional speed quality to the movement, and also means the bar does not need to be raised so high. Meaning more weight can be loaded onto the bar, requiring the athlete to impart more force and velocity onto the bar. Therefore, this is an excellent conditioning exercise for all sports.

Start Position

The start position for this lift is the same as the push press (see Figure 104 or 105, either can be used).

The Descent

- Prior to any movement, the athlete braces the trunk.
- The knees are now bent to an angle of 130–140°, and, following this countermovement, rapidly extend the ankles, knees and hips to explosively send the bar upwards.
- At the same time, the elbows are rotated around the bar.

The Ascent

- The hips, knees and ankles extend explosively to send the bar upwards.
- After completing the triple extension, the athlete drops under the bar by re-bending the hips and knees (trunk remains upright) and catches the bar in an overhead position with the elbows fully extended (Figure 108).
- The centre of mass is acting through the heels in the catch position, with the bar directly above the back of the athlete's head.

Figure 108: Push jerk catch position

Finish Position
- Maintaining the fully extended arm position, complete the lift by fully extending the hips and knees, with the arms remaining locked until the athlete is standing fully upright (see Figure 109).

Figure 109: Push jerk finish position

The Split Jerk

This is a high-speed movement combining the explosive extension and countermovement actions of the jerk with unilateral leg actions in catching the weight and returning to a standing position. This makes the lift another excellent conditioning movement for all sports.

Start Position
- Both the start and alternative start positions for this lift are the same as for the push press.

The Descent
- Prior to moving, the athlete inhales and braces the trunk.
- The first movement is an explosive countermovement, into a quarter-squat position under the bar, with the centre of pressure towards the middle of the foot and the trunk upright (see Figure 106).

The Split Lift
- From the bottom of the countermovement position, the athlete rapidly extends the ankles, knees and hips to explosively send the bar upwards.
- After completing the triple extension, the athlete drops under the bar and simultaneously splits the legs (into the same pattern as demonstrated in the split clean/snatch – see Figure 91 on page 86) and extends the elbows.
- The bar is therefore caught in the finish position, which is a lunge position with the bar extended fully overhead (elbows locked, bar directly above the back of the head) (Figure 110).
- The front foot should land (remembering that this is a slide, not a jump) flat on the ground, with the rear foot landing on the ball of the foot.

- The athlete's centre of mass should be over the middle of the imaginary Murray Cross (see Figure 91, on page 86). This puts the athlete in a well-balanced position (Figure 111).
- From the catch position, move the front foot backwards, then the back foot forwards, until the feet are level.
- The lift is completed with the feet together, bar in the extended overhead position and directly above the back of the head.

Figure 110: Split jerk catch position (front view)

Figure 111: Split jerk catch position (side view)

Many coaches often ask: 'Why do my athletes need to be able to lift anything above their head: they never do this movement in sport.' While it may not be obviously specific for many sports, there are tremendous transfers of training benefits to performance that can be gained from athletes incorporating these lifts into their training programmes. As well as the ability to control weight above the head, which is an important component of many sporting performances, full extension of weight overhead challenges the musculature throughout the body's kinetic chain, thus really developing the neuromuscular control of the whole body. This significantly challenges the body to maintain postural integrity in three dimensions.

Supplementary Exercises

The following exercises are multiple-joint exercises coaches may find useful to include in a training programme in addition to the core lifts, as required by the specific demands of the sport.

The Shrug

The shrug element of the clean and snatch lifts is often the worst-performed part of the lift by many performers. The ability to explosively shrug the shoulders is vital in helping the bar maintain the upward momentum created by the extension of the leg joints and also keeping the bar pulled in close to the front of the trunk. The shrug also forms the basis of many sport-specific movements and skills. This lift is different from the traditional bodybuilding shrug, which is a slow movement designed to develop the *trapezius* muscle (large muscle at the base of the neck).

Figure 112: Shrug start position (clean grip)

Figure 113: Shrug top position

- This lift can be performed with either a clean (close) or snatch (wide) grip.
- The athlete begins in the power position for either the clean (with bar mid-thigh, as demonstrated in Figure 112) or the snatch (with bar against upper thigh) grip.
- The wrists should be slightly flexed (to help the bar move up the front of the body) rather than out and away from the body.
- The elbows should be fully extended and point along the line of the bar. The elbows shouldn't bend at all during the lift: When the elbows bend, the power ends.
- From here, the shoulders should be explosively raised straight up towards the ears in a violent, straight upwards motion (Figure 113: as opposed to the circular, upwards–backwards motion of the bodybuilding shrug). A common mistake is to bring the neck down, so the ears meet the shoulders; this should be avoided, ensuring the shoulders are always raised instead.
- The lift is completed by the bar returning (under control) to the start position.
- Performing this lift from blocks often helps the athlete, as they do not have to lift the bar as far to get to the start position and can rest the bar in between repetitions. Again, if the weight is too heavy for the athlete's grip, straps can be used to aid the holding of the weight (Figures 112 and 113).
- In order to really get the athlete to perform this as a 'violent' motion, it is often beneficial to put relatively heavy loads onto the bar, even with beginner athletes. As the bar should stay close to the body and the athlete will be in the power (jump) position during the lift, there is little pressure on the back during this movement, as long as it is executed correctly.

Bench Press

- This lift works the pectorals in the chest in a horizontal abduction motion, and the triceps (elbow extensors) on the back of the arm.
- The athlete lies flat on the bench, with knees bent and feet flat on the floor. The feet should remain on the floor throughout the lift.
- The buttocks and shoulder blades should be kept in contact with the bench while the back is flat and the chest is expanded.
- The athlete holds the bar with a medium (over-grasp) grip, with the bar directly above the chest (Figure 114).
- Inhale and brace the trunk musculature prior to lifting, then lower the bar directly to the chest, slightly lower than nipple level (Figure 115).
- When pressing to the starting position, the bar is pressed upwards and slightly back towards the shoulders ('J' lift).
- A spotter is important in free weight bench-press exercises (see Figure 116) to ensure the weight can be lifted off the athlete's chest should they get into any difficulty.

Figure 114: Bench press start position

Figure 115: Bench press bottom position

Close-grip Bench Press

This is an adaptation of the bench press outlined above. In order to put more emphasis on the arm extension (triceps) component of the exercise, the grip can be narrowed, to anything from shoulder-width to 10cm apart. As the bar is lowered, it must be ensured the elbows are kept pointing forwards.

Figure 116: Close-grip bench press bottom position, with spotter

Inclined and dumb-bell bench presses

This exercise can also be performed with the bench inclined (to an angle between 1–45°). This increases the workload on the upper portion of the chest. The exercise can also be done with dumb-bells, which increases the coordination and stability required around each shoulder joint as the lift is performed. Similarly, these variations can be combined, to enable the lifter to perform an inclined dumb-bell bench press (Figure 117).

Figure 117: The inclined dumbbell bench press

Dumb-bell Pull-overs

This is an excellent conditioning exercise for sports where an overhead pulling motion (eg football throw, javelin throw, judo throw) is a key component of the performance.

- The athlete begins seated on a bench that is inclined to between 30–70°, holding a dumb-bell between both hands.
- The hands are pointing upwards, with the thumbs joined around the dumb-bell one way and the fingers around the dumb-bell the other way.
- The back is held flat against the bench, head facing forward and feet flat on the floor throughout the lift.
- The athlete begins by bracing the trunk musculature, inhaling, and bringing the weight as far behind the head as possible (Figure 118).
- From here, the athlete uses the chest muscles to pull the dumb-bell forward to a mid-point position in front of the head (Figure 119), before returning the bar to the start position under control.

Figure 118: The dumb-bell pullover (start position)

Figure 119: The dumb-bell pullover (mid-point position)

Single Leg Squat

This is an excellent conditioning exercise for developing balance and control in the leg, also for overloading the muscles of the quadriceps, hamstrings and gluteals, which control hip and knee positioning during sporting performances. The required technical/coaching points for this exercise are the same as for the normal squat, although the athlete will now also have to work hard to keep the hips level as they descend through the lift. Below is a series of increasingly complex progressions that can enable an athlete to develop this exercise as their competency increases.

Each of these exercises can be performed with:

- no bar (easiest version – the athlete should follow the learning progression suggested below)
- dumb-bells held at the side
- a medicine ball held at the chest in front of the athlete
- a barbell in a squat grip (behind the neck)
- a barbell held in a front squat position, on the front of the shoulders
- a barbell held straight above the head (the narrower the hands are, the more difficult the exercise)
- dumb-bells held straight above the head (very advanced exercise).

Swiss ball single leg squat:

The athlete should stand with the ball level and the middle of their back against a wall. They need to ensure at the start of the movement that the hips are level and the knee of the standing leg is in line with the ankle (incorrect position illustrated in Figure 122). The standing foot should be flat on the floor, with the shoulders pulled back and down (holding the £5 note) and head up (Figure 120). Keeping the trunk muscles braced and the knee of the standing leg in line with the hips and ankles (if they could look down, the athlete would be able to see the big toe past the knee as they squat), the athlete should roll down the wall until the hip joint passes below the level of the knee. They should hold the position for a count of 10 and then return to the start position.

Figure 120: Swiss ball single leg squat (start position)

Figure 121: Swiss ball single leg squat (moving towards the bottom position)

Figure 122: Swiss ball single leg squat showing incorrect knee alignment

Once this has been mastered, the athlete can progress to a smaller ball (eg a medicine ball is ideal), which provides less support for the athlete.

Figure 123: Medicine ball single-leg squat (bottom position)

A bench can also be used for single-leg squats. This makes the action less dynamic but it does tend to put more emphasis on controlling the balance and positioning of the lead knee in relation to the front (Figure 124). The progression to this is to perform the exercise standing on a box, so the athlete is required to flex the hip and knee of the standing leg sufficiently to allow the heel of the non-standing leg (which has the toes pulled up towards the knee – known as 'toes dorsiflexed') to touch the floor. The hips should remain level throughout this exercise, which can be done with or without a bar (Figure 125).

The single-leg Cossack squat is an advanced exercise that really challenges dynamic balance, as well as single-leg strength. These can be performed from a bench either with or without dumb-bells (Figure 126).

**Figure 124:
The single-leg squat
with leg on a bench**

**Figure 125:
The single-leg squat
from a box**

**Figure 126:
The Cossack squat**

The Lunge

This is another version of the single-leg squat and is one of the most versatile conditioning exercises which, with some imagination from the coach, has enormous potential for sport-specific variations to the central principles/technique. For example, all of the progressions suggested above for the bar positioning in the single-leg squat can be applied to the lunge exercise. It can even be adapted so the bar begins in one position (eg behind the head) and is pushed into another position (eg extended arms above the head) at the midpoint of the lift, bringing in additional coordination requirements.

Start position
• The start position for this lift is the same as for the push press: head facing forward, chest high, shoulder blades pulled back, trunk upright, feet together, and bar held as desired by the athlete (Figure 127).

The Lift

- Prior to making the first movement, the athlete inhales and braces the trunk/gluteal musculature.

- From here, the athlete deliberately flexes the hip of the leg that will be leading the movement (refer to Figure 128). The knee of this leg should also be flexed, both to an angle of 90°. The athlete should alternate the lead leg, in order to ensure balanced development.

- The athlete now takes an exaggerated step forwards with the lead leg, which is planted flat on the ground.

- At the same time, the athlete will come onto the ball of the foot on the trail leg and lower the knee of this leg to a bottom position approximately 3–5cm off the floor.

- The trunk should be kept upright throughout the movement, with the centre of mass being directly above the midpoint between the two legs (see Figures 129–131).

- To return to the starting position, push back forcefully with the lead leg to return to the starting position. Repeat with the other leg.

- This can be done on the spot (alternating the front foot), by walking forward (so each step naturally alternates the front foot) or, if the athlete is to be really challenged in terms of strength, balance and coordination, by walking backwards.

Figure 127: Lunge start position (bar in front)

Figure 128: Lunge first movement (bar in front)

Figure 129: Lunge bottom position (bar in front)

Figure 130: Lunge bottom position (bar behind the head)

Figure 131: Lunge bottom position (bar extended above the head)

The in-line lunge

One means of really emphasising the role of the gluteal muscles to control hip positioning (especially in sports movements involving lateral force control) is to perform an in-line lunge (both forwards and backwards). Using all the technical points described above, the athlete places the lead foot only sufficiently far enough in front of them to enable the knee of the bent rear leg to touch the back of the front ankle. This means there is a straight line between the front foot, the lower portion of the rear leg and the rear foot. Having a straight line on the ground aids the athlete in executing the movement correctly.

Figure 132: The in-line lunge

Lunge and Press

This lift can also be performed with a pressing action (either with a barbell or dumb-bells), by forcefully extending the arms above the head, as the step with the lead leg is taken. This means that as the front foot lands, the arms are fully extended, with the bar directly above the head. The trunk remains upright throughout (see Figure 131).

Controlling Rotations in a Lunge

The exercise can also be done holding a weighted disk, or medicine ball, and rotating it from side to side every time the athlete takes a step (see Figure 133). This continual shifting of the weight (and therefore the athlete's centre of mass) will really test postural control. Performing the exercise with an uneven weight on each end of the bar (Figure 134) or holding one dumb-bell in a straight-arm position (Figure 135) will have a similar effect.

As with any lifting technique it should be remembered that the aim is not for the coach to be as rapidly creative and progressive as possible, but for the performer to demonstrate sound basic technique mastery at each successive level of complexity prior to the movement being made more challenging to execute.

| **Figure 133:** Trunk twists lunges | **Figure 134:** Lunges with bar loaded unevenly | **Figure 135:** Lunges with single dumb-bell in an overhead position |

The lunge exercise variations, as described above, are linear in nature, in that the front foot moves forwards. However, as sport is multi-directional, this conditioning lift can be manipulated to allow the athlete to train for this. As long as the athlete follows the principles relating to the major steps of the lift[23], the lift can be adapted so the front foot placement is open (to the side away from the body as demonstrated in Figure 136 – note the knee is still moving in the same line as the toes), closed (to the side across the body, as demonstrated in Figure 137) or even behind the athlete (as demonstrated in Figure 138). This can be done with the bar at the shoulders, or with a pressing/arm-extension action, or random combinations of all of the above. This type of pattern is known as a 'round the clock' lunge sequence.

**Figure 136:
Midpoint lunge
with open step**

**Figure 137:
Midpoint lunge and
press with closed step**

**Figure 138:
Midpoint lunge (bar
behind neck)
backward step**

Bent-over Row

- The athlete can perform this exercise with either a closed under-grasp grip, or an over-grasp claw grip (see Figure 139), depending on which might be more appropriate for the athlete's particular sport. Alternating grips between sets is a common strategy.
- The hands should be held slightly wider than shoulder-width apart.
- The athlete lifts the bar into the jump position using the floor-to-thigh lifting technique as described in the power clean.
- The athlete assumes a shoulder-width stance, with feet shoulder-width apart and knees slightly flexed.
- The athlete leans the torso forward to 10–30º above horizontal (see Figure 139) and looks ahead/slightly upwards.
- The chest should be high, shoulder blades pulled back together and the back should be straight.
- The lift begins with the elbows fully extended (the bar should not touch the floor).
- From here, the athlete braces the trunk musculature and inhales, then pulls the bar into the trunk (see Figure 140) using the arms and pointing elbows upwards during the movement.
- The athlete should maintain knee, head and torso position, keeping the back flat at all times.
- The bar is returned to the starting position to complete the lift.

**Figure 139: Bent-over
row start position**

**Figure 140: Bent-over
row top position**

Dumb-bell Curl and Press

- The athlete stands with dumb-bells in each hand, holding them with an under-grasp grip, sideways on, with palms facing forward.
- The feet should be shoulder-width apart, flat on the floor with legs slightly bent.
- The head should be up, shoulder blades pulled back together and the chest up (see Figure 141).

Movement 1: Curl

- Keeping the elbows next to the body, the elbows are flexed and the dumb-bells are raised to shoulder level (see Figure 142).

Figure 141: Curl start position

Figure 142: End of curl

Movement 2: Press

- Once the dumb-bells are at shoulder level, the athlete rotates the wrists so the palms are again facing forward (Figure 143).
- From here, the elbows are extended vertically, so that the dumb-bells are raised to full arm extension (see Figure 144).
- At the end of this movement, the dumb-bells are returned to the start position.

Figure 143: Beginning the press

Figure 144: End of the press

Alternative Dumb-bell Curl and Press Combination

This exercise is another that is very versatile, as the curl can be combined with a single-leg squat movement in the legs, or the press turned into a push jerk or split jerk.

Shoulder Press

This is the same movement as the push press, but the power to move the bar comes from the deltoids in the shoulder and triceps in the arm, rather than transferring power from the leg drive. In this way, the legs stay still throughout the movement.

**Figure 145: Shoulder press
start position**

**Figure 146: Shoulder press
top position**

Alternative Shoulder Press

One suggested variation of this lift is to raise the bar from the front, lower it behind the head, and then push it from behind the head (Figure 147), lowering to the front. This exercise can also be performed with dumb-bells if more unilateral movement control is needed to be developed.

Figure 147: Shoulder press (from behind the neck) start position

Dumb-bell Flies

This is another exercise that works the pectorals in the chest in a horizontal adduction (inward punching/hugging action) movement of the shoulder.

- The athlete lies face up on a bench, with feet flat on the floor, holding the dumb-bells with a closed, over-grasp grip, with the dumb-bells facing each other.
- To get into the correct start position, the dumb-bells are pressed to an extended arm position above the chest, with the palms of the hands facing inwards (see Figure 148).
- From here, the elbow is slightly bent (to an angle that will remain constant from this point throughout the lift) and then the dumb-bells are lowered, under control, in a wide arc, until the dumb-bell is at the same height as the shoulder (Figure 149).
- Both arms should lower (and later rise) at the same rate.
- Once the dumb-bells are in the bottom position, they are returned to the starting position. This is done by the pectoral muscles pulling the dumb-bells towards each other (keeping the angle of elbow flexion constant) to make the arms return to the start position.

Figure 148: Dumb-bell flies start position

Figure 149: Dumb-bell flies bottom position

Upright Row

This exercise strengthens the muscles around the neck, upper back and shoulder girdle, in an upward pulling motion.

- The athlete stands with the head up, shoulder blades back, chest high and feet flat on the floor, shoulder-width apart.
- The bar is held in an over-grasp grip with the arms fully extended.
- Prior to any movement being made, the athlete inhales and braces the trunk and gluteal muscles (Figure 150).
- From here, the elbows are flexed, pulling the bar up the front of the trunk until it reaches a position level with the top of the chest.
- The athlete's elbows should be above the level of the bar at all times (Figure 151).
- From this position, the athlete lowers the bar, under control, to the start position.

Figure 150: Upright row start position

Figure 151: Upright row top position

Dip

This is an excellent conditioning exercise for the triceps muscles (responsible for straightening the arm) and it can also be adapted to train the chest as well. This exercise uses the athlete's own body weight to provide resistance, although when they can cope with this for the required number of repetitions, additional weight can be added to a belt around the waist, so they are continually overloaded to stimulate development.

- Using a dip bar (or gymnastics parallel bar, depending upon equipment availability), the athlete hangs from the rails with straight arms, leaning slightly forward (see Figure 152). The further the lean, the more the chest muscles become involved in the action.
- From here, the body is lowered, under control, until the elbows are bent to a 90° angle (see Figure 153).
- The elbows are then straightened and the body driven upwards, as rapidly as possible, until the athlete returns to the start position.

Figure 152: Dip start position   **Figure 153: Dip bottom position**

Rope Climbing

This classic exercise from physical education is a fantastic means of developing total body strength. From first progressions, where it doesn't matter how the athlete does it (they just have to get up the rope!), to more advanced versions (eg upper body only [Figure 154]) this is a fantastic conditioning exercise for athletes from any sporting background.

Figure 154: Climbing ropes is a great conditioning exercise

Pull-ups (Chin-ups)

This is another exercise that develops strength through lifting your own body weight (until such a time as additional weight needs to be added to facilitate overload). This exercise can be performed with an under-grasp grip (see Figure 156) or an over-grasp grip (see Figure 155), or it can be made more sport specific. For example, the judo athlete performing the exercise could grip a judo 'Gi' draped over the chin-up bar and a rugby player could grip a rugby shirt or simply a piece of rope.

- The athlete begins by hanging from the bar, with arms fully extended (see Figure 155 or 156).
- From here, the athlete pulls themself up, so the chin comes level to, or above, the bar (Figure 157 on page 106), then returns under control to the start position.

Some might argue this action should occur with the body in a straight position. However, sport is about generating power through total body movement. If the athlete finds it beneficial to use the lower body to generate the momentum required for the movement, then this is acceptable, especially at the early stages of training. Similarly, if the full range of movement can not be achieved, then the athlete should be encouraged to perform as complete a range of motion as possible, particularly if grip strength is important to the sport for which they are training.

Figure 155: Pull-up start position (over-grasp grip)

Figure 156: Pull-up start position (under-grasp grip)

Figure 157: Pull-up top position

Press-ups

For some, the basic press-up is an excellent conditioning exercise. For those who find it easy, it can be progressed to cover greater degrees of difficulty.

To perform the basic exercise, the hands should be placed shoulder-width apart on the floor. The trunk should be in a straight-line position (head, shoulders, pelvis neutral, back flat, hips, knees and ankles), as shown in Figure 158. From here, and maintaining the straight line position, the elbows are flexed until they are bent to greater than 90° (or the chest is two centimeters off the ground, whichever is first, Figure 159) before the athlete returns to the start position.

Figure 158: Press-up start position

Figure 159: Press-up (midpoint)

This exercise can be made more complex by performing it with hands together (emphasising smaller muscle groups, eg Figure 160), raising the athlete's centre of mass (eg by raising the feet – Figure 161. This can be progressed all the way into a handstand press-up) or by changing the balance position (eg one-handed press-ups – Figure 162).

Figure 160: Press-up (start position) with hands close together

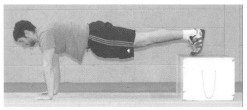

Figure 161: Press-up (start position) with raised centre of mass

Figure 162: One-handed press-up (bottom position)

Strength Balances

This group of exercises are often referred to as 'core stability' exercises. Basically, they are designed to focus the athlete's ability to control the shoulder and pelvic girdles in increasingly challenging positions. It is important to note that these exercises alone will not make the athlete significantly stronger. Also, the exercises described previously all activate the postural muscles to a great extent. These supplementary exercises can also be used within programmes to aid the recruitment and overload of the postural muscles in any athlete.

The idea during any of these exercises is to maintain the braced trunk position, and keep the distance between the navel (belly button) and the xyphoid process (small groove at the top of the rectus abdominis – the six-pack muscle) constant throughout the exercise.

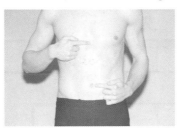

Figure 163: The distance between the xyphoid process and the navel should be constant throughout these strength balances

The Bridge

The athlete lies down on their back, with feet shoulder width apart and knees bent to 90°. To make it easier, the arms can be laid on the floor, or more advanced by raising them in the air (reduced surface area in contact with the floor – see Figure 165). From here, the athlete braces the trunk musculature, and lifts their pelvis off the floor, stopping when their knees, hips and shoulders form a straight line. This stable position needs to be maintained for a count of 10–15 seconds, then released and repeated. Athletes who feel pain in their hamstring or lower back are not utilising the gluteal muscles, and/or the trunk musculature.

Figure 164: The Bridge

The Single Leg Bridge

This is a progression of the bridge exercise. The athlete lies down on their back, with feet shoulder width apart and knees bent to 90°. The arms can be laid on the floor (easier), or raised in the air (reduced surface area in contact with the floor (making this more advanced, see Figure 165). From here, the athlete braces the trunk musculature and lifts their pelvis off the floor, stopping when their knees, hips and shoulders form a straight line. From here, the athlete maintains this stable hip (the hips need to stay level) and knee (in line with the toes) alignment for a count of 10–15 seconds, then the leg is returned to the start position and the other leg is raised.

Figure 165: The Single Leg Bridge

Superman

The athlete kneels on all fours on the floor, ensuring the knees are directly below the hips and the elbows directly below the shoulders. The shoulders should be pulled down and back, as if jamming the shoulders into the ribs and the ribs into the pelvis. Keeping the pelvis in a neutral position (maintained by bracing the trunk musculature and activating the back muscles, as described above), the athlete extends the arm (Figure 164) from the shoulder, so it clears the floor. The athlete must avoid hyper-extending the back and should work to maintain a neutral pelvis position. Variation on this exercise can be achieved by maintaining a three-point balance position while raising the legs (Figure 165). A two-point balance position can also be achieved by raising alternate arms and legs simultaneously (maintaining level hip and shoulder positions – Figure 166), and by raising the arm and leg on both sides of the body (Figure 167).

Figure 164: Superman – three-point balance raising one arm

Figure 165: Superman – three-point balance raising one leg

Figure 166: Superman – two-point balance raising opposite arm and leg

Figure 167: Superman – two-point balance raising the arm and leg on the same side of the body

The Plank

The athlete lies on their stomach, with their hands together under their chest and the elbows tucked in under shoulders. Bracing the trunk musculature and keeping the distance between the navel and the xyphoid constant, the athlete raises the trunk off the floor, keeping the forearms and feet in contact with the ground and the head up (Figure 168). There should now be a straight line between the ear, shoulder, back, hip, knee and ankle. Relaxing the abdominal brace will cause the loss of the neutral pelvic position and some shearing of the lower back/pelvic girdle will be evident (Figure 169). Being detailed in the analysis of this movement is important if the athlete is to reap the appropriate benefits.

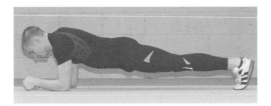

Figure 168: The plank

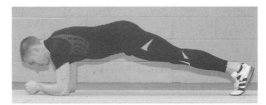

Figure 169: The plank with inappropriate position

The first progression from here is to change the exercise into a three-point balance, by raising one leg while maintaining a level hip and shoulder position, holding for 10 seconds, and then alternating legs.

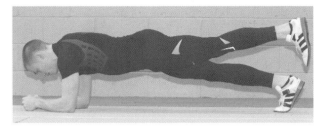

Figure 170: The plank with one leg raised

This exercise can also be done with the chest facing upwards.

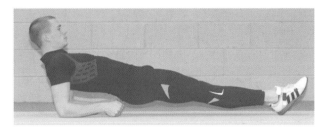

Figure 171: The reverse plank with straight-line body position

Making this into a two-point balance increases the number of dimensions that the athlete must control movement in. Moving onto one side (still resting on the elbows) means the forward/backward lean and straight line body position must all be controlled by the athlete. This can then be advanced by reducing the surface area in control with the ground (eg onto the hand, see Figure 173), making the athlete less stable again.

© Action Images/Reuters

Figure 172: The side plank on the elbow

Figure 173: England cricketer Monty Panesar performs the side plank with a straight arm during a gym session

Handstands

The athlete should try and make him or herself as tall as possible, reaching their feet to the sky, while maintaining an upright posture (Figure 174a). The athlete can use a wall to balance against if necessary. The athlete should face the wall, with the feet on the wall, hands on the floor, and walk the body up the wall into handstand position (Figure 174b). Most athletes are not strong enough to kick up into a handstand when facing away from the wall. Once this can be held for a minute, progressions can include handstand press-ups, or walking on the hands, with the same objective in mind.

Figure 174a: Handstands

Figure 174b: Walking up the wall into the handstand position

Trunk-conditioning Exercises

Crunches

Crunches are considered to be the easiest of the trunk-conditioning exercises to perform.

- The athlete lies on the floor, with the knees bent to 90° and feet flat on the floor.
- The hands should be folded across the chest (easiest method) or holding onto the ears, but they should not be put behind the neck (see Figure 175). The chin should be tucked onto the chest.
- From here, the athlete curls the trunk towards the legs until the upper back is off the mat, keeping the lower back and feet on the floor (see Figure 176). Coaches should emphasise that it is important not to bounce from the shoulders.
- This position is held, then the trunk is slowly lowered (under control) until it is back into the start position.

Figure 175: Crunch start position

Figure 176: Crunch top position

Cycled Crunches

- The athlete lies on their back on the floor, with the hands holding on to the ears, elbows pointing towards the feet and the toes dorsiflexed.
- The athlete raises the feet and legs off the floor together, keeping a slight bend in the knees (this takes the pressure off the lower back).
- From here, the left leg is bent, with the knee moving up towards the head (maintaining the toes pulled towards the knees).
- Simultaneously, the trunk is flexed and rotated about a stable pelvis, which remains in a neutral position, while the lower back remains flat on the floor.
- The left elbow is brought to meet the right knee (see Figure 177).
- From here, the athlete returns to the start position under control, before repeating the action with the opposite arm and leg.

Figure 177: Cycled crunches

Vertical Leg Shoots

- The athlete lies on the floor, with the hips bent to 90°, knees extended so the soles of the feet are pointing straight up in the air, with the hands folded across the chest.
- Keeping this angle at the knee joint, the athlete uses the lower abdominal muscles to tilt the pelvis back towards the head, so the angle of the hip is increased and the feet are thrown up towards the sky (see Figure 178).
- The athlete briefly holds this extended position and then returns to the starting position under control.
- This action is repeated, but it is important the flexion/extension action of the hips between repetitions does not cause the legs to lower and rise. This would cause momentum to be generated, which makes the movement a lot easier.

Figure 178: Vertical leg shoots

Vertical leg shoots with medicine ball
This is an advanced progression of the above exercise. Holding a medicine ball (the weight of which depends upon the athlete's capabilities) between the knees, with the knees bent to 90º, the athlete repeats the leg shoot motion, this time trying to get the medicine ball as high as possible with the hip drive.

Figure 179: Vertical leg shoots with medicine ball resistance (top position)

V-sits

• The athlete lies on their back on the floor, with the arms extended fully behind the head (with hands pointing away from the body) and the feet and legs raised off the floor together (toes dorsiflexed – see Figure 180).

• There should be a slight bend in the knees to take the pressure off the lower back.

• From here, maintaining a neutral pelvis position, the athlete performs a jack-knife manoeuvre, flexing the trunk and bringing the thighs towards the trunk (as if the upper and lower body segments were coming to meet each other at an imaginary line coming up from the hip joint in the start position).

• The legs should remain stiff with knees slightly bent, at the same angle throughout the movement.

• The athlete extends the arms above the head until the trunk has reached full flexion, at which point they are brought forward to meet the feet, as the 'V' position is achieved.

Figure 180: V-sits top position

Springboks

- The athlete lies on the floor, with the knees bent at 90° and feet flat on the floor. The feet should be restrained by a partner, who could also hold the athlete's calf muscles for support (Figure 181).
- From here, the athlete performs a powerful sit-up action, engaging the braced abdominal muscles to move the trunk forwards (Figure 182).
- As the athlete moves to the top of the sit-up, they now engage the hip extensor (glute and hamstring) muscles to drive the athlete up into a standing position, using the support from the partner (who will need to pull through the calf muscles) as little as possible (Figure 183).
- The athlete finishes in the standing position (Figure 184).

Figure 181: Springboks – start position

Figure 182: Springboks – top of the sit-up

Figure 183: Springboks – drive to standing

Figure 184: Springboks – finish position

Windscreen Wipers

The athlete lies flat on the back, hips flexed at 90° and legs straight, with the soles of the feet pointing towards the ceiling. Keeping the same angle at the hips and knees and keeping the back flat to the floor, the athlete lowers the legs to the side so they touch the floor at approximately 90° to the body. From here, and without using the upper body to do anything other than stabilise the position, the athlete returns to the start position and then lowers the legs in the other direction.

Figure 185: Windscreen wipers

Roll-outs

Roll-outs really emphasise postural integrity within an athlete, by fully challenging the eccentric control abilities of the pelvic and shoulder girdles; they are, therefore, reasonably advanced exercises that should be approached with caution. As with most exercises, there are ranges of progression of a roll-out, starting with the athlete on the knees, with both hands shoulder-width apart on a barbell pulled close to the body.

- The athlete inhales and, maintaining the abdominal brace (keeping a straight line between the shoulder and the knees) and the arms locked, rolls the barbell forward.

- The first target is for the athlete to be able to keep rolling the bar out until the straight arms form a 90° angle with the athlete's trunk (Figure 187). When learning this exercise, this is as far as the athlete may be able to go.

- From this position, to challenge fully shoulder girdle strength, the athlete should now continue to roll the bar forward, maintaining a straight line between knees and trunk, until the arms are pointing straight forward (at 180° to the body, which is now perpendicular to the floor, see Figure 188).

Figure 186: Roll-out on knees (start position)   **Figure 187: Roll-out on knees (mid-point position)**   **Figure 188: Roll-out on knees (end position)**

- From this end position, the trunk and hip flexor muscles should be concentrically contracted to pull the athlete back to the start position (maintaining the straight line body position throughout).

- Once this becomes mastered, the athlete should progress to performing the exercises on their feet (extending the length of the body chain that needs to be controlled, see Figure 189). Another progression is to use dumb-bells, rather than barbells, which places different stressors on the shoulder joints during the movement.

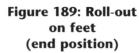  

Figure 189: Roll-out on feet (end position)   **Figure 190a: Roll-out using dumbbells (in two hands)**   **Figure 190b: Single arm dumb-bell roll-out**

Vault Twists

This exercise gets its name from its popularity with pole-vaulters.

- The athlete begins by hanging from a chin-up bar (or similar, as available), with hands in an under-grasp grip and trunk fully extended (Figure 191).

- From this position, the athlete braces the trunk musculature and uses the lower abdominal and hip flexor muscles to pull the feet upwards and to one side of the body (alternated with each repetition) until the soles of the feet point towards the ceiling (Figure 192). This position is held, and then the athlete returns to the start position, under control.

- An advancement of this sees the athlete twist the body fully around the bar and use the trunk musculature to raise the hips above the level of the bar, with feet still pointing towards the ceiling (see Figure 193).

Figure 191: Vault twists (start position)

Figure 192: At the top of the movement, with legs to one side of the body

Figure 193: Advanced version – the feet are above the bar, pointing towards the ceiling

Candlesticks

This is an advanced conditioning exercise for trunk, hip and groin musculature that emphasises the development of eccentric strength in the trunk as well as concentric strength.

- The athlete lies on a bench (or the floor) with head, shoulders and top of the back in contact with the bench.
- The trunk should be flexed, with the pelvis and legs pointing to the ceiling. The hands should be holding something that can act as an anchor point behind the head of the athlete (see Figure 194).
- From this position, the legs are lowered, slowly and under eccentric control of the trunk musculature, towards the ground. The trunk is not lowered to the ground.
- This lowering continues until the trunk body is in a straight line (see Figure 195).
- From here, the abdominal/trunk muscles contract concentrically and you return to the starting position.

Alternative Candlesticks

This exercise can be further advanced by the addition of a rotational movement in the trunk-lowering phase of the exercise, raising to a parallel position and then rotating to the opposite side on the next repetition.

Figure 194: Candlesticks start position

Figure 195: Candlesticks bottom position

Machines and Free Weights

All of the conditioning lifts recommended in the previous section have been bodyweight and other free-weight exercises; these are very important for sports performers. But why shouldn't athletes begin to develop strength on machines? These machines, after all, have the advantage of allowing the athlete to be able to train without a spotter in assistance (if a training partner is not available) and they require little technical skill to use. However, the fact the machine controls the movement of the exercise means they effectively eliminate any training of the stabiliser muscles acting around a joint in a lift. They effectively isolate a joint movement in one dimension, whereas the physiological requirements of sport lie with joint stability and strength in three dimensions.

Indeed, joint isolation does not relate well to the concept of specificity or transfer of training benefits to performance, as almost all sports skills are multi-joint in nature and strength training needs to promote total body development and inter-muscular coordination of muscles around various joints, in order to reflect the needs of the game. It is for this reason that strength-training sessions should focus on multiple-joint lifts that stress the entire body and do not focus on individual body parts. Two to three sessions of such workouts per week also allow every body part to receive quality workouts rather than just one. Similarly, machines encourage detraining of the core postural muscles that control pelvic, trunk and shoulder stability, leading to postural instability – a poor base from which to develop limb power and one that could possibly lead to movement dysfunction and lumbar back pain in many adolescent and adult athletes. Therefore, the focus of an effective strength-training programme should be based on the use of bodyweight exercises (especially really challenging gymnastic exercises and free weights).

Weight Training and Physical Maturity

One of the most frequently asked questions by coaches and parents revolves around the age at which someone should begin to use weights in their resistance training. Unfortunately, there is no simple answer to this question, for one principal reason: it is accepted that children have individual rates of physical development and many cross-sections of body shape and size can be seen within any one age group. For this reason, chronological age can only be used as a rough guideline for training progression.

It should be remembered that strength is always trainable in a child of any age. In younger children, this can be developed through activities such as Swiss (physio) ball work, body-weight control exercises (such as the traditional press-up, squat thrusts, bench dips and sit-ups) and medicine-ball exercises. Having children undertake gymnastics training from an early age will probably give them the best possible start to their athletic careers, in terms of being able to control postures and utilise the right muscles to perform the correct tasks.

The pre-adolescent years can be characterised by poor coordination, due to the accelerated development of the nervous system and rapid growth of the skeleton (particularly in terms of the trunk, a concept referred to as peak height velocity, or PHV). However, free-weight techniques are skilled movements that need to be learnt to benefit the dexterity of the young athlete. In Britain, we have traditionally been held back in our development of young individuals for too long, by having an over-developed sense of caution about the general use of strength training, particularly with weights, which has prevented children undergoing this vital learning stage. When children undergo this training, after having reached the appropriate stage of development to work with resistive masses, they already have a well-developed technique base. For many adult athletes, the lack of development of a safe and effective technique is the biggest barrier to being able to train with weights effectively.

Prior to PHV, strength gains occur largely as a result of neurological improvements. Neural development benefits, and therefore strength gains, can be aided by the young athlete learning the techniques and movements of free-weight lifting. This can be achieved by learning and practising the techniques with a broomstick, and need not involve lifting any significant mass. However, as technical competency improves, the resistive mass of the bar can be progressively and gradually increased, so the athlete is working against progressively increasing loads and developing strength and athletic potential.

It has long been thought by coaches, parents and teachers that young athletes should not lift weights until they have gone through the adolescent growth spurt. Lifting weights prior to this was thought to cause such detrimental effects as stunting children's growth, or damaging the *epiphysial* plates (growth plates) in the bones through shearing or compressing forces. However, it is clear from researched principles and anecdotal evidence this simply isn't true, and improving a young athlete's potential through weight lifting is a valuable aid to athlete development (Pierce et al., 2008; Byrd et al., 2004).

Figure 196: Instruction of young Scottish judo athletes by Dr Kyle Pierce of the US Weightlifting Development Centre at a sportscotland **workshop**

'The potential for growth plate injury may be less in the prepubescent...the growth plate is actually much stronger and more resistant to shear stress in children than adolescents.' (Micheli, 1988: in Pierce, et al., 2007)

Following PHV, hormonal influences mean the muscular component of strength can be positively influenced. These hormonal influences suggest the best time for females to begin to benefit is at the onset of PHV, whereas in males, testosterone levels begin to peak 12–16 months after PHV. A parent or coach monitoring the height of their child on a regular basis can identify the onset of PHV fairly easily.

Age apart, it should be remembered that poorly planned, poorly performed and over-strenuous resistance training is as dangerous for adults as it is for children. **Whether working with a child or an adult, it is important to realise technique needs to be taught, and training needs to be supervised, by an experienced and knowledgeable coach.** The coach should be educated and qualified according to the standards of the UK Strength and Conditioning Association and work in an appropriately managed environment.

How Much to Lift and How Many Times

As identified in Chapter 2, the size-recruitment principle of muscle fibres is important in designing a strength-training programme. To fully develop the Type IIx fibres essential for power production, the weight lifted needs to be very heavy or the movement very powerful. This nature of weight is not going to be lifted many times, however. This is where the concept of the repetition maximum (RM) (Fleck and Kraemer, 1997) becomes important, as it relates to the maximum number of repetitions that can be completed with a given load. For example, a 1RM of 100kg in an identified lift means that an athlete can lift a maximum (single lift) of 100kg. Similarly, a 3RM of 70kg means that this weight can be lifted a maximum of three times in a given exercise. As is illustrated in Chapter 10, coaches should be aware that not every set is a repetition maximum effort (eg three repetitions at 70% is not a 3RM).

This information can be used to shape how the strength-training programme is put together, by manipulating the number of times the weights are lifted (repetitions) and the number of blocks of repetitions completed (sets) per exercise.

Table 5: General guidelines for constructing a training session

Objective	Repetitions per Set	Resistive Mass and Speed of Movement	Suggested Recovery Time Between Sets
Power	1–4	Loading sufficient to allow explosive movement: 70–85% of 1RM in Olympic lifts, 50–60% in back squats	3–8 minutes
Maximum strength	1–4	Maximal load. Intention is to lift explosively, but load on the bar will result in a slow movement	3–5 minutes
Strength	3–8	As explosive as resistive mass will allow (it won't be as fast as power training, but will be faster than maximal strength lifts)	3–5 minutes
Strength and size increase	8–10	Controlled and rhythmical movement with as much speed as resistive mass and fatigue will allow. Sports performers should not lift weights slowly	2–3 minutes
Cardiovascular endurance	12+	As fast as fatigue will allow	1 minute

In order to develop power, it is important to train all of the fibre types. However, imagine you are lifting the heaviest weight you possibly can (your maximal lift) – will this be a fast or slow movement? The answer must be, despite using all of the fibre types, the movement will be slow. This is due to the mass upon the bar, however, not a result of the athlete trying to move slowly (if the athlete did try and lift a maximal weight slowly, it is guaranteed not to move). Therefore, there is a definite need to combine these maximal lifts with an element of speed. Generally speaking, there should never be any reason to intentionally attempt to lift a weight slowly; athletes should always be encouraged to lift as rapidly as possible. However, with the lower repetitions, it is not always possible to lift the weight rapidly, no matter how hard an athlete tries, as has already been identified. So how does this develop power? This is done by manipulation of the weight the athlete lifts, to allow explosive speed to develop, which is achieved through training[24] using between 70–85% of an athlete's 1RM (eg in a snatch or clean lift), and 50–60% 1RM (eg in a back squat) and lifting this weight explosively. This allows peak power (ie force x velocity) to be generated, as shown in Figure 197.

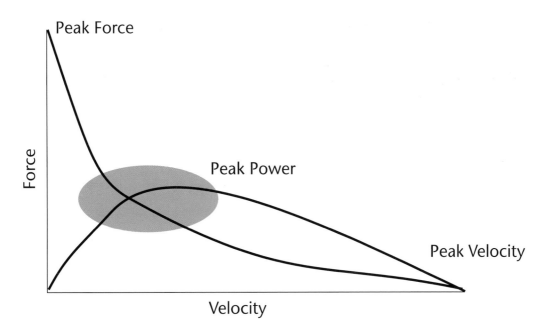

**Figure 197: Peak power occurs at 70–85% of maximum strength
in the clean and snatch**

As with any aspect of fitness, monitoring and testing the strength/power development of an athlete is one of the primary functions a coach can fulfil. These tests provide the coach with a range of information essential in programme planning. Firstly, the tests should provide baseline data about how strong the athlete is prior to commencing the programme. This is vital, as a coach needs to be able to determine whether the programmes being implemented are working or not and how much progress each individual athlete is making. Therefore, tests to assess the current status of an athlete are also needed periodically. The data from these tests not only allows the coach to determine what strengths and weaknesses to work on, but also to set objective goals for the athlete to work towards. Such examinations can be formal – planned months in advance, as part of a long-term programme – or they can be more spontaneous, allowing the coach to test the current situation. Whatever the circumstances, the test should conform to certain rules in order to be effective. These rules are as follows. Tests must:

• replicate the competitive demand of the sport (ie test biomechanically similar movements)
• be simple and repeatable, so there can be a realistic comparison between test results over time
• be interpretable (ie the coach must understand the implications of the results and rapidly apply them to the developed training programme).

The standard form of testing strength is to record a repetition maximum for a given lift in athletes who are fully competent technically. The standard lifts used in the majority of sports are one or two lifts from clean, snatch, squat and bench press (as an indicator of upper-body strength). This is because the multiple-joint actions of these lifts are biomechanically similar to many of the actions required within a multitude of sports. The most common repetition maximum tested in sports is either one, three or five. This is because very few sports require maximal strength to be tested in a one-off situation. However, to test using more than five repetitions means the explosive power elements important to the sport will not be tested adequately, and it is consequently not a valid test for the sport.

Once the appropriate lift and the required repetition range have been determined, the athlete should warm up appropriately, and begin by lifting 50% of their required repetition maximum. For example, if someone has a 3RM squat clean of 80kg, they should begin by lifting 40kg for three. After a 3–5-minute rest, this should be progressed to 80% of 3RM for three, then 90% of 3RM for three and then 100% of previous 3RM for three, and so on, until the athlete can not complete the required number of repetitions safely (and with sound technique) with the given weight. It is important to allow adequate recovery between attempts and also to not have too many attempts before maximum, in order to avoid unnecessary fatigue. The last weight to be successfully lifted for the given number of repetitions (in this example, three) should be recorded.

It is important coaches using testing of this type are confident in the technique of the athlete tested. If their technique is at all unstable, testing of this kind should not be used and the simple monitoring of training lifts as technique develops will provide coaches with sufficient data. Similarly, such tests must not be used if an athlete's training status is not 100% (ie they are nursing an injury or they are fatigued). Some lifts, such as the bench press or the squat, require competent spotters to provide assistance in returning the bar to the start position should the lifter fall.

Many times, especially when using strength lifts (squat, bench etc – it is not such an exact science with explosive lifts such as the clean and the snatch), a coach can estimate the athlete's 1RM (the maximum weight an athlete can lift once) based upon a 5RM training load. This is illustrated in Table 6, which shows that a 5RM is estimated to be 88% of a 1RM.

So, knowing a 5RM max (which is far less demanding on an athlete and should regularly be part of a training load) will enable the 1RM to be estimated.

Table 6: Calculating the training load for a lift based upon the 1RM in the squat (or using a RM to estimate 1RM)

Repetitions	Medium (%RM)	Medium–Heavy (%RM)	Heavy (%RM)	Very Heavy (RM)
1	85	90	95	100
2	80	85	90	95
3	78	83	87	92
5	74	78	83	88
8	68	72	76	80
10	63	67	71	75

As Table 6 illustrates, the calculation of a training load is based upon knowledge (or estimation) of the 1RM. More detail about training loads (very heavy, heavy, medium-heavy; medium, as examples) can be found in Chapter 10. However, it is important to realise that, for example, a 5RM is 88% (approximately) of a 1RM, whereas a medium five-repetition training load is 74% of the athlete's 1RM lift. This is a large difference in load, which needs to be accounted for when designing the athlete's strength training programme or, indeed, the optimum load to put on the bar for optimum power.

Example Training Sessions

Below are some example sessions taken from different sports. It is important to realise these are presented as ideas for how coaches can use the exercises shown earlier on in this chapter. Actual programming depends upon many factors, such as the level of the performer, individual training needs and the stage of the season.

Example 1: Rugby Forward

Objectives of session: Build size and strength

Stage of season: Off-season

Training age of athlete*: Two years

Exercise	Number of Sets	Number of Reps	Weight to Lift (% RM)	Movement	Duration of Rest Between Sets (minutes)
Push press (page 90)	4	5	80%	Explosive	4
Squat (page 68)	4	8	75%	Explosive	5
Pull from floor (snatch grip) (page 79)	4	8	75%	Explosive	3–5
Bench press (page 95)	4	8	80%	Explosive	3
V-sits (page 112)	4	10	–	Explosive raise, controlled lowering	3

*How long this person has been lifting weights

**Pull = first pull, followed by transition phase and second pull. Load to be lifted is based upon the snatch 1RM.

Example 2: Football

Objectives of session: Develop speed and strength

Stage of season: Late pre-season

Training age of athlete: Six years

Exercise	Number of Sets	Number of Reps	Weight to Lift (% RM)	Movement	Duration of Rest Between Sets (minutes)
Overhead squat (page 72)	4	6	75%	Controlled descent, explosive ascent	3–5
Clean (page 79)	4	4	85%	Explosive	3–5
Push jerk (page 92)	4	3	88%	Explosive	5–5
Stiff-legged deadlift (page 88)	4	6	80%	Controlled descent, explosive return	3
Candlesticks (page 115)	4	10	–	Explosive raise, controlled lowering	3

Example 3: Tennis
Objectives of session: Develop explosive speed
Stage of season: In competition
Training age of athlete: Three years

Exercise	Number of Sets	Number of Reps	Weight to Lift (% RM)	Movement	Duration of Rest Between Sets (minutes)
Pull (clean grip) from hang (page 84)	3	4	75%	Explosive	5
Squat snatch (page 78)	4	3	70%	Explosive	5–8
Split jerk (page 93)	4	3	85%	Explosive	5
Dumb-bell curl and press (page 102)	3	6	85%	Explosive return to start position	3

Example 4: Cross-country running
Objectives of session: Develop basic strength and postural control
Stage of season: Preparation period
Training age of athlete: Four years

Exercise	Number of Sets	Number of Reps	Weight to Lift (% RM)	Movement	Duration of Rest Between Sets (minutes)
Overhead squat (page 72)	4	5	85%	Controlled down, rapid to standing (with full control)	5
Split clean (page 85)	4	5	75%	Explosive	5
Push jerk (page 92)	3	5	80%	Controlled	3
Round the clock lunges with bar behind neck (page 100)	4	8 (one circuit for each leg leading)	85%	Explosive return to start position	3

Example 5: Swimming

Objectives of session: Develop start speed for freestyle event and flexibility

Stage of season: In competition

Training age of athlete: Six years

Exercise	Number of Sets	Number of Reps	Weight to Lift (% RM)	Movement	Duration of Rest Between Sets (minutes)
Front squat (page 71)	4	5	70%	Controlled lowering, explosive raising	5
Snatch from hang (page 78)	4	3	75%	Explosive	5
Push jerk (page 92)	4	3	75%	Explosive	3–5
Roll-outs (page 114)	3	10	–	Explosive up, controlled lowering	3
Vault twists (page 114)	5	1 minute hold	–	–	2

Further examples of strength training programmes can be seen in Chapter 10, where they are used to illustrate the concept of volume and training loads.

Summary

Important points for athletes:

- The athlete should control the weight; they should not let it control them. They should lower the weight in a controlled fashion, while raising the bar in an explosive, powerful manner.

- Make sure athletes are familiar with the correct technique for a lift. Most injuries occur because people lift weights too heavy for them and/or they use incorrect technique. Egos in the gym do not improve performance. Therefore, athletes should not attempt to lift weights to impress others – they should stick to their own limits and not follow the MOR-ON school of thought – ie thinking they'll put more weight on the bar, before being technically prepared for the extra kilograms.

- Before attempting any lift, always check the equipment being used is fully functional and not damaged in any way. Always make sure the plates on a dumb-bell/barbell are secured with a suitable collar, if appropriate.

- Intensity is the key to successful training. Maintain 100% focus, effort and concentration throughout the session.

- Encourage athletes to train with a partner for safety and motivational purposes. Spotters can aid lifting by helping athletes to complete repetitions they find difficult, thus helping them lift to failure (ie train maximally).

- Never train in cramped conditions. Ensuring that your athletes have enough space for a safe lift means they will not endanger themselves or others while training.

- Allow adequate rest (3–8 minutes) between sets of lifts involving major muscle groups. Lifts using smaller muscle groups do not need the same amount of recovery time.

- Do not ignore the conditioning of the abdominals and lumbar back, or the development of the postural muscles that control pelvic, back and shoulder stability.

- Strength and power are the changeable elements that can greatly influence the success of a sports performer at any level.

References

Brewer, C., Favre, M. and Low, L. (2005) 'Weight lifting for sports specific benefits', http://www.coachesinfo.com/category/strength_and_conditioning/

Fleck, S.J. and Kraemer, W. J. (1997) *Designing Resistance Training Programmes*. Illinois: Human Kinetics. ISBN: 978-0-873225-08-3.

Stone, M.H. (2000) 'Explosive exercise and training', *National Strength and Conditioning Association Journal*, 15 (3): 7–15.

Stone, M.H. (2002) 'How strong is strongenough? http://www.coachesinfo.com/article/index.php?id=246&style=printable

Stone, M.H. (2005) 'The use of weightlifting pulling movements in sports', paper presented at The UK Strength and Conditioning Association Conference, Loughborough, May 2005.

Further Information

Byrd, R., Baker, C., Pierce, K. and Brady, J. (2004) 'Young weightlifters' performance across time', http://www.coachesinfo.com/category/strength_and_conditioning/245

Pierce, K., Brewer, C., Ramsey, M., Byrd, R., Sands, W.A. and Stone, M.H. Opinion paper and Literature review: Children and Youth Resistance training. UKSCA Journal: Summer 2008 (available from UK Strength and Conditioning Assosciation. See Key Contacts)

Stafford, I. (2004) *Coaching for Long-term Athlete Development*. Leeds: Coachwise Business Solutions/The National Coaching Foundation. ISBN: 978-1-902523-70-9*.

Stone, M.H. (1990) 'Muscle conditioning and muscle injuries', *Medicine and Science in Sport and Exercise*, 22 (4):457–62.

Weight lifting for sports: UKSCA Coach education workshop (available from www.uksca.org.uk)

An introduction to core stability training: sports coach UK 'Developing your coaching' workshop.

* Available from **Coachwise 1st4sport**. For a full range of sports education and training equipment, please visit www.1st4sport.com or call 0113-201 5555.

Notes page

Notes page

Chapter 5
Plyometric Training

Introduction

Power (force x velocity) is a work rate: A measure of work done in a given time (distance/time). Rate of force development is the ability to produce maximal muscular forces very rapidly, which is very important in sports that rely on the acceleration component for powerful movements and skills. As identified in the previous chapter, the goal for most sports coaches is to train their athletes' ability to produce an increased force and then train the ability to produce this increased force in a shorter time period, before transferring the benefits of this increased force to executing a given skill.

Plyometrics are specialist strength/speed exercises enabling a muscle to reach maximal strength in a short space of time. This works by stimulating the stretch reflex, stretching a muscle and then relying on its elastic properties to produce greater forces than are normally possible in the reflex contraction (as the muscle returns to its resting length). In order to achieve this greater muscular force, the muscle must contract, following lengthening, within the shortest possible time.

Table 7: How does a plyometric work?

	Eccentric phase	Amortisation phase	Concentric phase
Demonstration			
Action involved	The prime mover (agonist muscles) is stretched.	Transition phase between eccentric and concentric phases. This should be as short as possible for the action to be effective.	The muscle fibres in prime movers are shortened.
Results of action	Potential energy is stored in the muscles and connective tissue. Stretch receptors within the muscle are stimulated.	Stretch inhibitors send signals to the central nervous system, which stimulates concentric contraction of agonist muscles.	Elastic energy is released from the muscles and connective tissue. Prime movers are stimulated to forcefully contract concentrically.

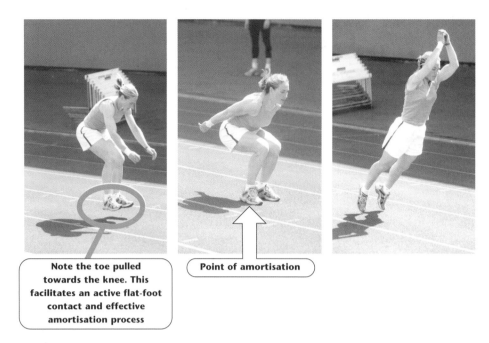

Note the toe pulled towards the knee. This facilitates an active flat-foot contact and effective amortisation process

Point of amortisation

Figure 198: The amortisation phase in a two-footed jump

The following drills use dynamic movements to achieve this stretch-shortening in a muscle, thus causing a faster concentric (reflex) contraction. Many people design plyometric routines that have a basis in track and field, such that they are based upon straight-line actions. However, this is not representative of the performance demands of all sports (invasion games, racket games etc which have extensive multi-directional actions). Regardless of the sport, it is a good idea that coaches utilise a routine of plyometric drills that are multi-dimensional in nature (ie incorporate the ability to effectively and efficiently control and express force in lateral and forward/backward movement).

Coaches need to ensure their athlete's body is suitably developed (ie their muscles have a good strength base) and is well trained before attempting such exercises. For example, the National Strength and Conditioning Association (NSCA) recommends the individual is able to squat 1.5 times their body weight before undertaking high-intensity (shocks, see page 129) plyometric training. Technique is also very important. Bad coaching and poorly executed technique lead to injuries. **A progressive approach to developing plyometric ability and technique is suggested within this chapter that will enable the coach to appropriately progress technique from a sound base**.

Coaches should use the following guidelines as an aid to coaching and not a replacement for strength-training instruction or experiential learning opportunity facilitated by a suitably qualified and experienced individual. Individuals with a history of stress-induced injuries to the feet, ankles, shins, knees, hips or lower back should not perform plyometric activities without consulting a chartered physiotherapist.

Classification of Plyometric Exercises

Plyometrics are classified according to the intensity of the exercise:

Jumps

These can be either in-place jumps (taking off and landing on the same spot) or standing jumps (which emphasise either horizontal or vertical components of movement from a stationary/standing position). Jumps begin and end with one or both feet on the floor and are usually performed in sets of 5–8 repetitions. Jumps form the lowest intensity of plyometric exercises and include many basic exercises such as skipping. Box jumps increase the intensity of the exercise by giving the athlete something to jump off, over or on to. The height of the box depends upon the size and strength of the athlete and the goals of the programme.

Hops

Hops begin and end with the athlete on one or both feet and are associated with a component of maximum horizontal distance. Training volume is usually measured by sets of 4–8 reps or by distance (ie covering 40–60m over a series of movements in a set). These are low- to medium-intensity exercises, although intensity can be augmented by increasing the vertical component of the hop (eg hopping over something).

Bounds

Bounds are the alternating movements associated with take-off from one foot and landing with the other, in repetitive sequence, usually with the aim of covering as much distance between each ground contact as possible. The fact these exercises require the high intensity transfer of body mass onto single legs means these exercises require significantly more control at the foot, ankle, knee and hip, and also more strength than hops or jumps. These are therefore classified as medium–high-intensity exercises and are usually undertaken in sets of 4–8 reps, or by covering a distance (eg 60–80m).

Shocks

These are very high-intensity plyometrics, which will place significant stress on the neuromuscular system and connective tissues. Shocks usually constitute an element of depth jumping (ie jumping down from a raised platform, a 40cm high box) and will have either a vertical component (ie jumping down and then up) or a horizontal component (ie jumping down and then out). This uses gravity and the athlete's weight to increase exercise intensity. Only an experienced performer who is sufficiently well trained to cope with the high stresses associated with shock training should undertake instruction of this nature. The platform height will vary according to the age, weight, training status and experience of the performer. The aim is to keep the minimum ground contact time and attain the maximum vertical height with the increased stimulus of the jump from a height.

An explosive athlete will be able to jump higher with a countermovement jump than from a squat jump. A countermovement jump starts with the athlete standing tall, then rapidly performing a quarter squat movement to stimulate a stretch-reflex enabling a powerful vertical jump that immediately follows (see Figure 199).

Figure 199: The countermovement jump

By contrast, a squat jump involves the athlete squatting down until the knees are at 90° and holding this position for several seconds, so that the following jump is performed from a static position.

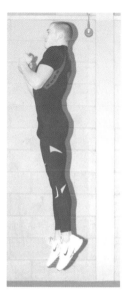

Figure 200: The squat jump

If the athlete does not achieve a higher jump with the countermovement, then there is no point in progressing with shock training; there is a need to revisit basic techniques and training principles with such an athlete.

Once the countermovement jump height is known, the coach should then test the athlete from a two-inch drop and measure the resulting jump. It is also important that landing technique is monitored. The two variables a coach is now looking to monitor are resultant jump height and ground contact time. Ground contact time is very difficult to measure without specialist equipment, such as a force platform or a switch mat, which may be available to some coaches. However, observation of technique (possibly aided by video review) and listening for a crisp, active, flat-foot contact are important indicators of ground contact time for the experienced coach.

Figure 201: Video review can aid coaching technique and doesn't have to use expensive equipment – most mobile phones will provide adequate pictures

A drop-jump from two inches should produce a greater resulting jump height than a countermovement. The coach can simply carry on increasing the drop height by two-inch increments until the athlete cannot maintain the height achieved in a countermovement jump, and/or ground contact time is (observably) increased (Figure 202).

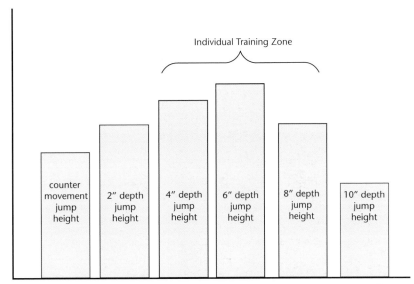

Figure 202: This athlete would be trained using drop/landings from heights of between 4–8 inches

Coaches should not undertake shock plyometrics with athletes who do not have a well-developed strength base and are not in excellent physical condition prior to commencing the programme.

Intensity of Plyometric Training

Plyometrics are classified according to the intensity of the exercise. Jumps are the lowest intensity, followed by hops, bounds and then shock jumps.

The intensity of a plyometric exercise can be reduced by lowering the centre of mass in a jump (ie starting from a bent-over position). They can be made more intense by decreasing the surface area of body contact (eg landing on one foot rather than two, although coaches should note this immediately doubles the intensity of the exercise, for which the athlete needs to be appropriately prepared, physically and technically). Even increasing either the horizontal or vertical distance jumped (ie additional vertical components place more stress on the performer than increased horizontal ranges of a jump). Many coaches make the mistake of advancing athletes onto single-leg work too quickly, before the joints and/or the supporting musculature are ready. This progression in intensity should be considered carefully. For example, an athlete performing a multi-directional jump (see Figure 263 on page 150) over hurdles on two feet might consider removing the hurdles (and just doing multiple direction jumps on a single leg), then putting small hurdles closer together in position before, after a period of time, coming close to performing the same drill, with the same height hurdles as with two feet.

By increasing the vertical component of a plyometric jump, a coach will make the exercise more intense than by increasing the horizontal component. Therefore, when seeking to overload an athlete doing an exercise, first seek to challenge the vertical component of the movement before increasing the horizontal component.

All of the horizontal and vertical movements described within this chapter can be made more difficult by performing them with the addition of a bungee cord. This should be tied around the waist and tensioned in the start position. Resistance provided laterally will increase the postural control the advanced performer will need to demonstrate in executing the movement. Resistance to the direction of movement (ie from behind in a horizontal jump, anchored to the floor in a vertical jump) will increase the amount of force necessary to complete the movement.

Progression

Plyometrics are skill-based, high-speed movements and as such can only be done when the athlete is in an unfatigued state. This means plyometrics need to be scheduled towards the start of a training week and at the start of training sessions, when the athlete is still fresh. Coaches should progress plyometric training from exercises of low intensity through to high intensity, following the principle of progressive overload. This principle should not only be applied over a number of successive training cycles, but also within individual sessions.

Some low-intensity plyometric exercises (eg single-leg hopping on the spot with the eyes closed) are excellent to incorporate into the warm-up routine, in order to activate the body's internal sensory (proprioceptive) systems and stimulate the muscles around the ankle and foot joints.

Plyometric activities are ideal for off-season training, following the period of strength development. Shock and higher-intensity plyometrics should not be used during periods when the playing or training volume is high, due to the recovery time the body needs after each session. Low-intensity plyometrics and medicine-ball drills are, however, ideal for such times. Plyometrics take a relatively longer time period to recover from than other training methods. Recommended frequencies therefore range from one session per week (low-intensity work with beginners) to three low-intensity sessions per week in an experienced performer. In an advanced athlete, very-high-intensity sessions may take up to 8–10 days for the body's neuromuscular system to fully recover.

Training Volume

Plyometric sets should comprise between 3–10 reps (the higher the intensity of the exercise, the lower the number of repetitions per set), with complete recovery (3–8 mins) between sets.

The following guidelines are based upon the principles outlined by the NSCA. Beginners should start off with no more than 70 foot contacts per session, and gradually progress up to 100. Intermediate athletes (or advanced athletes with large body masses) should utilise 100–120 foot contacts per session. Advanced athletes should work between 120–140 foot contacts in one session. Coaches should remember that plyometric work is about quality of performance and should therefore not exceed these totals, allowing plenty of recovery time in between sets. As described earlier, the intensity of all foot contacts is not the same. Coaches should remember that volume and intensity cannot be considered in isolation; there is a significant difference between the demands upon an athlete performing 120 jumps in a session versus 120 bounds versus 120 hurdle jumps. Therefore, consider that the higher the intensity of the exercises, the lower the volume should be in order for the athlete to fully get the benefit from the session and produce high-quality technique.

Plyometric Technique

Developing an Active, Flat-foot Landing

Technique is a factor that definitely limits the rate of progression of a drill. Coaches should never advance plyometric progressions beyond the ability of the athlete to maintain a correct landing posture. In plyometric exercises that involve landing on the feet, the coach needs to pay particular attention to the position of the foot upon landing. It is important the athlete does not contact the ground heel-first for two main reasons. Firstly, this increases the impact forces that travel up through the ankle joints into the knees and lower back and, secondly, this is a very slow position from which the athlete can accelerate into the next position.

Conversely, if the athlete attempts to land on the balls of the feet, the mass of the body (being accelerated into the floor by gravity) will cause the heels to come down into the floor and bring the centre of mass of the athlete back onto the heels. From this position, little upward and forward acceleration is possible. The impact (ground reaction) forces will also be absorbed over a longer period of time (probably resulting in a longer ground contact time and significantly increased – less effective – amortisation time).

Landing with the toes pulled towards the knees (ankle dorsiflexed) pulls the Achilles tendon (tendon at the back of the ankle) tight, and the calf muscles (gastrocnemius and soleus) tight. This means that the foot is now coiled and acting like a spring. When the foot now hits the floor (with an active flat foot), the tension in the lower leg enables the stretch-reflex to operate and the reflex contraction to accelerate the body upwards and/or forward.

Landing in a flat-foot position will also not cause the heel to be driven into the floor in the same way, and the centre of mass can remain above the balls of the feet, allowing rapid acceleration in whichever direction is required in the movement. In this type of exercise, athletes should therefore be coached to land 'flat footed'. That is, not exactly on the flat foot, but onto the ball of the foot with a very slight gap between the heel and the floor (world-renowned sprint coach Loren Seagrave always refers to this as 'the credit card rule': a credit card should be able to be slipped under the heels). However, if there are reduced vertical components to this force, and/or the athlete can control landing on a flat foot without the heel being lowered to the floor, then this should be encouraged by the coach.

Figure 203: An active flat foot landing is important – landing with a plantarflexed (pointed toe) is not correct

Plyometric movements should be fluid in nature. When landing/taking off, the athlete needs to ensure the hips are over the feet and the chest is over the knees. As with sound weight-lifting technique, the knees need to move along the same line as the toes[25]. If the knees start to collapse inwards upon landing (see Figure 204), due to weak muscles or poorly executed technique, it will result in injury.

Figure 204: Proper technique education and strengthening work in the gluteals is necessary to prevent the knees collapsing inwards upon landing

One progressive method for teaching effective plyometric technique is suggested later within this chapter.

It should be remembered that plyometrics are, for the most part, total-body exercises and so jumping and bounding with the legs should be accompanied by upper-body action. Jumps that use arm drive can be 35% higher than jumps from the legs only. The aim is for the athlete to generate as much height and distance as possible and, therefore, unless directed otherwise due to a specific training objective, the athlete should utilise every limb to generate power in the exercise.

Medicine-ball Exercises

These exercises may require a significant amount of space to perform. Adequate care should be taken to ensure the safety of the environment and persons around the athlete when undertaking the throwing of medicine/jelly (weighted rubber) balls. Working with a partner, to allow the ball to be retrieved, may be beneficial in these sessions.

These are low-impact plyometric exercises that can be incorporated easily into many different types of sporting actions and programmes. The basic idea is to generate power from a stretch-reflex movement forcing the ball away from the athlete in whichever direction is desirable.

Underhand Throw

The athlete squats down into a squat position, holding a medicine/jelly ball (henceforth 'the ball') with an under-grasp grip between the legs. From here, the athlete explodes into a vertical jump, throwing the ball as far in the air in front of them as possible. The aim is to achieve maximum height and distance.

Figure 205: The squat position

Figure 206: The vertical jump and throw

Viking Throw

This is similar in nature to the underhand throw, but the direction of the ball release is different. The athlete squats down, holding the ball with an under-grasp grip between the legs. From this position, the athlete explodes into a vertical jump, throwing the ball as high in the air behind them as possible.

Figure 207: Viking throw release

Ball Slam

The athlete stands tall, with knees slightly flexed, holding the ball above the head. Using as much force as possible, the ball is thrown to the floor so that it lands directly in front of the athlete, who should catch the ball as it rebounds up. Repeat in sequence.

Figure 208: Ball slam start position

Figure 209: Ball slam

Trunk Rotation

The athlete stands straight, with feet shoulder-width apart and with the ball in two hands, to the right-hand side of the body. Keeping the arms straight, the athlete twists further to the right, leading with the hips, and then forcefully reverses the twist to the left and releases the ball, with the aim of throwing it as far as possible. This is repeated by twisting to the other side.

Figure 210: Trunk rotation start position

Figure 211: Trunk rotation release position

Chest Pass

The athlete stands with feet shoulder-width apart and knees slightly bent. The ball is thrown to the athlete, who catches it and guides it back to the chest with both hands behind the ball. Explode the ball as far forward as possible. Perform 5–8 reps. This can also be adapted to a further partner drill with the ball being forced downwards against the floor as hard as possible, so it bounces on the floor midway between two athletes. Another variation could be that the ball is forced from the chest position as high as possible between two athletes.

Figure 212: Receive ball

Figure 213: Amortisation phase (transition from catch to forward push)

Figure 214: Explode forwards

Seated Chest Pass

This is carried out as above, but from a seated, inclined trunk position. The athlete sits on the floor, with legs out in front of the body. The trunk is leant backwards, until the angle between the back and the floor is approximately 45°. The athlete brings the ball to the chest, with both hands behind it, and explodes the ball as far forward as possible.

Chopping Wood

This drill can be done in pairs (with the partners standing approximately 10m apart) or as an individual drill. The feet should be shoulder-width apart and the trunk upright. The athlete holds the ball in both hands and rotates from the hips to bring the ball around to a point above the head (see Figure 216), and then forcefully propels the ball to the floor, either at an angle if throwing to a partner (see Figure 217) or straight into the ground if training as an individual. If training individually, the athlete catches the rebound and performs the exercise rotating in the other direction.

**Figure 215:
Start position**   **Figure 216: Hip twist,
bring ball over head**   **Figure 217: Forcefully
throw ball to floor**

Back Slam

The athlete starts by standing upright, with the feet shoulder-width apart and the ball held above the head. From here, the athlete forcibly contracts the hamstring muscles (to cause knee flexion) and at the same time the ball is slammed down to the floor, as hard as possible, behind the back.

Figure 218: Hold ball above head   **Figure 219: Slam ball to the ground**

Kneeling Serve

The athlete assumes a single-leg kneeling position (alternating the forward leg) and keeps the trunk upright. The ball starts directly above the head in two hands. Keeping the arms and the trunk straight and the head up, the athlete extends the shoulder back as far as they can and then explodes the ball forwards as far as possible. The kneeling position ensures that this stays as an upper-body exercise.

**Figure 220: Single-leg
kneeling position**

**Figure 221: Explode the ball
forwards from above the head**

This exercise can also be performed as a single arm exercise, with the emphasis on maintaining pelvic neutral position and keeping the hips level throughout the movement.

**Figure 222: Single-arm version
using opposite forward leg**

**Figure 223: Using the arm
and leg on the same side**

Hip Flexor Throw

The athlete stands with the ball between both legs, clasped by the ankle bones. Keeping the pelvis in the neutral position, the hips are explosively flexed and at the highest point the ball is released so that it is thrown forward as hard as possible into the arms of a partner.

Figure 224: Ball clasped between ankles

Figure 225: Extending the hip and the trunk

Figure 226: Ball thrown forwards by flexing hips

Rotation Drive

This is a drill for one, two or three athletes. The working athlete starts sitting down, with legs out in front and slightly bent. A server throws the ball from the left (or right) so that it can be caught in front (Figure 227). Using the momentum of the ball, when caught, rotate away from the server and touch the ball to the floor (Figure 228). From here, forcefully rotate the ball back to the other side of the body and touch the ball down (Figure 229). Immediately, rotate back to the other side and throw the ball as forcefully as possible (Figure 230).

This drill works best when there are two servers (one on either side of the working athlete) so that the drill progresses continuously. With two athletes, the server's throw and athlete's release need to be in the same direction, so that there will be one less rotation movement. One athlete can perform this drill by throwing the ball against a wall.

Figure 227: Receiving the ball from the left

Figure 228: Twisting to the other side

Figure 229: Forcefully twisting, from the trunk, back again

Figure 230: Twisting back to the right and exploding the ball away

Hamstring Curl

A hamstring curl is another excellent movement to complement heavy-resistance training in a complex drill (eg following a stiff-legged deadlift – see notes on complex training later in this chapter). The working athlete lies face down on the floor with the knees extended and the feet together. The spotter should stand so they straddle the athlete, slightly in front of the athlete's head and facing the athlete's feet. The spotter rolls the ball down the middle of the legs with sufficient force that it will stay on course and roll up the calf muscles (Figure 231). As the working athlete senses the ball reaching the area of the Achilles tendon (base of the calf muscle) the athlete should rapidly flex the knee joint, thus firing the ball upwards and into the hands of the spotter (Figure 232).

This will also test the athlete's proprioception and coordination (without which, the firing of the ball will not take place). The spotter should ensure the fired ball does not fall down onto the athlete's body or head.

Figure 231: The ball is rolled down the legs   **Figure 232: The ball is fired up to the hands of the spotter**

Medicine-ball Tennis

This is a game for 2–4 athletes that involves the medicine ball being fired across the net (or training area) to score points, in the same way as tennis. The service lines and court markings can be changed to reduce/increase the stress to the athlete, depending upon the mass of the ball and the power of the athletes. Each shot should be caught after one bounce, then the athlete twists with the shot (ie if the ball comes on the backhand side, the athlete should catch and rotate to the fullest possible range of motion for a backhand shot) and then explodes the ball back over the net. Drills can be set up to achieve the same effect, but they should be kept as open as possible, allowing the athlete to play shots from various foot and body positions.

Figure 233: Medicine ball tennis is an excellent game for tennis players and other sports performers to develop power

Figure 234: A steel-reinforced wall in the gym at the All-England Lawn Tennis Club allows athletes to train for explosive power and warm up dynamically during the Wimbledon tennis championships

Plyometric Exercises

It is important the coach remembers that all of the following exercises are subject to the variations in intensity outlined earlier on in this chapter.

Developing Landing Technique

Firstly, it is a good idea for the athlete to develop the musculature at the front of the shin to enable the toe to be effectively dorsiflexed. Exercises such as walking with the toe pulled back towards the knee (Figure 235) aid this in novice performers.

Figure 235: Walking while pulling the toes towards the knee

From here, bouncing repeatedly (without emphasising height or distance) upon an active flat foot encourages the correct landing technique (active flat-foot landing on a dorsiflexed foot). This can then be progressed to bounces over a 10m distance (encouraging many foot contacts).

Figure 236: Multiple flat-foot bounces

For increased coordination development and to provide a fun challenge for the athlete, coaches should not underestimate the benefit of skipping as a plyometric exercise.

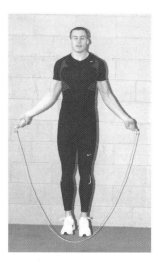

Figure 237: Skipping is a plyometric exercise with many variations

By stretching the arms high above the head, the athlete lengthens the kinetic chain and also isolates the legs and feet as the only propellants of the body. If the athlete stands next to a wall (reducing any chance of horizontal movement) the athlete can have an indicator (or target) of how high they are moving with each jump. This exercise should be performed as a series of multiple bounces on the spot, rather than single repetition jumps for maximum height.

Figure 238: Straight arm multiple bounces against a wall

Inserting small hurdles (or boxes/benches etc) into a 10m distance (as described earlier) will encourage the athlete to continually think about the flat foot landing technique as, with the increased time between taking off and landing (made necessary by the small hurdle), the athlete must think about the toes being pulled up and the ankle dorsiflexed. The tendency here is for the novice athlete to drop the toes (see Figure 239a) when the coach is not reinforcing technique.

© Steven Paston/Action Images

Figure 239a: Olympic medallist Kelly Sotherton teaches a jumping technique to novice athletes (note the pointed toes) using hurdles with small bounces in between – compare with Figure 239b, the experienced athlete who maintains a dorsiflexed ankle.

Figure 239b: Experienced athlete with dorsiflexed ankles

Specific Exercises: Jumps

Countermovement Jumps

The athlete squats down into a quarter-squat position and then explodes upwards as high as possible, using the whole body to generate maximum vertical force.

This can be performed as a repetitive action (one jump straight into the next), with a tuck position at the highest point of the jump (ie a tuck jump), or with a pike position (ie a pike jump) encouraging the athlete to adapt the movement position. The athlete can also use this as a test of ability to jump with maximum vertical height (ie a standing vertical jump) or maximum horizontal power (ie a standing long jump).

Figure 240: From standing into countermovement position

Figure 241: Maximum countermovement jump

Figure 242: Tuck jump top position

Figure 243: Pike jump top position

Standing Box Jump

From the countermovement position (see Figure 244), the athlete jumps from a position of approximately 60cm away onto a box or over a hurdle. The height of the box/hurdle is determined by the training status of the athlete (the usual range is 40–70cm high).

Figure 244: Box or hurdle jump

Ball Throw to Box Jump

The athlete stands approximately 60cm back from a box/bench that is 40–70cm high and wide enough to jump onto. Holding the ball with an under-grasp grip between the legs, the athlete squats down into a countermovement squat and then explodes into a forward jump onto the box/over the hurdle, throwing the ball in the air as far behind as possible (Figure 247).

Figure 245: Start position

Figure 246: Squatting down for ball throw

Figure 247: Throwing and jumping

Figure 248: Landing on the box

Cycled Split Squat Jump

The athlete stands in the lunge position (ie with one leg fully extended forward and the other behind the midline of the body) with the trunk upright. The athlete jumps vertically as high as possible, with little or no arm swing. While in the air, the athlete quickly switches leg position from front to back, landing in the lunge position with the legs reversed. This is then sequenced, so that the landing of one jump becomes the start of the next jump. The front leg should be alternated at the start of each new set.

Figure 249: Cycled split squat position

Figure 250: Cycled split squat mid position

This exercise can also be performed with a box, or between boxes, with a slight height difference between each box. This is a fairly advanced exercise allowing the athlete to adapt to chaotic landing positions and limb position differences, as would be necessary in a game or performance on changing surfaces (eg running cross-country). The athlete should alternate the position of the higher box between front and back.

Figure 251: Cycled split squat on uneven boxes

Resisted Horizontal Jump

This drill utilises bungee cords attached to a belt around the waist to provide resistance to the movement. The athlete performs a standing long jump, as high as possible, against the resistance of the bungee cords. The addition of resistance will encourage the activation of more nerves in firing more muscles. The athlete should perform four reps, then remove the resistance and immediately perform two long jumps, as high and long as possible.

The athlete jumping towards differently numbered/coloured cones, but keeping the location of the bungee anchor the same, can make this drill multi-directional in nature. This will mean all jumps will be assisted in one direction, but resisted in another. Athletes can start off jumping around the cones in number order, but to progress this exercise, the coach can call a cone number or colour. This progression adds a thought element to the drill, preventing an athlete from anticipating the next jump.

Figure 252: Resisted horizontal jumps

Resisted Vertical Jump

Using weighted vests or bungee chords can also resist vertical jumps. Coaches should be aware that bungees resist movement in a manner not necessarily useful for developing acceleration, as the point of the jump where the rate of acceleration is greatest is the point which is least resisted (as the athlete accelerates from the floor, the bungee is least stretched). However, at the point where the body momentum is slowest (towards the top of the jump), the bungee resistance is the greatest. Devices with accommodating resistance, such as the Vertimax™, control this phenomenon.

Figure 253: Resisted vertical jumps

Clap Press-up

The athlete starts off in a press-up position – elbows straight, back flat, legs straight and head up. From here, the elbows are flexed, lowering the trunk to the floor. From the lowest position of the movement, the athlete explodes upwards so the hands leave the floor. Clap the hands once and repeat upon landing. Clapping the hands helps the athlete to contact the floor with the wrists flexed (fingers pulled back towards elbows). This increases the stiffness of the muscles and tendons in the forearm (in the same way that the dorsiflexed toe pulls the muscles of the lower leg tight), increasing the stretch-reflex response.

Figure 254: Clap press-up

Specific Exercises: Hops

Choo-Choo Trains

This is an excellent exercise for working with groups of athletes. It encourages an active flat foot landing, correct hip positioning, as well as coordination and cooperation between individuals, making this a fun drill.

The athletes line up one in front of the other, with the athlete at the front having their right foot held by the right hand of the athlete behind them (and so on down the line). From this start position, the challenge is for the chain of athletes to hop (without losing contact of the hands) 15–20m without the chain breaking and with the fewest number of foot contacts possible. The next repetition should be done with the other foot held. The drill can also be repeated with the athlete having their foot held by the athlete in front of them.

**Figure 255: Choo-Choo trains
(leg held behind)**

**Figure 256: Choo-Choo trains
(leg held in front)**

Double-leg Speed Hop

The athlete stands in a half-squat position, with feet together. Keeping the feet together at all times is important; if they come apart, the tendency is to touch the feet down at different times and this should be avoided, as it does not train bilateral power. The athlete should jump upwards and outwards, aiming for as much height and distance as possible. In flight, they should use a double-arm forward swinging action, as if reaching for a ball, and straighten the body. They should land in the starting position and repeat the movement.

Figure 257: Double-leg speed hop landing

Figure 258: Take off for second jump

This can be progressed to a single-leg hop and then on to a directional change.

Figure 259: Single-leg speed hop

Multi-directional hops are carried out in response to either a verbal stimulus or a visual stimulus, for example a ball being dropped.

Stair Hop

Using a two-legged take-off and landing, the athlete hops up a flight of 4–10 steps of 20–40cm in height. To increase the intensity, the athlete can progress to a one-legged take-off and landing, as long as the athlete is sufficiently strong enough to cope with this.

Figure 260: Stair hop

Lateral Hurdle Hop

The athlete stands on one side of a hurdle or cone 30–40cm in height. Using a two-footed take-off, the athlete leaps sideways over the cone, with as much height as possible, lands on the balls of both feet and immediately jumps back in the reverse direction. If this is too advanced, a simpler version of this exercise involves the use of a step or exercise box. The athlete hops laterally onto the box, makes quick contact and hops off. Advanced progression of the lateral hurdle hop is to move the hurdles further apart, or to repeat the exercise but work on one leg (again, this more than doubles the intensity of the exercise).

Figure 261: Lateral hurdle hop

Double-leg Zigzags

Place 4–8, 30–60cm-high hurdles (or lower if necessary) in a zigzag pattern, with approximately 45–60cm between each hurdle. Keeping the feet together and arms by their side, with elbows flexed to 90°, athletes use a double-arm action and a double-foot jump, in a diagonal direction, to clear the first hurdle. The athlete needs to keep the shoulders pointing forward and concentrate on bringing the knees high. On landing, the athlete immediately takes off, changing direction, and jumps diagonally over the second hurdle. This diagonal continues all along the chain of hurdles for one set. Variation can be achieved by altering the angle of the hurdles to each other, the height of the hurdles or by alternating between single- and double-leg jumps if the athlete is sufficiently strong enough to control the technique and body position during the exercise. In advanced progressions, athletes can also face different directions and/or jump forwards/backwards in response to a call from the coach.

Figure 262: Double-leg zigzags

Multi-directional Jumps

The athlete starts in the middle of a square of four mini-hurdles, between 40–70cm in height. The athlete uses a two-footed take-off and landing, and then jumps forward over the hurdle in front of them, immediately springing back to the start position upon landing. The athlete immediately jumps over the hurdle to the left, springing straight back into the middle of the square. Minimising the time in contact with the ground (and still facing forward), the athlete immediately jumps backwards over the hurdle behind them, back into the middle and then to the right, finishing up in the middle. This equates to one set.

The above exercise can be made more difficult by numbering the hurdles 1, 2, 3 and 4. The coach then calls out the direction of the next jump as the athlete lands. This means the athlete is not able to anticipate the direction of the next jump and manipulate landing accordingly. The advanced progression of this drill is to perform the exercise on one leg, then carry out the next set on the other. However, coaches need to be confident that the athlete is sufficiently strong and technically competent enough for this progression.

Figure 263: Multi-directional jumps

A variation of this can be achieved by placing the hurdles in a zigzagged line, with the athlete jumping forward (or backwards) over the hurdles which are angled to each other.

Figure 264: Zigzag jumps

Specific Exercises: Bounds

Standing Triple Jump

From a standing position, the athlete performs a countermovement jump (see page 129), as high and far forward as possible. Landing on one leg (alternate between the left and right), the athlete immediately takes off (again jumping as high and far forward as possible), landing on the other foot. Again, the athlete immediately takes off and lands as far in front as possible.

Figure 263: Standing triple jump (start)

Figure 264: Standing triple jump (landing one: hop)

Figure 265: Standing triple jump (landing two: step)

Figure 266: Standing triple jump (landing three: jump)

Alternate Leg Bound

The alternate leg bound involves moving in an exaggerated running style characterised by a strong hip and knee drive to a position in which the thigh is parallel with the ground. This can also be completed with a single-arm action (as in running, with the opposite-arm-to-opposite-leg action) or a double-arm action (with both arms swinging together). The athlete starts with a rocking step: arms by the side and one foot slightly in front of the other, as if the athlete was about to take a step. From here, the athlete jumps forward, with as much distance and height as possible. In flight, the athlete needs to prepare for, and land on, the opposite leg, and take off immediately upon landing. The front leg should be alternated at the start of each new set (typically, a set equates to one series of 6–10 bounds).

Figure 267: Alternate leg bounds step 1

Figure 268: Alternate leg bounds step 2

Specific Exercises: Shock Jumps

Coaches should be careful to follow the guidelines for progression in shock jumps described earlier within this chapter. Remember, that depending upon the training age, experience and strength levels of an athlete, what is a shock drill for one athlete may not be as stressful for another athlete (or may be more stressful!). The athletes development should guide the coaches' use for such drills.

Multiple Hurdle Hops

The athlete stands about 60cm back from the first hurdle (this drill should have between 4–8 hurdles in sequence, with the number and distance between the hurdles – 1–2m – determined by the capabilities of the individual athlete). The athlete jumps over the first hurdle in an explosive manner, using a double-leg take-off. The trunk should be kept upright and a double-arm forward-swinging motion should be used. Maintaining the upright trunk posture and ankle dorsiflexion (see Figure 270) throughout the flight allows landing with an active flat-foot contact. As the athlete lands on the other side of the hurdle, they should, with minimal ground contact time explode upwards, getting as much height and distance as necessary to clear the next hurdle and land in the middle of the following hurdles. The arms are important in this action. This action is completed along the exercise sequence.

© Action Images/Reuters

Figure 269: Olympic gold medal heptathlete Carolina Kluft performs hurdle hops in training

Figure 270: Multiple hurdle hop drill

Box Jump to Maximum Long Jump

The athlete stands about 60cm back from a 40–70cm-high box or bench. From here, the athlete jumps onto the box in an explosive manner, using a double-leg take-off. The trunk should be kept upright and a double-arm forward-swinging motion should be used. As the athlete lands, they should explode off the box, getting as much height and distance as possible (the arms become important in this action). As soon as they land, the athlete immediately jumps as far forward as possible (as in a standing long jump). This can be modified so that the athlete jumps upwards on landing, thus performing box jumps to maximum vertical jumps.

Figure 271: Box jump to long jump

Figure 272: Take-off from box

Depth Jump to Box

Place 4–8, 40–70cm high wooden boxes 1–2m apart (using boxes or benches that are wide enough to jump onto). The athlete either stands on top of the first box in the sequence (Figure 272) to start the exercise or he/she stands about 60cm back from a box/bench. From here, the athlete jumps onto the box in an explosive manner and uses a double-leg take-off, keeping the trunk upright and using a double-arm forward swinging motion. As soon as the athlete lands, they should jump off the box. The higher the jump, the more intense the landing impact will be for the athlete. This will require some experimentation. Make sure that, when the boxes are set up, there is adequate room between them to allow the athlete to jump appropriately. On landing on the ground, the athlete immediately jumps onto the next box, and this is continued along the line of boxes.

Variation can be achieved by altering the height of the boxes, the distance and angle between boxes, and by alternating between single- and double-leg take-offs.

Figure 273: Depth jumps between multi-height boxes

Depth Jump to Hurdles

Place a hurdle 1–2m away from a 40–70cm high box. The athlete jumps off the box, keeping the knees very slightly bent in the air. Landing appropriately, with the legs shoulder-width apart and knees flexed upon landing, the athlete then immediately explodes over the hurdle. The arms should swing as high as possible in a forward direction and propel the body as high as possible, concentrating on maximal effort. Variation can be achieved by obtaining two vaulting boxes of similar (and appropriate) height and placing the second one after the hurdle. After clearing the hurdle, and upon landing, the athlete then jumps onto the other vaulting box. This may require someone spotting the athlete as they land on the second box, to ensure the athlete doesn't fall off.

Advanced progressions of this drill incorporate directional changes as the athlete lands. For example, the athlete clears the hurdle, jumps backwards over it (or another hurdle placed laterally), lands and explodes onto another box.

Figure 274: Depth jump to multi-hurdle jumps

Depth Jump to Power Twist

This drill begins with the athlete standing on top of a box in front of a series of 4–6 mini hurdles (20–30cm high) in preparation for an in-depth jump to the floor. The athlete then performs an in-depth jump from the box. On landing, the athlete immediately jumps up in the air and performs a 90° turn as they clear the first hurdle. On landing, the process is repeated, but the second jump is through 180° as the second hurdle is cleared, and so on through the sequence until all the hurdles have been cleared.

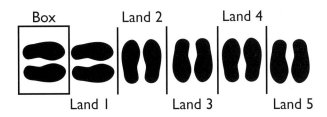

Figure 275: Landing pattern for depth jump to power twists

Figure 276: Power twist shock jumps

Abdominal Down and Up

This is a shock plyometric for the abdominal and trunk musculature. The athlete needs to work with a spotter and lie flat on the floor, with the spotter standing behind the athlete's shoulders. The athlete's head should be on the floor, midway between the spotter's legs, and holding the spotter's ankles for support. The athlete bends the legs slightly and then flexes the hip joint until the feet point towards the sky. Maintaining a neutral pelvis and back position, the spotter pushes the athlete's legs towards the ground in a forceful manner. The athlete should allow the feet to be accelerated towards the ground, but prevent the feet touching the ground before forcefully returning the legs to the starting position.

This can be advanced by the spotter alternating the angle at which the feet are pushed towards the floor, thus working the trunk musculature through different ranges of motion.

Figure 277: Abdominal down and ups

Figure 278: Abdominal down and ups with angled pushes

Complex Training

Experienced individuals may wish to combine strength training with plyometric activities for maximum benefits (as demonstrated by Harrison, 2007). For example, a maximal squat set, followed by a rest of 3–5 mins, can then be followed by sets of cycled split squat jumps, depth jumps into high jumps, or a bench press followed by a set of explosive chest passes with a medicine ball (after a 2–3-min recovery period).

This complex training method allows the maximal strength exercises to recruit large numbers of motor units in sports-related movement patterns (refer to Chapter 4) and the same motor units to be applied to a powerful and explosive movement. Basically, it is a method that tricks the body – the neuromuscular system is potentiated (activated) by the strength exercises, so more motor units will be recruited than would be possible voluntarily for the plyometric exercise. This allows the training effect to be maximised.

Summary

Key points to consider when undertaking plyometric training:

- Athletes need to warm up thoroughly.
- If an athlete experiences muscular or joint problems, stop immediately.
- Athletes should wear quality footwear, which provides ankle support and has adequate, but not too much, cushioning in the sole.
- Use a flat landing surface with good shock-absorbing properties. Hard surfaces such as concrete should be avoided. Surfaces such as sprung-loaded floors are not appropriate – they interfere with the elastic properties of the muscle as it operates in a plyometric exercise. Nor are heavily cushioned surfaces such as a crash mat suitable, as they absorb too much energy and ruin the stretch–shortening mechanism of the exercise. The best surface is a tartan athletics track.
- If boxes or benches are used, make sure they are sturdy and have a non-slip surface.
- Make sure the athlete has an adequate area for training. Do not put athletes at risk from obstacles (or others) that may encroach onto their activity.
- The work should be of a high quality. Therefore, ensure athletes are adequately rested between sets and do not exceed the recommended volume guidelines.
- Technique is very important – if in doubt, seek appropriate expertise. As with sprinting, you should use the ball of the foot to apply force to the floor, in order to accelerate the body off the ground. Care should be taken to ensure a stable landing on a flat-foot position.

Further Reading

Chu, D.A. (1996) *Explosive Power and Strength: Complex Training for Maximal Results.* Illinois: Human Kinetics. ISBN: 978-0-873226-43-1.

References

Harrison, D. (2007) *Complex training for maximum plyometric benefits* UK strength and conditioning Association Annual Conference, Largs, Scotland, May 2007.

Chapter 6
Developing Speed and Agility

Introduction

In sporting terms, speed relates to traversing the distance between two points in the shortest possible time. Speed development is therefore sport specific; while running speeds may enable an athlete to win a race, intercept a ball or beat an opponent rapidly, fast limb speed is essential to numerous activities, including striking, kicking and throwing. Speed is the product of reaction time (the time taken to detect and respond to a stimulus) and movement time (the time from the beginning of a movement to its completion). Movement time can be seen as the product of acceleration (the time between the starting movement and reaching top speed) and achieving top speed (the maximum possible amount of metres per second that an athlete can move).

When undertaking training to improve the speed of athletes, the coach should consider designing training to improve the elements of reaction time, acceleration, agility and movement technique, all of which should be incorporated into the programme. Top speed, which comprises stride length and stride frequency and is reached after about 25m of movement, is largely unimportant for some athletes. For example, in tennis, players are never required to sprint more than 15m maximum. In many sporting contexts, speed work is typically seen as necessary with an element of directional change. The fast bowler in cricket does not necessarily need to have exceptional running speed, since the final approach is rarely undertaken at maximum pace. Nevertheless, the player must be capable of achieving a final, effective bowling action as a consequence of fast, coordinated limb movement. Similarly, goalkeepers in hockey and soccer rarely have to develop good running speed, as they rarely have to cover large distances at maximal speed. They do, however, need rapid limb and total-body speed, so quick reaction speeds can be achieved whenever the goalmouth is threatened.

There is limited value, therefore, in a coach spending large volumes of time working on developing the correct sprinting technique[26] in many sports performers. However, effective and efficient running technique does train, through appropriate joint positioning, the correct muscles to perform the correct actions at the appropriate stage in a muscle action sequence. Therefore, running drills should be designed to establish efficient and error-free movement, by emphasising certain components relating to rapid movement (factors which will be outlined in detail later in this chapter), should be incorporated into the training sessions for all sports and positional demands within various sports. The most efficient way to do this is to put these into the session warm-ups, as designed by the coach, and these can be easily incorporated into dynamic flexibility routines (see Chapter 7).

Multiple-sprint sports place acute demands on the ability of an athlete to react and move quickly in all directions, often with an associated change in direction, while maintaining postural control (joint positioning determines muscle recruitment and action) and the ability to effectively strike a ball or beat an opponent. The components of speed vital to a sports performer are, therefore, acceleration (a component of power) and agility.

Speed and acceleration may be the most vital physical abilities (besides sport-specific technique) that ultimately influence an athlete's competitive level.

Training to develop an athlete's running speed should be aimed at achieving:

• strength and power (through the training methods identified in Chapters 4 and 5)
• efficient movement technique (the body parts must work together in an effective and synchronised – coordinated – manner)
• the efficiency of the anaerobic energy-delivery systems.

The Key Principles

Speed can only be developed by running (moving) maximally. Sub-maximal running will not allow the neuromuscular system to adapt to speed training. If the athlete is not able to run with 100% effort, their speed will not improve.

Maximum speed development should be treated as a skill and should therefore not be developed when fatigued (unlike speed endurance). Therefore, it is essential sufficient recovery time (eg 2–5 minutes, longer for really maximal efforts) be allowed between sprint repetitions. Remember, also, that speed should be developed sport specifically. Therefore, distances, angles of running and sport-specific equipment (pads, racket, ball) should be incorporated into 25–50% of the sprints (depending upon the number of times the athlete will be running with/without the equipment during a game), to enable effective transfer to the athlete's activity in a game.

Sprinting Technique

There are a number of mechanical principles a sprint coach would seek to coach a sprinter when developing track technique. All of these principles are outlined below and illustrated in the pictures shown in Figure 280, page 161. This demonstrates the many similarities between track sprinters, people running with a ball at their feet and people running in a game.

Body Position

Athletes, typically, should have a slight forward lean (10–15cm) after the start. The back should be flat, with the hips tilted forward (pelvis in neutral), and the trunk musculature braced (see page 107: the distance between the belly button and the xyphoid process – below the breastbone – should remain the same).

Heel Recovery (Rear Heel Kick Action)

Heel recovery is the product of the hip extensor muscles (glutes in the buttock) driving the centre of mass forward and the support leg springing off the ground. Therefore, the greater the running speed, the higher the heel should kick up as the leg moves through the air and the knee punches forward. The heel should be tight to the buttock at the top of the action, with the thigh above the horizontal position. The heel of the recovery leg should travel above the opposite knee, with the toes dorsiflexed. Improper height of this action will hinder the speed of the leg turnover.

Preparation for Ground Contact

The ankle should be dorsiflexed in preparation for ground contact. The athlete should maintain the forward body lean (by not standing up or leaning back) and the top of the thigh should be above horizontal. The athlete's foot should contact under, or just behind, the body's centre of mass (which will be a point on the ground under the middle of the stomach). Contact between the ball of the foot and the floor should be a pushing motion, as it is this (rather than a pull) that generates the forces for forward momentum.

The gastrocnemius (large calf muscle) flexes the knee at high speeds, with the heel rising as the knee drives forward.

The hamstring muscle flexes the knee at high speeds (something which it is not designed to do – often causing injuries) with the heel rising yet knee not moving forward as far/fast.

Dorsiflexion at the ankle: The stiff foot contacts the floor, ground reaction force and action from the gluteal muscles drive the athletes centre of mass forward.

Plantarflexion at the ankle: The pointed foot lands toe first and the athlete lowers onto the balls of the feet. This means that forces are absorbed (lost) upon landing, there is a longer ground contact time, the hips drop and then rise again as the hip flexor drives the centre of mass forward.

Figure 279: Joint positioning of the ankle determines both the speed of ground contact and the recruitment of the leg muscles. Coaches should take care to emphasise the correct joint position to avoid such movement compensations in their athlete (Seagrave, 2007)

Ground Contact Phase

The athlete should force the thigh towards the ground. The foot should be pointed straight ahead and should not pronate (ie inwardly rotate at the ankle) excessively. The athlete's foot should contact the ground with an active flat foot (ie coached to land on the ball of the foot with a slight gap between the heel and the ground). The centre of mass of the body should drive (through the hip extension action of the gluteals) forward in a straight line, with additional force coming from the ground reaction of the foot and associated extension of the ankle, knee and hip. After the athlete pushes off, the foot motion is one of lift, reach and pull through (as if to reach and then pull back, in a manner that would allow the athlete to grab grass with the ball of the foot).

Arm Action

The athlete's arms should be flexed to 90–100°, with no elbow flexion or extension in the forward movement and should drive forcibly backwards motion about the shoulder joint. As the arm is driven backwards, there will probably be some elbow extension, which facilitates the biceps muscle at the front of the upper arm being stretched. This will occur with a forceful backward movement as a natural phenomenon – it is definitely not something that should be actively coached. It will then initiate a stretch-reflex which aids the rapid forward motion of the arm. There should be minimal lateral movement, which reduces speed by causing shoulder rotation. When moving forwards (a reaction to being accelerated backwards), the athlete's hands should not cross the mid-line of the body but should rise to the level of the chin and backwards beyond the hips (the 'hips to lips' movement). The elbow drive backward will speed up the leg action, therefore the faster the athlete moves the elbows, the quicker the athlete's feet will move. Coaches can demonstrate this by asking athletes to keep their hands by their side and jog on the spot. Then, keeping their arms still, get the athletes to move their feet as fast as they can. Without decreasing leg speed, introduce the arm action as well (driving the arms bacwards as fast as possible) and note what happens to their leg speed (it will increase).

Hand Action

The athlete's hands should be relaxed. While it does not matter in terms of speed whether the hands are open or closed, it is hard to imagine anyone being ready to catch a ball (important in many sports) with the hands clenched into a closed fist. Hands clenched tightly create tension in the shoulders, which restricts shoulder movement.

Head Action

The athlete's head should stay facing forward in a relaxed upright position to allow the athlete to monitor what is going on around them and should not sway in any direction. A stable head position allows the eyes to scan around and make decisions about what is going on in the game in front of them. A swinging head means this important action is not possible. The athlete's jaw should be loose and relaxed at all times (hence the term 'jelly jaw' associated with sprinting).

Head up: Maintain erect posture and line of sight

Arm drive from the shoulder, elbows stay bent at 90°, allowing large deltoid muscles to drive the arm action

High-knee drive into stride allows ankle of recovery (in-flight) leg to clear (travel above) the knee height of the driving leg

Straight-line body position between head, shoulder, hip, knee and ankle of driving leg

Minimal distance between recovery leg, ankle and thigh allows faster/more efficient travel of recovery-leg cycle

Ankle fully extends at the end of the leg drive

Ankle joint dorsiflexed in preparation for landing on the ball of the foot

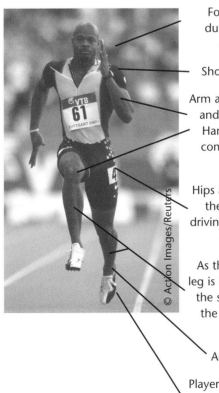

© Action Images/Reuters

© www.actionplus.co.uk

Forward trunk lean during initial phases of acceleration

Shoulders are relaxed

Arm action: Opposite arm and leg forward/back. Hand of forward arm comes up to the level of the chin

Hips are high enough off the ground to allow driving leg to extend fully off the ground

As the heel of the front leg is highest, the angle of the shins in both legs is the same (ie the shins are parallel)

Ankles dorsiflexed

Player pushes off from ball of foot (large surface area) and minimal heel contact with the ground

Figure 280: The basic component of efficient acceleration technique

!

Sound sprinting technique is reliant on the development of the technical consistencies outlined on the previous page and in Figures 279 and 280. However, not all of these technique points need to be developed in performers from all sports. In short, not every sport requires a sprint performance in order to be successful. For example, a tennis or squash athlete must run with a racket in their hand at all times during the game and, in moving between court positions following shots, the athletes do not reach an upright position very often. Also, the end result of movement is not to get somewhere as quickly as possible, or to get past someone as quickly as possible, but to arrive at a defined point in sufficient time, with appropriate body position and postural control, to intercept the ball and return it to the opponent territory in as attacking a manner as possible. However, key principles relating to active flat-foot contact moving on the balls of the foot, having the shoulders relaxed and keeping the head up should all be worked on in accordance with the principles of speed development, as these will also aid in appropriate muscle recruitment. Coaches should avoid the phrase 'on your toes' as the toes have a small surface area and do not provide a stable platform from which to exert a force. This common phrase also encourages athletes to land with 'ballet-dancer's toes', (ie toes pointing down, rather than the preferred active, flat-foot landing described previously in Figure 279).

Differences between track sprinting and other sports-specific speed can be found in the patterns of acceleration. In track athletes, this pattern is to react, accelerate, attain maximum velocity and then maintain velocity endurance for as long as possible/necessary.

It is somewhat different in team sports/invasion activities, where the athlete has to make a decision to react to one of a range of stimuli, accelerate, then typically decelerate, change direction, straighten and re-accelerate, either into space or maybe into a body contact situation. These differences in acceleration pattern should be considered by a coach when they are putting together the speed development activities for the athlete.

For example, in tennis, where the need is to arrive at a defined point to intercept a ball, the acceleration pattern will be different from a games player (football, rugby) who is seeking to move into space or attack as quickly as possible. This means the first step in tennis will, in many circumstances, be a big one resulting in the player landing with a heel strike to effectively position the body (see Figure 281a). Whereas a games player or track athlete requires small, power generating steps to overcome inertia and apply force into the ground to accelerate the body and would never want the heel to touch the floor (Figure 281b). Note however, some things (eg dorsiflexed ankle to allow the gluteals to drive the hips forward) are common in both situations.

Figure 281: Acceleration mechanics of a tennis player (a) and other athletes (b) including those with a disability (c) may be different due to the sports-specific requirements of movement, however, the guiding principles of speed development remain the same.

Developing Sprint Technique

The following drills are typically used to develop sprint technique. They can also be incorporated into a warm-up, as part of a dynamic mobility routine.

Seated Arm Action

The athlete sits with their legs straight and drives the arms in a sprinting motion (as described previously) as fast as possible. The faster the backward drive of the arm movement generated, the faster the sprinting leg action will be in a full movement. The athlete should try to lift their bottom off the floor using the arm action only in this drill.

Figure 282: Seated arm action

Wall Drill One: Single Leg March

The athlete stands with feet flat on the floor, ankle dorsiflexed, with arms straight and the trunk leaning to approximately a 45° angle. There should be a straight line between the shoulder, pelvis (which is in neutral, with the trunk braced), knee and ankle (see Figure 283). From here, the athlete should go to the 'ready' position, with the knee 'punched forward' (it is a common mistake that the knee should be brought high, rather than forward) and the toe dorsiflexed, so the sole of the foot is parallel with the floor. The toe should now be behind the knee, so there is a shin angle the same as the body lean, and this angle should be the same in both legs (ie the shins are parallel). The foot in contact with the floor should remain flat and the toes dorsiflexed. From here, keeping the standing foot flat and the body angle and straight position the same, the athlete should fire the glutes on the raised leg so the hip extends and leg comes down towards the floor, contacting the floor in a dorsiflexed position. The speed is not important to start with (it can be sped up as technique become proficient): the key thing is being able to maintain the correct body position as described.

Figure 283a: Wall drills straight-line body position

Figure 283b: Wall drills straight-line body position common errors (toes plantarflexed, loss of body position, loss of body angle)

**Figure 284: Wall drill
ready position**

**Figure 285: Single leg march
finish position**

Wall Drill Two: Single-Leg Drive

From the straight-line body position, one knee is driven forward (towards the wall) into the ready position (Figure 284). All technique points are maintained (toes dorsiflexed, positive shin/body angle, knee forward, toe behind knee), then the glutes are fired to drive the leg towards the ground, returning the foot (still dorsiflexed) to the start position. Speed can be added as the technique becomes proficient.

**Figure 286: Single-leg drive
start position**

**Figure 287: Single-leg drive
finish position**

Wall Drill Three: Two-step

As above but starting with one leg forward in the ready position. From here, the raised leg is driven backwards to the floor (initiated by a firing of the gluteal muscles) at the same time as the knee of the opposite leg is fired forward. Maintaining all the technique points is essential throughout this sequence. Once the athlete is proficient at this drill, sequences of three or more repetitions can be added together.

Figure 288: Step one   **Figure 289: Step two**

Aligning the Heels

The athlete moves in a walking motion, bringing the lead leg through with the ankle in a dorsiflexed position, with the heels moving as close to the buttocks as possible. The athlete extends the leg from here in a normal motion. The coach should place emphasis on allowing (but not forcing) the heel to come up to the buttock, with the knee driving forwards, not upwards.

Figure 290: Aligning the heels

Straight-leg Bounding

With straight legs (and maintaining the opposite arm/opposite leg pattern), the athlete keeps the ankles dorsiflexed and performs alternate straight leg bounds. Keeping the knees straight at all times, the floor contact is through an active flat foot.

Figure 291: Straight-leg bounds

Skips for Height and Distance

Move with an easy, rhythmical, skipping action, working the arms and aiming for long, high skips. The arm swing should be a loose, swinging movement, controlled from the shoulder. Everything should work in a straight line as the athlete moves.

Figure 292: Skips for Height and Distance

Pull-through

Extend the leg in front of the body (like a hurdler), with the knee forwards (see Figure 293a). Extend the knee so the leg is straight (Figure 293b) and then bring the leg down and contact the ground with the ball of the foot slightly behind the trunk, in a powerful motion (Figure 293c).

Figure 293: Pull through sequence

Acceleration Stride Sticks

Place sticks on a grassy surface, starting them 45cm apart and progressively increase this to two metres. Use approximately 20 sticks. The athlete sprints through the sticks as fast as possible, touching one foot down between each stick. The foot–ground contact should be with an active flat-foot and as quick as possible, and the athlete's knee driven forward. If possible, the coach should record the time between the first and second foot contacts, and the time it takes the athlete to complete the course.

Figure 294: Acceleration stride sticks

Fast Feet

From a standing start, take as many small steps as possible over a 10m distance. Then jog for 10m and repeat. The aim is to get the body used to moving as quickly as possible. The coach should emphasise quick turnover, with the legs moving in front of, not behind or under, the body.

Figure 295: Fast feet

Side Drives

Sprint forward with a lateral movement every three steps. The coach should place emphasis on shifting the body weight onto the driving leg at the point of direction change (the forward and lateral angles at both of the shins should remain the same) while maintaining forward motion and speed.

Figure 296: Side drives

Starting Drills

In sports, athletes need to be able to react quickly to a stimulus, whether this be sound (eg a call, a starter's gun) or visual (eg the opponent's play) from a number of different body positions. Common positions include from the floor (after a tackle), going through a transition from walking or jogging, landing on one or two feet (after making a smash or performing a blocking move) or from an extended lunge position (eg after reaching for a drop shot in squash).

The coach needs to recognise the variety of starting positions common within the sport they coach. The coach then needs to incorporate combinations of all of these positions into speed and agility practices in order to ensure the athlete is able to maximise their potential explosive development. As with many coaching drills, the only limitation on the variety of these starting positions is the coach's imagination.

Up Tall and Fall

The athlete stands with their feet together and leans forward into a partner (if available), who should take the weight of their body as they lean forward. It is important a straight line is maintained between the head (which should face forwards), shoulders, hips, knees and ankles as the athlete leans. This straight-line position, with the feet remaining in the dorsiflexed position, a credit card-width distance between the ground and the heel, is referred to as the drive position. Once the partner has the athlete's full body weight, they should step to one side, causing the athlete to fall forward. (If no partner is available, the athlete should maintain the correct body position and fall forward until the point where they over-balance.) As soon as the support is removed and the athlete falls forward, they should immediately accelerate away. If body position is lost (check the head is looking forward and the straight-line body position is maintained) gravity will probably cause the athlete to fall over.

Figure 297: Arsenal manager Arsene Wenger demonstrates to players the 'up tall and fall' start position during a training session at Arsenal's training ground. Coaches should note the head should be facing forward not looking down throughout the movement.

Flying Start

The athlete accelerates into a sprint from a five metre jog.

Figure 298: Acceleration from a flying start

Off the Floor

The athlete lies on the floor, facing the direction of play (ie the direction of the sprint) or away from the direction of movement (depending on which is more appropriate for the sport). In one movement, the athlete should get off the floor, turn and sprint in the required direction.

Figure 299: Getting off the floor

Side Shuffle

The athlete side-steps left and right between two cones placed 2–5m apart, concentrating on moving on active flat feet (remember the credit-card rule). On an appropriate signal (eg 'Go'), the athlete straightens and accelerates forwards.

Figure 300: Side shuffle

Figure 301: Acceleration on cue

Partner Jumps

The athlete jumps continuously on the spot with varied landing patterns (eg land feet together, feet apart, feet crossing over) as directed by a partner/the coach. On the command 'Go', or another stimulus, such as a ball drop, the athlete breaks into a sprint. This will enable them to practise moving off any foot.

Figure 302: Partner jumps

Reaction Drills

Speed is the product of reaction time (the time taken to detect and respond to a stimulus) and movement time (the time from the beginning of a movement to its completion). Training an athlete's reactions is therefore a very important part of training. In a game, athletes need to react to the visual stimulus, for example, the movement of a ball or another athlete, as well as possible verbal stimuli, such as 'man-on', or a pre-set call to initiate a move. Therefore, in training, athletes should practise reacting to this type of stimulus. Reaction drills always need to be done in pairs or larger groups (three or more athletes) in order to be effective. As with many of the drills outlined in this chapter, these drills lend themselves very well to warm-up sessions for all sporting activities.

Crazy-ball Drills

Take a crazy (reaction) ball[27] and bounce it to a partner, making them move to the direction of the bounce to catch the ball.

Figure 303: Crazy-ball drills

Other games can be invented for the crazy ball, as well as the partner throws outlined above (eg throw the ball for the athlete and call a number to determine how many bounces it should do before the athlete catches it).

'Catch Me if You Can' Drill

Two athletes face each other, five metres apart. Athlete 1 jogs backwards, Athlete 2 follows, keeping five metres apart. Athlete 1, when ready, shouts 'Go' and turns and sprints. Athlete 2 has to catch Athlete 1 before they run 15m. This drill can be varied by Athlete 2 calling and Athlete 1 reacting or by a third person calling and both athletes having to react.

Figure 304: Catch me if you can

Cut-offs

Athlete 1 starts at the point marked * and sprints to one of the markers. Athlete 2 reacts and tries to cut Athlete 1 off before they reach the marker. Variety can be introduced by having a third person call out 'left' or 'right', thus both athletes have to react to a verbal stimulus. Similarly, a third person can indicate, using hand signals, the direction of sprint to Athlete 2. Athlete 1 then has to react to the movement of Athlete 2 (see Figure 305). This version can be progressed by having Athlete 2 side-step left or right within a defined area, in response to hand signals from Athlete 3. This might involve the following variations: left hand up, side step left; right hand up, side step right; left arm pointing vertically and right arm horizontal, sprint to right cone; left arm horizontal and right arm vertical, sprint to left cone. Athlete 1 should react to the movements of Athlete 2 and mirror them appropriately.

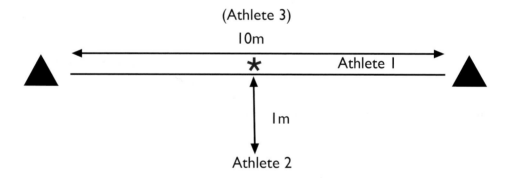

Figure 305: Cut-off set-up

Ball-drops

Athletes can also train reaction times and decision-making in response to visual stimuli, by using ball-drop drills. Two athletes stand five metres apart, facing each other (Figure 306). When Athlete 1 drops a ball from an outstretched hand, Athlete 2 accelerates towards the ball and attempts to catch it before the second bounce (Figure 307).

**Figure 306: Ball-drops
start position**

**Figure 307: React and catch the
ball after one bounce**

To develop decision-making skills, use two balls as follows: Athlete 1 has a ball in each outstretched hand and drops one of them for Athlete 2 to react to accordingly. Coaches will notice how this necessitates the athlete changing body position away from the split-step start to a more neutral, two-footed stance, to allow acceleration in either direction in response to the ball-drop.

Figure 308: Decision-making and ball-drops

By introducing more athletes, a sequence of such decision-making/reaction-developing opportunities can be practised. Each athlete should stand five metres back from the person in front, and drop their ball as soon as the working athlete has caught the ball in front. The emphasis is on making the athlete work to react to the ball-drop: they should not therefore have to wait for the person in front to drop the ball. This will also mean that another athlete has to be available to catch balls that are caught and passed by the working athlete. By altering the angle at which the athletes are placed, these drills can also be used to practise directional change (in accordance with agility practices outlined herein).

Acceleration

Acceleration can be viewed as the ability to rapidly propel a stationary body, or to rapidly increase pace. Acceleration improvement can make a significant difference to the effectiveness of any sports performer. Acceleration is determined by the length of time it takes an athlete to reach top speed (or reach the object/space they are moving to), and is directly proportional to the application of force to the ground; the greater the force applied, the greater the acceleration.

Correct technique is important in developing maximal accelerations, as the body's ability to exert a force will depend upon it being in the correct position. Therefore, it is important that the appropriate drills outlined herein are undertaken in conjunction with the appropriate (multi-joint) resistance-training exercises and plyometric activities.

Below are detailed examples of drills designed to improve an athlete's acceleration. Coaches should remember that, as well as changing the starting stimulus and position, the angle of sprints should also be adapted (ie design the five-metre sprints to run diagonally to the left and right, as well as straight on) in order to vary the patterns and make them more representative of specific sport requirements.

Acceleration Sprints

• 10 lots of five-metre sprints (100% speed) with active recovery between reps.
• Active recovery – three minutes.
• Seven lots of 10m sprints (100% speed) with active recovery between reps.
• Active recovery – three minutes.
• Five lots of 15m sprints (100% speed) with active recovery between reps.

Hollow Sprints

• Mark a 100m course into 20m intervals.
• Jog 20m, sprint 20m (50% speed), cruise 20m, sprint 20m, jog 20m. (Concentrate on changing pace into the sprints.)
• Active recovery.
• Repeat two sets of 4–8 reps.

Gear-change Sprints

• Mark out 100m in 20m segments.
• Run between these segments, increasing the pace every 20m (jog, stride, 75% speed, 90% speed, 100% speed).
• Active recovery.
• Repeat two sets of 4–8 reps.

Flying 10s

• Mark out a 30m course into a 20m section and a 10m section.
• Start running at 50% speed and increase the pace with each stride, until you are at full pace by the end of the 20m. Maintain maximal speed for a final 10m.
• Active recovery.
• Repeat two sets of 6–8 reps.

This can be changed into 40m (20m acceleration, 20m sprint) or other distances, as is relevant for the sport.

Resisted Drills

Some of the drills outlined in this section can be performed with a bungee cord, attached by a harness or belt with a resistance, either from a person holding a bungee, or a weighted sled (this should not be so heavy that it interferes with technique development: An example of good practice is shown in Figure 309). Wearing a weighted vest will also achieve the same effect. If such equipment is not available, a manual resistance (ie a partner hanging on to your hips as you run) can be just as effective, as long as they do not interfere with the athlete's movement. The purpose of such resistance work is to increase the resistance to the sprint. In basic terms, this will require more nerves to fire, thus making more motor units active in the movement. This is not something that can be achieved voluntarily; it will only occur in response to an increased resistance.

However, it is desirable that movement technique does not suffer as a result of this resistance. It is important, therefore, that the resistive load does not add more than 5–10% of body mass to the individual. Overloading the resistance will simply lead to technique being lost.

It is recommended that athletes using resistive drills run several successive drills with the resistance added and then, immediately after, run the same pattern without the resistance.

This is known as contrast training: the neuromuscular system will continue to operate as though the resistance were present, thus training the muscles to operate in that manner all the time. This works in a similar way to the principles of complex training (adding plyometric work to resistance-training sets) and will make the athlete faster over time.

Figure 309: Italian striker Christian Vieri performs resisted sprints during a national squad training session

Agility Drills

Agility can be considered as the ability to precisely and quickly change direction or body position. In most games, athletes will be required to undertake directional change quickly and precisely, after many varied distances, with rapid movements (usually between 2–20m). Acceleration is therefore an important part of all agility drills. As well as enhancing an athlete's performance, good agility training will also aid injury prevention, as the athlete will be used to rapid and reactive changes of direction and speed.

Coaches should bear in mind that, as with all training, there should be a progression in the challenge of the task. Dot drills and ladder drills (detailed overleaf) are great for specific technique purposes and, once technique is sound, for warm-up purposes. However, the athlete needs to move from closed drills of this nature (where the athlete reacts to their thoughts or a limited stimulus-response selection) to ones where the agility technique is much more determined by the environment of the sport. This can include unpredictable bounces, speed and spin on a ball, the surface, the decisions of other players etc, if the technique is eventually going to become stable under performance conditions.

Figure 310: Belgium's Justine Henin-Hardenne undertakes an agility discipline

The basic principle of direction change involves the need to create the necessary positive shin angle for effective movement, in the same way that the shin angle is important for straight line sprinting. To achieve this, when the athlete wants to move in a given direction, they should be coached to push off the outside of the leading foot (a hard thing to learn to do) and the inside of the trailing foot. Another key principle for the coach to remember is that any time the athlete wants to change direction, they should never have their navel between their feet: the centre of gravity needs to move outwith the stable position of support.

© Action Images/Reuters

Figure 311: Skiers have long understood the importance of weight transfer through the feet, the importance of shin angles and the importance of controlling the displacement of centre of mass of the body at speed

The following drills form ideal components of warm-ups for all sessions, allowing an athlete to practise the movements and attain exceptional technique without the need for additional sessions. The drills are also non-fatiguing and so form ideal rehabilitation/active-recovery sessions.

These drills lend themselves to resisted efforts through the use of bungee cords and harnesses, to facilitate neural recruitment of the optimal number of fast-twitch (explosive) muscle fibres. To achieve maximal training effect using such equipment, unresisted efforts should immediately follow resisted efforts.

All of the following drills should be undertaken with a focus on maintaining good technique: focus on active flat-foot contact, elbows should be angled at 90° and arm driven backwards from the shoulder. Ankles should be dorsiflexed, the shin angles maintained at 45° and parallel to the lean of the trunk, and the trunk should be kept stable.

Dot Drills

Putting some markings onto a floor or a 1m x 1m rubber mat can easily create a dot matt. The aim is for the performer to hop from dot to line or dot (depending upon the combination in a pattern), using the inside or outside of the foot in contact with the floor to change the angle of the shin and move the position of the athlete's centre of mass, under control, around the mat. Maintaining a dorsiflexed toe and controlling the ankle, knee and hip positions during the landing is very important during these movements.

Figure 312: The dot matt

Rope-ladder Drills

There are many possible variations for rope-ladder drills, using one or two feet. Coaches should realise they all are designed to train the body to positively change the position of the centre of mass of an athlete and control this movement. They also encourage correct foot contact and proprioception, as well as agility. Rope ladders (with foot holes approximately 30cm square) are excellent tools for this drill but for complete drill adaptability, the coach can chalk or tape the structure on a suitable surface. Rope-ladder drills provide coaches with the opportunity to bring much variety to training.

It should be noted that in all of the following example drills, as the athlete exits the rope ladder, they should immediately accelerate at 100% pace for 5–10m, to allow a contrast effect to occur.

© Action Images/Reuters

Figure 313: England defender Ashley Cole works on ladder drills to challenge his body's ability to move his centre of gravity. Coaches should note the head should be up during the drills, ensuring an efficient posture can be maintained

The following diagrams (Figures 314–322) show the order in which to place the feet for each drill.

Quick step:
Run through the ladder, putting both feet in every hole along the ladder.

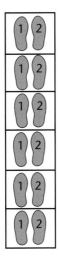

Miss a hole:
Two ladders are placed side by side. Run through, missing out every other hole on the respective left/right side.

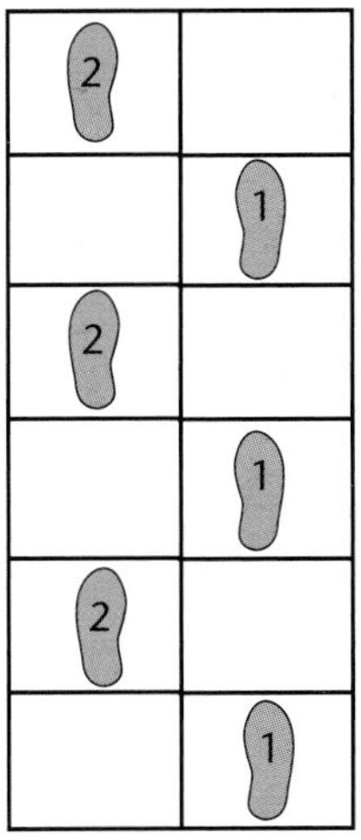

Figure 314: Rope-ladder drills – quick step

Figure 315: Rope-ladder drills – miss a hole

Side step:
Run sideways along the length of the ladder, putting both feet in every hole.

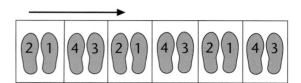

Figure 316: Rope-ladder drills – side step

Lateral push:
Working sideways along the length of the ladder, begin at position (a), step forward into the first square of the ladder with the right foot, then follow this with the left foot (position b). Now push off diagonally and backwards with the right foot in a position in front of the next square and follow this with the left foot (position c). Repeat this sequence along the length of the rope ladder. This should be reversed in the next repetition.

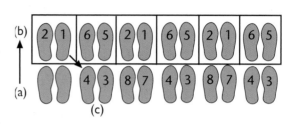

Figure 317: Rope-ladder drills – lateral push

Bunny hops:
Stand with feet together. Bounce through alternate holes, keeping feet together. Spend a minimum amount of time in contact with the ground.

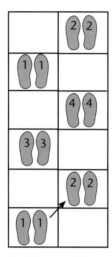

Figure 318: Rope-ladder drills – bunny hops

Cross-steps:
Forward running movement, putting the right foot in every other left hole, and left foot in alternate right holes.

Figure 319: Rope-ladder drills – cross steps

Single-leg hops:
Use two ladders, with a 30cm space between them. On the left foot, hop two spaces forward (a). As soon as possible upon landing, hop one space back (b). Hop diagonally across to other ladder, and land on the right foot (c). Jump two spaces forward (d), back one (e), and across diagonally, to land on left foot (f). Repeat up the ladder.

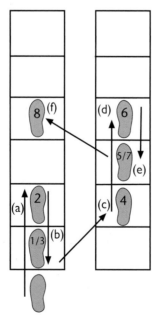

Figure 320: Rope-ladder drills – single-leg hops

Icky shuffle:
From start, put left foot then right foot into hole (a), then left foot out and forward (pushing off with the right foot), followed by right foot (b). Then right foot into hole (c) followed by left. Right foot out and forward (push off with the left), followed by right (d), etc.

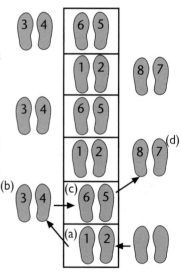

Figure 321: Rope-ladder drills – icky shuffle

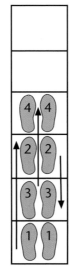

Double jumps:
The athlete starts with the feet together, jumping two holes forward, then one hole back. Repeat the pattern up the ladder. Spend as little time in contact with the ground as possible. This can also be performed on a single leg as a progression.

**Figure 322: Rope-ladder drills
– double jumps**

Ladders can be used in many drills as well as in isolation. An example from tennis is shown in Figure 323, which combines an advanced ladder drill (ie directional change in response to a partner's movement, requiring the athlete's attention to be away from the foot position) with a reaction component and a plyometric drill.

Baseline drives:
Coach (holding medicine ball) moves left or right. Player mirrors directional change in ladder. After 2–8 direction changes, coach throws medicine ball to either their left or right in front of the ladder so it is one to two steps away from the player. This should not be accompanied by any verbal warning, ie this is a visual stimulus. Player explodes out of ladder, picks up ball and throws it explosively (either forehand or backhand) over the net.

**Figure 323: Rope-ladder drills
– baseline drives**

Progression in all of these drills can be achieved by the athlete not looking at their feet (which needs to be encouraged as soon as possible from the start if technique is to be progressed), by speeding the movement up, or by the athlete having to catch, pass or hit a ball being fed to them. When practising these drills on court, the athlete should rapidly accelerate into a five-metre sprint at the end of every agility drill.

Agility Technique Practices

Cross-over Lunges

From a standing lunge position, the athlete brings the left (or right) foot across in front of the body, keeping the ankle dorsiflexed and facing forward upon landing, so it is completely perpendicular to the direction of the body's travel (see Figure 324a). The knee of the front leg should be directly over the toes upon landing. The centre of mass of the athlete should be switched out with the base of support, so the nose of the athlete is now over/outside of the knee of the front leg, which is now holding most of the athlete's body mass. The athlete remains close to the ground as they move into the end position. Depending upon the objective of the drill, the back foot of the athlete should either remain on the floor, facing forwards (Figure 324b), on the balls of the feet (movement drills), or, if emphasising muscle recruitment (for example the role of the gluteus medius in controlling the hip joint), then the back leg coming off the floor to emphasise the shifting of the bodyweight outside the base of support (Figure 324a) is appropriate. From here, the athlete pushes off the outside of the front foot back to the start position, and repeats the drill to the other side .

Figure 324a: The correct foot positions during cross-over lunges

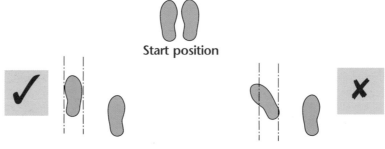

Start position

Correct finish position:
Foot pointing forward, perpendicular to the direction of movement, heel pushed across, so foot falls inside imaginary tramlines running at 90° to the direction of movement.

Incorrect finish position:
Toe leading the movement forward, dorsiflexed position lost in the ankle, foot not contained within the imaginary tramlines. This is an unstable position that may result in injuries.

Figure 324b: The correct and incorrect foot positions during cross-over lunges

Kareoka

The athlete turns sideways-on to the direction of movement. The athlete should keep the ankle dorsiflexed throughout this drill. The first step is to bring the rear leg behind the athlete's body (Figure 325a). Pressure on the inside of the rear foot brings the front foot back across in front of the body (Figure 325b). The athlete now brings their knee forward (as if punching a wall) in front of the body (Figure 325c), then drives the foot back to the floor, contacting and driving with the outside of the foot (Figure 325d) which will drive the body sideways (Figure 325e), so the athlete returns to the start position.

This sequence is repeated moving in one direction, then repeated with the athlete facing the same way, but moving in the other direction. This means the lead leg is reversed from the right to the left.

Figure 325a: Kareoka first step – behind the body

Figure 325b: Kareoka second step – knee in front of the body

Figure 325c: Kareoka third step – punch the front knee across the body, note the dorsiflexed ankle.

Figure 325d: Kareoka fourth step – ground contact

Figure 325e: Kareoka fifth step – the finish position

Back-pedal

The athlete stands in a low stable position, with the buttocks low, back straight, and chest and head facing forward. Keeping the ankle dorsiflexed the athlete lifts the left (next step right) foot and reaches the foot behind them. Keeping low and keeping the shoulders square, the athlete contacts the floor with the ball of the foot and pulls themselves backwards with the foot moving down onto the heel, aided by the toe being pulled towards the shin. As the weight transfers onto the planted left foot (now behind the body), the momentum will cause the front foot to rise from the floor (if the toes remain dorsiflexed). Therefore, the coach should encourage the athlete to show them the bottom of their shoes on the front foot as the athlete's weight transfers backwards. The opposite arm–opposite leg principle still applies in this drill.

This drill can be progressed into linked movements, such as back pedalling, or sprinting forwards or laterally. When this happens, the coach should make sure that, at the point of direction change, there should be no extra steps on the spot, but, because the athlete will have a 45° body angle, they will be able to plant their feet (a double-foot plant and push is much more effective than a single foot) and immediately use this to drive forward into a sprint.

Figure 326: Back pedal

Angled Back-pedal

This skill is particularly useful for athletes who need to look forwards while tracking backwards and to the side. It involves learning to push off from different parts of the feet to produce a resultant movement pattern.

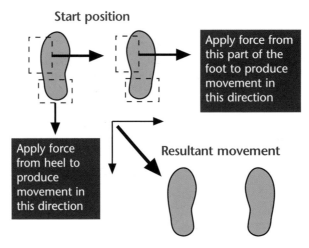

Figure 327a: Angled back-pedal movements result from learning to apply forces from the heel and the side of the foot

Figure 327b: Angled back pedal

As the athlete moves at the 45° angle backwards, the feet, hips and upper body should be kept facing forward (square). This means the athlete will be able to respond to any necessary stimuli and change direction by pushing off from the relevant parts of the foot. If the hips point in any direction other than forward, the athlete will not be able to respond rapidly to any required directional changes needed, which opens up the opportunities for an opponent to pass the athlete on the inside (the side which the body has turned away from).

This drill can also be progressed into linked movements, such as back pedalling, or sprinting forwards or laterally. When this happens, the coach should make sure that, at the point of direction change, there should be no extra steps on the spot, but, because the athlete will have a 45° body angle, they will be able to plant their feet (a double-foot plant and push is much more effective than a single foot) and immediately use this to drive forward into a sprint.

Sport-specific Agility Drills

One of the best things about speed and agility training is that most aspects of this type of training can, and indeed should, be very easily accommodated into the warm-up and technical session drills. Again, the only limitation to the scope and range of reaction, explosion, agility and acceleration practices that can be incorporated into drills is the coach's imagination. The example drills illustrated in the following pages have been modified to allow for the role demands of the individual sports to be trained. The stimulus initiating the athlete's acceleration also needs to be varied, to allow for the process to be as sport specific as possible.

Some examples follow of agility drills devised for, and used with, athletes at the highest level in the relevant sports. They are based on the dimensions and markings of the playing area and are designed to replicate various movements the athlete may experience during a specific activity. Once again, the basic idea is for the coach to adopt the principles upon which these drills are based and utilise their imagination and knowledge of the game, to devise specific drills to suit particular session or athlete needs. All of these drills are suitable for inclusion in warm-ups, as well as forming the focus of a session. They can also all be adapted for enhanced neuromuscular activation with the use of bungee resistance. Combinations with ladders, or inclusion of other factors such as reaction drills (ie ball-drops), serve to make these drills progressive, reflective of the actual game and a lot of fun for the athletes.

Example 1: Tennis

- The player (wearing bungee resistance) starts at X.
- The coach calls out a cone number. The player sprints to the respective cone, (touches cone/plays a shot/ throws ball) and returns to X.
- Repeat five times, with two reps unresisted.

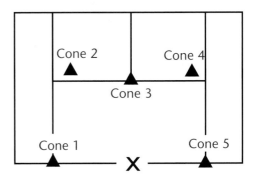

Figure 328: Up and drive

Example 2: Basketball

This drill can be performed by the player sprinting forwards, running backwards or side-stepping. From the start position, the player sprints around outside of the circle in an anti-clockwise direction. At 1 (or in response to a shouted command), the athlete cuts in and sidesteps straight across circle. When the athlete reaches the other side, they sprint in a clockwise direction, until 2 (or verbal command), and then cuts inside again. The coach should vary the length of sprints around the perimeter.

Alternatives:

- Running forwards, cutting in and out of each cone (emphasise pushing of each foot).
- Running backwards.
- Keeping the back squared to the inside of the circle, turning and sprinting across the circle.
- Keeping the front squared to the inside of the circle, turn and sprint.

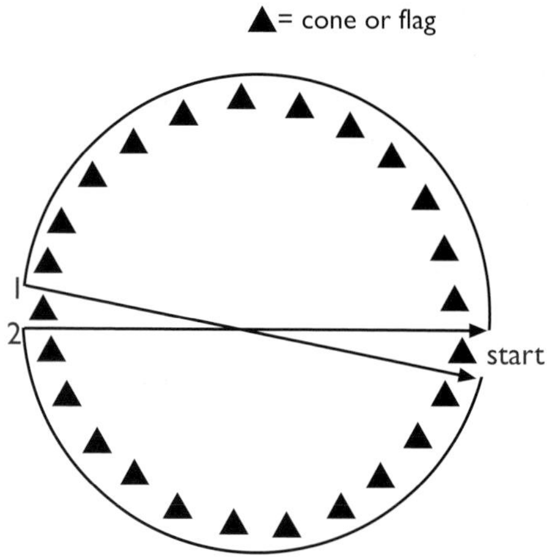

▲= cone or flag

Figure 329: Circle cuts

Example 3: Rugby League

- The player is in the start position.
- They sprint the pattern shown, touching the outside of each line with their foot.
- From here, they sprint to Cones 1–5 depending on either a visual or verbal cue from the coach.
- The player should run the drill in the opposite direction as well.
- A further variation is to side-step between the lateral lines (rather than sprinting forward).

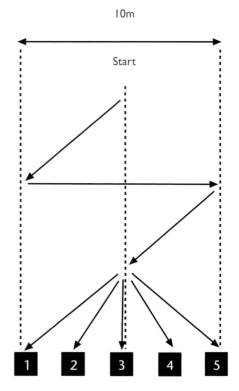

Figure 330: Lateral run

Example 4: Squash

This drill ideally needs two belts and four bungee chords (fixed to the belts on the front, back, left and right sides of the athlete), which are either held by four people or doubled up and looped around poles/fixed objects to anchor the resistance.

However, this drill can be performed in the same manner without resistance if this is not available. The order of the cones can be randomised in order to progress the complexity of the drill.

- The player begins at X.
- From here, they sprint forward around A.
- They run backwards to B.
- They sprint forwards to X.
- They side-step right around C.
- They side-step left across to D.
- They side-step right back to X.

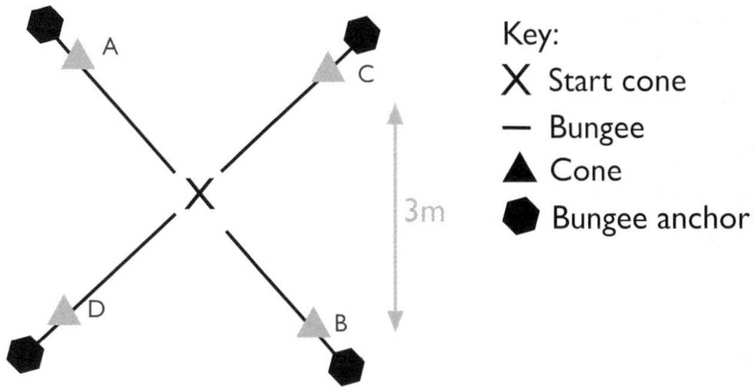

Angle of cones can be altered to allow forward or diagonal movements. This drill can also be performed with a lunge position at A–D to make this more sport-specific.

Key:
X Start cone
— Bungee
▲ Cone
⬢ Bungee anchor

3m

Figure 331: The 4s drill

Coaches should take every opportunity to make training as efficient as possible by integrating agility drills with technical practices. It is essential athletes perform such drills under pressure, in response to match-specific movement patterns and with sport-specific equipment. Such drills also help to accustom the young performer to the spatial orientation of the playing area. This is important, as spatial awareness is often a deficient quality in pre-adolescents.

Example 5: Football

This drill might apply to a centre forward, whose movement pattern might typically be to:

- back-pedal to draw the defender away from the ball to create space
- accelerate forward into the space, taking the defender with them
- angle-back-pedal into the space at the side of them (watching the ball all the time)
- turn and accelerate into the space now created behind the defender as the ball is played over the top of them into the space.

This drill replicates these movement patterns:

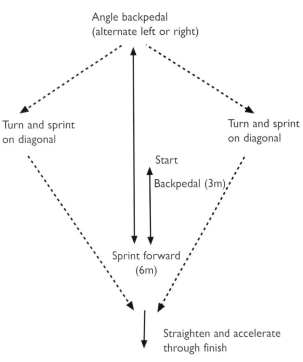

Angle backpedal (alternate left or right)

Turn and sprint on diagonal

Turn and sprint on diagonal

Start

Backpedal (3m)

Sprint forward (6m)

Straighten and accelerate through finish

Figure 332: A centre-forward's agility drill for football

Developing Top Speed

This is the maximum speed athletes are able to reach. It occurs after the acceleration phase (usually the first 20–40m, depending on the sport/event). Therefore it is best improved by sprinting over longer distances, although again consideration needs to be given to the game/positional role in this. Athletes should not just run in straight lines during these training sessions and should incorporate angular and directional changes into such athletic drills as appropriate, to make them more game specific.

Sports performers who regularly have to run at maximal speeds would be well advised to spend time with a high-quality/specialist sprint coach who can build upon the basic technique points covered within this text to develop the appropriate technique at maximum speeds.

Medium-distance Sprints

- 5 x 30m sprints (1–3 minutes recovery between each repetition)
- Walking active recovery (3–5 minutes)
- 4 x 35m sprints (1–3 minutes recovery between each repetition)
- Walking active recovery (3–5 minutes)
- 6 x 25m sprints (1–3 minutes recovery between each repetition)

Pyramid Sprints

The pyramid sprints work primarily on building and maintaining speed.

- 4 x 20m pyramid sprints then active recovery
- 3 x 25m pyramid sprints then active recovery
- 2 x 40m pyramid sprints then active recovery
- 1 x 60m then active recovery

Ensure each set and rep is followed by complete active recovery. Reps per distance can be increased by two over a period of weeks but remember that speed work is not based upon high volume of activity.

20-40-60s

- 5 x 20m maximal sprints (100% effort) with active recovery between reps
- Walking recovery 2–5 minutes
- 5 x (2 x 20m) maximal sprints with 180° turn (100% effort) with active recovery between reps
- Walking recovery 2–5 minutes
- 4 x 60m maximal sprints (100% effort) with active recovery between reps

Testing Speed and Agility

All of the below tests are based upon a coach timing with a stopwatch, which all coaches have access to in one form or another. The coach always instructs the athlete to respond to a 'Go' command. This means there is an element of reactions involved on the part of the athlete (this is more effective than the coach attempting to start the stopwatch when the athlete decides to move).

If the coach is lucky enough to have access to photoelectric cells, which time movement electronically by recording the time between an athlete breaking light beams. The athlete can choose when to begin moving, as the clock will not start until they cross the light beam (this removes reaction time from the recorded time).

Testing Linear Speed

Speed is about covering a distance in the quickest possible time. Therefore, testing linear speed is relatively simple involving a tester with a stopwatch and some space. Common distances to measure speed over are 0–5, 0–10, 0–20 and 0–30m. However, track and field athletes may want to measure linear speed over 100m.

It should be noted, speed tests also include time trials over certain longer distances (400m, 800m etc), or distance covered in a certain time, although the longer the distance, the greater the number of variables (eg endurance status) a coach will need to consider. As this chapter has focused on maximal speed, we will consider this.

The start position of the speed test can be determined by the coach, as befits the nature of the sport that is being trained for. Static standing starts are the most common, and easy to administer (coaches should remember to use the same starting positions when comparing two test scores). The tester should stand next to the finish line, so as accurate a 'stop' score as possible can be achieved.

On the 'Go' command from the tester (stopwatch started), the athlete runs as fast as possible over the determined distance. The stopwatch should be stopped as the player crosses the finish line. Two tests should be performed over differing distances with complete recovery available between each test. (If photoelectric cells are used, they can be placed at different distances along the course, so, for example, speed at 10 and 20m can be recorded, as well as 30m, on a 30m sprint. This avoids fatigue due to repetition. Athletes are encouraged to slow down/decelerate gently after passing the respective finishing lines in order to maximise the effectiveness of their performance. Time should be recorded in seconds (to the nearest 0.01).

The Modified T-test (Y-test)

This speed agility test records the ability of the athlete to change direction at pace, either running backwards, forwards or sideways. This requires quick movement, balance and coordination, and is important for athletes requiring evasive movements and rapid directional changes.

The Y-test is a modified T-test (popular in American football), which replicates the demands of many intermittent high-intensity sports. Performers should be allowed one familiarity attempt prior to having two test attempts (best score is recorded).

On the figure below, the triangles (cones) are those used in the tests, with the circles indicating the measurements needed to set the test up.

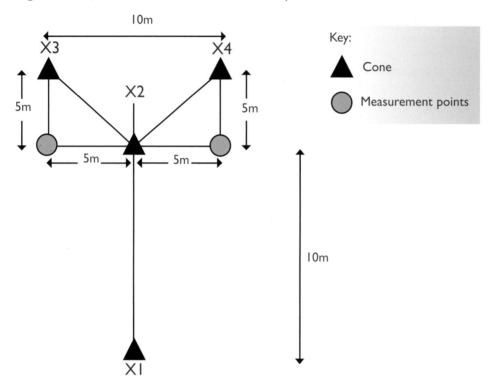

Figure 333: The Y-test set-up

The athlete begins at X1, facing X2. On the 'Go' command (stopwatch started), the athlete sprints to the left-hand side of X2.

At X2, the athlete sprints to X3. At X3, they touch the ground (outside of the cone) with the left hand. (Coaches should note that the decision of whether to touch the cones with the hands or the feet rests with them, as they see fit for the nature of their sport. It is important, however, that there is consistency between tests on this issue).

Immediately, the athlete turns and sprints back to X2. The athlete must come around X2 (ie passing as close to the cone as possible, but between X1 and X2), and sprints to X4 touching the ground with the right hand. Now, the athlete turns, sprints back to X2, passing around the cone between X2 and X3 and crosses the start line (X1) on the right-hand side (direction of travel) of the cone. The watch is stopped as the athlete crosses X1. The completion time is recorded in seconds (to the nearest 0.01).

The Pro-test

The pro-test measures 180°-turning speed and 0–5 and 0–10m sprint abilities in one test. This has been popularised and used extensively in soccer and rugby.

As illustrated in Figure 334, two lines are set up (or marked with two cones), 10m apart, with one cone placed in the middle of these lines (so it is five metres to each line). On the 'Go' command, the athlete sprints to their right at maximal speed. When they reach the line five metres to their right, they touch this with their right foot (or hand, as is determined to be appropriate). Hasegawa (2007) recommends putting a ball on the line, so the player touches this with their foot – the ball moves, and the coach knows the athlete has touched the line. The athlete then pushes off their right foot (touch and turn is one movement) and sprints 10m across to the far line, where the turn is performed with the left foot. The athlete then sprints back to the middle, and the stop-watch is stopped as the player crosses the line.

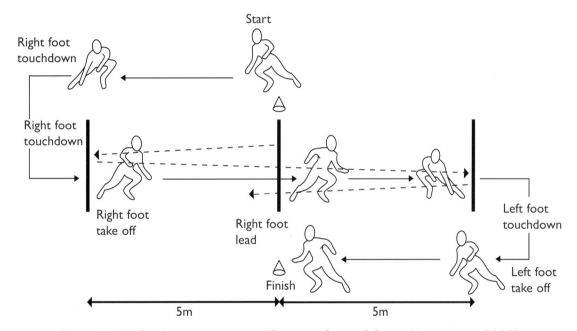

Figure 334: The Pro-test set-up (figure adapted from Hasegawa, 2007)

Other tests

Coaches may look at the tests outlined above and decide there is not sufficient backward movement in them for their sport, or their athlete(s) do not need to be able to turn through 180°. These observations are valid and coaches should be comfortable with designing their own tests for use, as long as the principles of validity (it actually is a speed test) and reliability (as much as possible is done to ensure that the same tests can be repeated in the same conditions with the same person on the stopwatch) are observed. Analysing the movement patterns from a particular sport can then form the basis of such tests, some suggestions for which appear in Figure 335.

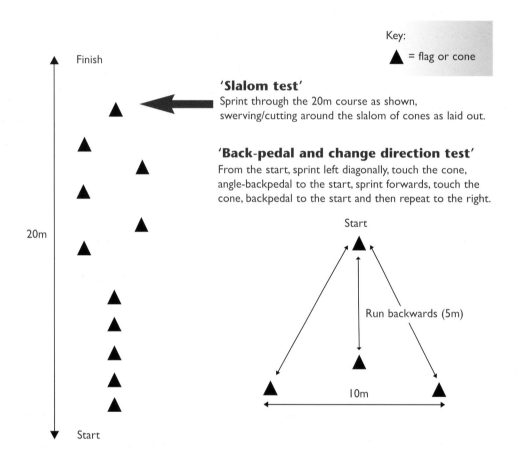

Key:

▲ = flag or cone

'Slalom test'
Sprint through the 20m course as shown, swerving/cutting around the slalom of cones as laid out.

'Back-pedal and change direction test'
From the start, sprint left diagonally, touch the cone, angle-backpedal to the start, sprint forwards, touch the cone, backpedal to the start and then repeat to the right.

Start

Run backwards (5m)

10m

Finish

20m

Start

Figure 335: Some suggested agility tests for coaches to use

Summary

When designing acceleration and agility practices, there are a number of factors the coach needs to consider:

- What is the purpose of the drill? This is the fundamental question that will influence all other factors. Once this has been decided, it is important to attend to specific factors such as:
  - In a performance, from which starting positions do athletes have to react quickly?
  - With which stimulus will I (the coach) start the drills?
- What is the nature of movement required?
  - **Acceleration** (0–20m): What angles will the athletes need to run at/from?
  - **Agility** (direction changes): What is the angle of turns that should be considered; what type of movements; how many direction changes form a typical movement sequence?
  - **Top speed** (20–100m): How far will athletes be required to run in an average sprint (this should comprise the majority of distances in practices) and a maximum distance sprint. To calculate the furthest range for training sessions, add 10m to the aforementioned distances.

Coaches should build the carrying of sports equipment (rackets, balls, sticks) into a percentage of the drills undertaken, in order to improve the efficiency of the performer during the game.

References

Seagrave, L. (2007) 'Developing speed technique in sports performers UK', Strength and Conditioning Association Annual Conference, Inverclyde National Sports Centre, Scotland, May 2007.

Hasegawa, H. (2007) 'Strength and Conditioning in Soccer', ETSU Sports Performance Enhancement Consortium Coaches College, Tennessee, December 2007.

Further Reading

Brown, L., Ferrigno, V. and Santana, J.C. (2000) *Training for Speed, Agility and Quickness*. Illinois: Human Kinetics. ISBN: 978-0-736002-39-1.*

Coachwise 1st4sport (2001) 'Speed Training Drills' video. Leeds: Coachwise 1st4sport. *

Pearson, A. and Hawkins, D. (2005) *SAQ Youth*. A and C Black. ISBN: 978-0-713670-42-4. *

Ward, R., Dintiman, G.B. and Ward, R. (2003) *sports speed*. Illinois: Human Kinetics. ISBN: 978-0-736046-49-7.

* Available from **Coachwise 1st4sport**. For a full range of sports education and training equipment, please visit www.1st4sport.com or call 0113-201 5555.

Notes page

Notes page

Chapter 7
Warming Up for Training

Introduction

Much has been written over the years about the warm-up for a session and how it should do 'what it says on the tin' (ie increase the temperature of the muscles in the body). However, this is more probably a by-product of the major objectives for this part of the training session. This is written deliberately, as the warm-up has often been treated by many athletes as something done before training. This, and the impression that it is about doing activity to increase core temperature, has often resulted in an entirely different psychological approach being taken to this part of the session (ie 'we'll just do a few laps and have a chat about something completely unrelated to the session') rather than treating it as an important part of the session, which the coach should really emphasise.

Typically, the warm-up has three major objectives:

• To prepare the athlete physically for the following performance (training or competition).
• To prepare the athlete mentally for the following performance.
• In a competition, to prepare the athlete for the environmental conditions in which the performance must be undertaken (crowd, weather, under floor etc).

Many coaches have followed the principle that, in order to get muscles warm, a jog around the track/pitch is necessary. However, any form of appropriate activity, with an increasing intensity but the appropriate psychological focus, can achieve this. The warm-up therefore becomes an excellent opportunity for practising the movement patterns and techniques allowing the right muscles to fire at the right time and in the right manner to maximise performance and minimise the chance of an injury occurring. Movement skills based upon dynamic mobility exercises are ideal for this purpose.

Dynamic Mobility

Dynamic mobility usually involves rhythmic-type movements that may extend to full range while focusing on putting the joints in the right positions so muscles can work appropriately. The aim of this book is not to confuse coaches with the names of muscles or the movements they are responsible for, but it is important to understand that a coach placing emphasis on correct technique in a warm-up is important.

The term dynamic flexibility refers to the maximum range of movement (ROM – explored in more depth in Chapter 8) of a joint during a movement, or its ease of movement within the obtainable ROM. This method of stretching has sometimes been criticised as exceeding the elastic limit of the tissues as a result of the repetitive bouncing actions. However, dynamic (movement) stretches should prepare the muscles for the impending exercise by working rhythmically through sport-specific ranges of movements under direct muscular control and should therefore gradually increase the elastic range of the tissues without causing acute overreaching. As the drills below outline, these exercises can include such activities as speed and agility technique drills and movements relating to the specific activities that will be undertaken in performing any sport-specific actions. For example, consider twisting movements, diagonal movements of the trunk and vertical and horizontal movements.

© Action Images/Reuters

Figure 336: The German national football team perform a dynamic warm-up prior to training during the 2006 world cup

© Action Images/Reuters

Figure 337: The England cricket team use dynamic mobility exercises to prepare for a training session

Dynamic stretches should be used in preparation for training and sports performance. At this time, dynamic methods help to increase muscle temperature, temporarily increase the plastic potential of the muscles and help the neurological activation of muscles that will be used in a performance. Stretches performed at this time should be turned into a creative routine to mirror most types of activities within the game, such as running, turning, jumping, rotating, hitting and lunging. More forceful, explosive stretches (ballistic stretches) that utilise momentum and velocity should also be undertaken in a warm-up following rhythmical dynamic work. Ballistic stretches have an important role in preparing for training/participation in sports. Indeed, if such ballistic actions are not practised at appropriate speeds, then injury may occur in performing explosive actions. Ballistic stretching, when undertaken, should only take place in a properly controlled environment and should be progressively introduced when the individual is well warmed up, is fully aware of the dangers involved in the stretch and knows how to properly execute the movement.

So, why is dynamic stretching advocated in performance preparation rather than the more traditionally used static stretches? This requires some physiological explanation. Explosive plyometric actions (see Chapters 2, 4 and 5) in the muscles occur as the stretch reflex (stretch–shortening) mechanism operates. This is a protective mechanism in the body, which initiates a strong reflex contraction when the stretch receptors in the muscle perceive that the rate of change in muscle fibre length is too rapid or too forceful. For example, when landing from a squat jump, the quadriceps muscles are stretched rapidly. The stretch receptors within the muscle sense this change and limit the rate of stretch by initiating a reflex concentric contraction (ie a shortening of fibre length). End-of-range static stretching, when held for any period of time, can switch this stretch reflex mechanism off. This can be demonstrated in a static hamstring stretch:

- The athlete sits on the floor, with legs out straight in front of them.
- Keeping the head up (this helps to avoid curvature in the lumbar spine) and back straight throughout, they reach down the legs with both hands until a comfortable end position is reached (they should feel a definite stretching sensation but no pain).
- The athlete will hold this position for a count of 10 (at least six seconds) and then relax.
- Now, they should try to stretch a little further. They should find they are able to do so, because the mechanisms that inhibit the extent of the stretch in the muscle have been switched off.

As sports need a power base that relies on the stretch–shortening cycle to facilitate explosive movements, then the inhibition of the stretch reflex mechanism is not desirable. This inhibition will not only have an acute and immediate effect, but there is also evidence to suggest subsequent levels of power production can be reduced by up to 40% for a period of over an hour following static stretching.

The following dynamic stretches are therefore suggested as examples (whole books could be written on such ideas) in order to maximise the physiological potential of the athlete. Coaches will need to be aware that athletes may, initially, not be psychologically prepared for performance following a dynamic stretching routine, in the sense they may not perceive that they have actually stretched the muscle at all.

Athletes who have spent many years preparing for training and matches by undertaking a static stretching routine may not feel they have done any stretching at all in the movement education. Coaches need to overcome such concerns in the athletes by firstly having an extended education phase, to familiarise athletes with the concepts and movements involved in such a routine, and secondly, by initially allowing athletes time within the routine to evolve their own ideas about how best to maximise the benefit of such a routine.

Dynamic Stretching Exercises

All of the stretches described below are highly adaptive and can be modified to incorporate specific movements from individual sports or specific pieces of equipment, such as a ball or stick.

Similarly, the sequences the coach utilises can be based upon the requirements of the session but, as a basic principle, the progression should follow that the less-intense exercises precede those more intense in nature.

The renowned speed coach Loren Seagrave recommends the following structure to a dynamic warm-up (Seagrave, 2007):

- Movement exercises for coordination
- Movement exercises for stability
- Muscle activation exercises
- Mobilisation exercises.

Lunges

The lunge is an exercise that can be adapted in a number of ways to incorporate different stretching actions. From a standing position, the athlete deliberately flexes the hip of the leg leading the movement. The knee of this leg should also be flexed, both to an angle of 90°. From here, they take an exaggerated step forwards with the lead leg, which is planted flat on the ground. They now flex the lead knee, moving so that it is shifting along the same line the toes of the lead foot are pointing in (Figure 338). At the same time, the athlete comes onto the ball of the foot on the trail leg, and lowers the knee of this leg to a bottom position that is approximately 3–5cm off the floor. The trunk should be kept upright throughout the movement, with the centre of mass being directly above the midpoint between the two legs. This can be performed as a forward and backward walking movement to ensure bilateral work.

Figure 338: Lunge

This exercise can be developed so the lead leg is placed at a number of different angles (eg in Figure 339), allowing a range of fibres to be stretched. It is important for the athlete to ensure the knee of the lead leg is flexed in a line that is the same as the toes of the foot of the lead leg. The movement can also be performed with a trunk rotation, so the upper body is turned away from the lead leg at the bottom of the lunge position (Figure 340). At all times, the head should be held high and the chest facing upwards.

Figure 339: Angled lunge

Figure 340: Lunge with rotation

One exercise that should definitely be included in a routine is the in-line lunge (forward and backwards), which encourages balance and ankle and hip stability. The knee of the trailing leg should contact with the ground immediately behind the heel of the front leg, so there is a straight line formed between the toe of the front leg, the heel of the front leg, the knee of the rear leg, the shin of the rear leg and the toes of the rear leg (using lines on a back/court/pitch to aid the straight line positions between the front knee and and the back foot is useful for the performer. See Figure 341).

Figure 341: The in-line lunge

Galloping

The athlete starts with one foot in front of the other (eg the left foot in front of the right). Keeping the ankle dorsiflexed and in contact with the floor, with an active flat foot, the athlete brings the back foot up to meet the front foot, then moves the front foot forward. The toes should be kept facing forward throughout the drill.

Figure 342: Galloping

In and Outs

This is a great exercise for loosening up the groin region, which is tight in many athletes. The athlete moves into a semi-squat position, with the hips higher than the knees and the trunk leaning forward (in this instance). The toes point straight forward at the start of the drill, with the hands staying in front of the body. From here, the athlete keeps low (the challenge here is to not change the height of the body between the transitions) but rotates the hips and turns the feet out, so that they point directly along the length of the body (Figure 344) upon landing with the toes dorsiflexed. The athlete then returns the feet to the starting position, remaining low all the time.

**Figure 343: In and outs:
feet forward**

**Figure 344: In and outs:
feet flared out**

Trunk Rotations

The athlete stands with feet shoulder-width apart and arms fully stretched above the head. From here, they rotate their body around to the left (five rotations) and right (five rotations), keeping the arms straight so that the hands make big circles as they move.

Figure 345: Trunk rotations

Stars

The athlete lies on their front with arms and legs spread out into a star shape. From this position, the athlete raises the left arm and right leg as high as they can and wiggles them up and down through the full range of movement for 10 seconds. This should then be repeated for the opposite arm and leg combination.

Figure 346: Stars top position

Figure 347: Squeeze position

After this has been repeated on each side, the athlete raises both arms and legs together and then squeezes them together as tightly as possible for a count of 10 (Figure 347).

Alternating Squat Thrusts

The athlete starts in the press-up position, with a straight line between shoulders, hips and ankles. It is useful, if possible, for the athlete to have their feet on a line when they are in the press-up position (Figure 348). From here, the athlete pushes the feet forward to a position where they are between the athlete's hands (which stay flat on the floor). In this position, the athlete may be on the balls of the feet, although this is not desirable (Figure 349). From here, the athlete extends back to the start position (making sure the toes reach the line they started on) and from there moves them forward again, but this time to a position where the feet are outside of the hands and are flat on the floor, pointing straight forward (Figure 350). From here, they return to the start position again. This pattern is then repeated.

Figure 348: Squat thrusts start position

Figure 349: Squat thrusts middle position

Figure 350: Squat thrusts wide position

Back Crucifixes

The athlete lies on their front with legs outstretched, feet together and arms at 90° to the body (a crucifix position). The athlete should keep their hands in the same place and their shoulders in contact with the ground, then attempt to rotate their trunk to the rear, touching the left foot to the right hand (Figure 351). This should be done with the ankle in a dorsiflexed position throughout the movement. The coach should ensure that the athlete moves the foot to touch the hand, rather than moving the hand down to make the movement easier. The athlete then returns to the start position and repeats the stretch to the other side.

Figure 351: Back crucifix mid-position

Front Crucifixes

The athlete lies on their back, in the crucifix position, with arms straight out to the side and legs together. Keeping the hands and shoulders in the same position, the athlete alternates between touching left foot to right hand and right foot to left hand.

Figure 352: Front crucifix mid-position

Knee Rolls

The athlete lies on their back, with knees pulled tight into the chest and arms wrapped around the legs, preferably behind the knees to avoid stressing the knee joint. From this position, the athlete rocks backwards and forwards, increasing the range of movement with each roll.

Figure 353: Knee rolls

Disco 1

The athlete stands tall, with feet shoulder-width apart and right arm extended to a position at 90° to the body. Keeping the arm straight out and fully extended, the athlete brings the left knee up to the right elbow, keeping the pelvis in a stationary, neutral position, the abdominal region braced (distance between the belly button and the chest the same) and the ankle dorsiflexed. At the top of the range of movement, the athlete returns the foot to the ground and contacts with an active flat foot. The athlete should repeat to both sides.

Figure 354: Disco 1 mid-position

Disco 2

As with the above exercise, but this time the leg is kept straight and the toe dorsiflexed, whilst it is raised to the right hand.

Figure 355: Disco 2 mid-position

Standing Hamstring Swings

The athlete stands on one leg (holding on to another athlete or a static object for support, if needed), with the pelvis in a neutral position, ankle dorsiflexed and head looking forward. Keeping the upper body stationary, the athlete swings the non-standing leg forwards and backwards, allowing momentum to gradually increase the range of the swinging motion and keeping the swinging leg straight at all times. The drill is repeated on the opposite side.

Figure 356: Standing hamstring swings

Lying Side Leg Raise

The athlete lies on the floor on their side, making sure the body is in a completely straight line. Keeping this straight line, the athlete raises the upper leg vertically. As they do this, the ankle should be dorsiflexed and the heel kept high pointing towards the ceiling. The athlete should imagine they are using the foot to pour water from the toes, so that, as the foot is raised, the toes point downwards – this causes the gluteal muscles to raise the leg, rather than the hip flexor muscles in the groin. This also means the athlete should not lean forwards or backwards during the movement but should remain on their side throughout.

Figure 357: Lying side leg raise

Lying Straight Leg Raise

The athlete lies on their back, with one knee bent to 90°, with the foot flat on the floor. The other leg is straight, with the foot pulled back towards the knee. Keeping the shoulders and hips on the floor and the other leg straight (with the toe dorsiflexed) the athlete lifts the straight leg as high as possible and returns it to the floor. This needs to be repeated on both sides. The exercise can also be done with both legs straight, lifting one at a time in an alternate sequence.

Figure 358: Lying straight leg raise

Press-up to Side Crucifix

The athlete starts in the press-up position, with arms straight and a straight line between the ankles, knees, hips, back and shoulders (Figure 359). The athlete performs a press-up and pushes up onto the left or right side, with the arm straight. The body should remain in a straight line (looking front on, there will now be a straight line between the neck and the space between the legs). There should be no forwards or backwards lean of the body (Figure 360). From here, the athlete raises the arm and leg, pointing them towards the sky (Figure 361). This position should be held for three seconds (although it can be prolonged by the arms and legs being raised and lowed between the two positions shown in Figures 360 and 361 five times) before the athlete returns, under control, to the press-up position, and the exercise is repeated on the other side.

Figure 359: Start position

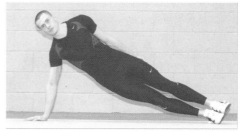

Figure 360: Push off one side into side crucifix

Figure 361: Leg and arm raises

Single-leg Stiff-legged Deadlift

This is a single-leg version of the exercise described in Chapter 4. The athlete stands on one leg, which is slightly bent at the knee (but held stiff in this position throughout the lift). From here, the athlete should brace the trunk musculature, dorsiflex the ankle of the other (non-standing) foot and, (keeping a straight line between the ankle, knee, hip and shoulder of the non-standing foot at all times), reach the heel as far back as possible while leaning the trunk forward (hingeing at the hips). This continues until the upper-body/raised leg are parallel with the floor. During this time, the coach should ensure the athlete's hips and shoulders remain level (horizontally), which may sound easy but many find extremely difficult to do properly. Once the parallel position (Figure 362) has been achieved and held for two seconds, the athlete can return, under control, to the start position.

An advanced version (only to be attempted when the above is mastered) of this is for the athlete, once the midpoint position has been achieved, to rotate the trunk and unsupported leg externally (so the outside of the hip turns towards the sky in this position), maintaining the levelness of the hips and shoulders, and the straight-line position between the trunk and the ankle of the raised leg (Figure 363). From here, the trunk is rotated back to the 'normal' midpoint (Figure 362) and the athlete returns to the start position. This movement should be repeated on both legs.

Figure 362: Single-leg SLDL – midpoint

Figure 363: Single-leg SLDL – advancement of the midpoint position

Standing Groin Swings

The athlete stands on one leg (holding on to a static object for support if needed), with the pelvis in a neutral position, ankle dorsiflexed and head looking forward. Keeping the upper body stationary, the athlete swings the non-standing leg from side to side, across and away from the body, allowing momentum to gradually increase the range of the swinging motion and keeping the swinging leg straight at all times, with the foot level (heel of the swinging leg leading the movement, not the toe). The drill is then repeated to the opposite side.

Figure 364: Standing groin swings

Hip Rotators

This can be performed as a walking exercise, in both a forwards and backwards direction. The athlete starts with their hands resting behind their head and the elbows pointing away from the body. They take a step forward with the left foot, then bring the right foot forwards so the knee of the right foot is brought outwards and as high/close to the right elbow as possible. This is achieved with a rotation movement of the hip joint – the step begins with the foot behind the athlete's body and ends with the foot in front of the athlete's body. Upon landing, the athlete makes the same rotation movement with the left foot. After a number of repetitions, the athlete should undertake the same movement in reverse, rotating each leg in turn from a position in front of the body, to one behind, at the end of the step.

Figure 365: Hip rotators

Sprint Pull-throughs

The athlete stands on one leg (holding on to a static object for support if needed), with the pelvis in a neutral position, ankle dorsiflexed and head looking forward. The athlete lifts the left leg to a high-knee position in front of the body by flexing both the hip and the knee (Figure 366). Then, maintaining the height of the knee and the dorsiflexed position of the ankle, extends the knee to a straight position (Figure 367), and then extends the hip so that the leg is pulled through underneath the body (Figure 368). The active flat foot should contact with the ground just behind the mid-line of the body.

Figure 366: Sprint pull-throughs – high-knee position

Figure 367: Sprint pull-throughs – foot-extended position

Figure 368: Sprint pull-throughs – moving-to-ground-contact position

Walking High-knee Grabs

The athlete should perform a forward and, later, a backward walking action, keeping the trunk upright and the head high. With each step, as the athlete raises the knee, they put their arms around the shins and pull the knee as close to the trunk as possible (while keeping the trunk upright). This position is held briefly, then released, and the foot lands as the athlete steps forward. This action is then repeated with the other leg.

© Danny Moloshok/Action Images/Reuters

Figure 369: Maria Sharapova performs a walking high-knee grab as she warms up for training at the US Open

Butt Kicks

This is a commonly used exercise for developing sprint technique. The athlete moves forward by flicking the heels up to touch the buttocks, driving the knee forward (it should not be done with the knee pointing down towards the floor – this action rarely happens in sport) and contacting with the floor with an active foot. The ankles stay dorsiflexed throughout the movement. At the same time, the athlete drives the arms backwards from the shoulders in a sprint-arm action (opposite arm, opposite leg), with the elbows bent at 90° and hands moving from level with the hips to level with the chin.

Figure 370: Butt kicks

Squats

This is exactly the same exercise as performed in weight training. The athlete's head should be up at all times, chest high and back straight. The knees and hips should flex fully, dropping the buttocks as close to the floor as possible. The feet should remain flat on the floor throughout the movement.

Figure 371: Squats

Low Walks Forward and Backward

The athlete simply walks, with exaggerated steps, 15m forwards and then 15m backwards, but from a squat position. The coach should instruct them to start in a half-squat position and walk as they would be if the ceiling height was set at this level and they could not stand up between steps. The athlete should hold a braced trunk position and maintain a dorsiflexed ankle.

Figure 372: Low walk forward and backward

Skip and Scoop

This is a combination exercise whereby the athlete performs two skips followed by a lunge, in which they scrape the knuckles along the floor as the lunge is performed. Performing this exercise in a forward and backward manner will ensure the lunge movement is performed with alternate legs leading.

Figure 373: Skip

Figure 374: Scoop

Shoulder Swings

This upper-body movement can be combined with a number of different movements, such as the lunges. The athlete keeps the trunk and head upright throughout the movement and rotates straight arms as close to the ears as possible in both a forwards and backwards direction.

Figure 375: Shoulder swings

Arm Throws

This is a two-phase stretch. The athlete keeps the head up and the trunk upright, driving the arms backwards at shoulder height to open up the chest, leading with the elbows (Figure 376). The athlete then returns the arms to the front of the body, keeping them at shoulder height, before driving them back again, this time straightening the arms and leading with the hands (Figure 377).

Figure 376: Arm throws elbows leading

Figure 377: Arm throws hands leading

Other exercises easily incorporated into dynamic flexibility routines include forward and backward skipping variations, plank variations, jumps and medicine ball exercises (see Chapters 4 and 5). Also, there are a number of drills commonly used within speed and agility technique drills, such as fast-feet, wall-drills, kareoka, backpedal and skipping variations (Chapter 6). Other skill-specific or dynamic balance activities can be incorporated into this stage of the training session as well (see Figure 378).

© Action Images

Figure 378: David Beckham prepares for training by warming up his balance mechanisms on a trampet as part of a dynamic warm-up routine

Summary

- The preparation period prior to performances in training and/or competition (the period traditionally known as the warm-up) is very important for the physical conditioning of the athlete.

- Dynamic stretching and mobility movements are highly adaptive to sporting demands and should be used by coaches in the preparation for performance.

- The warm-up presents opportunities to reinforce specifically the movement qualities and technical movement skills of the athlete, as well as preparing the athlete mentally.

- Joint positioning will determine muscle function and the quality of the movements performed in the exercises should be reinforced by the coach at every opportunity: it is not doing the exercises that is important – it is how they are done that makes the difference.

References

Seagrave, L (2007) *Developing speed technique in sports performers,* **sport**scotland four-day workshop for academy coaches, Scotland, May 2007.

Notes page

Notes page

Chapter 8
Developing Flexibility

Introduction

Flexibility refers to the range of movement (ROM) possible around a joint, or a series of joints, in the body. It is important in an athlete, as optimum ranges of movement in the musculoskeletal system can improve an athlete's performance by increasing the range of a joint movement. The greater the ROM, the more situations the athlete will be able to perform a skill in and the more skills they will be able to perform. There is also a possibility (less well proved than is commonly thought) this may also reduce the chances of the athlete getting injured; this is probably because there is less chance of an athlete over-extending a joint or muscle during a movement. ROM is limited by a number of things, some of which can not be directly altered through training, as outlined below:

- **Joint Structure** – Different joints in the body have greater ranges of motion than others, as a joint's structure determines its function and range of movement. Ball-and-socket joints, such as the hip and shoulder, move in all directions, whereas a hinge joint, such as the knee, will only bend and straighten in one direction.

Table 8: The relationship between joint structure and range of movement

Type of Joint	Structure	Example	Normal Movements
Ball and socket	Ball-like head of one bone into the depression of another bone.	• Hip. • Glenohumeral joint in the shoulder.	Three-dimensional: flexion and extension, abduction and adduction, rotation.
Ellipsoidal	Oval-shaped *condyle* fits into the elliptical cavity of another bone.	• Joints between radius, saphoid and lunate bones in the wrist.	Movement in two planes: flexion and extension, abduction and adduction.
Gliding	Flat surfaces rest against each other.	• The *carpal* bones in the hand. • Joint between the *navicular* and *tarsus* bones in the foot.	Movement in two planes: flexion and extension, abduction and adduction.
Hinge	Concave and convex bone surfaces that fit together.	• Elbow (*humeral–ulna*). • Knee (*tibia–femur*). • Ankle (*tibia–talar*).	Flexion and extension in one plane of motion.
Pivot	Rounded or pointed surface articulates with a ring structure formed by a bone or bone and ligament (ie a peg through a hole).	• *Atlas* and *axis* vertebrae in the cervical spine. • Proximal (nearest the body) attachment of the radius and ulna in the arm.	Rotation is the primary movement (eg when turning your arm over, the radius rotates to allow the palm to turn).
Saddle	Convex surface (rider) articulates with concave surface (saddle) of another bone.	The thumb: where the *metacarpal* articulates with the *trapezium* of the hand.	Movement in two planes: flexion and extension, and rotation.

- **Muscle Bulk** – This is demonstrated in some well-muscled performers who can not bend their arms throughout the full range of movement because their bicep muscles get in the way and limit full ROM. This must not be confused with the old wives' tale that the more muscle someone has, the less flexible they are. Many athletes have very large amounts of muscle and are very flexible.

- **Age** – Children are naturally more flexible than adults, although this ability is lost as the child grows towards puberty, unless it is maintained through training. Basically stated, children are at their most flexible very early in life; after that, it is a case of use it or lose it.

- **Gender** – Females tend to be naturally more flexible than males.

- **Activity Level** – The more active a person is, the greater the level of flexibility they would tend to have.

However, the major limiting factor to ROM is the elasticity (the ability to return to resting length after being stretched) and the plasticity (tendency to take on a longer length after a stretch) of the muscle fibres, tendons and ligaments of an athlete. These factors can be positively altered by stretching and by working through a full range of movement when doing weight training and other strength/conditioning exercises.

The Importance of Stretching

Although not as important as thought previously, stretching is the training method that enables flexibility to be developed. Stretching can be used to improve both static and dynamic flexibility. Static flexibility relates to the range of movement possible in a passive movement (ie one that requires no direct muscular action). External forces, such as gravity, a partner, or a machine, provide the force that enables the stretch to take place. Dynamic flexibility relates to the range of joint movement possible during active movements. Dynamic and static stretching methods can be used to improve dynamic and static flexibility, but they also have different uses in the training routine.

Flexibility Training

Stretching is often associated with warming up and cooling down. While it is appropriate that different stretching methods are employed by coaches in preparation for, and immediately following, performance, this is not where flexibility is developed. As one of the fitness variables potentially influential to performance, flexibility should have training sessions devoted to its improvement, through regular stretching sessions that are performed for extended periods of 30–60 minutes.

It is during such times flexibility is permanently increased, although it will be lost if this training is stopped or if the athlete does not continue to perform sport and conditioning skills through the full ranges of movement. As with all adaptations to training, the rule of 'use it or lose it' applies. Recovery, and a further reduction in the incidence of injuries that may occur as the athlete undergoes a rigorous training routine, will be massively aided by such flexibility training sessions. If combined with imagery and visualisation training, and appropriate music, these sessions can be very beneficial for relaxation and refocusing. Such sessions are most successful if undertaken in a quiet room, with appropriate accompanying music and at the same time every day, following a routine developed by the individual. These sessions should last 25–30 minutes and should stretch all of the major muscles.

Figure 379: England player Steven Gerrard performs a full-range static stretch as part of his training programme

Developing a Stretching Routine

Stretching routines should start in the middle of the body to ensure the major muscle groups are mobilised first, thereby allowing for greater potential flexibility in the smaller muscle groups. Therefore, the order of stretching in the routine should be:

- back (torso)
- hips (pelvic region)
- hamstrings
- groin
- quadriceps
- calves, ankles, feet
- shoulders
- arms, wrists
- neck.

Static Stretching

Static or slow stretching is possibly the oldest and the most common stretching technique in use. This involves taking a joint and its associated muscle group(s) to the end or near-end of range and holding the lengthened position as the muscle tension slowly decreases. Stretches should be held at the end position for a time period of between 15–40 seconds, with 2–4 reps completed per stretch. Lengthening a muscle to its ROM and holding it there in a static stretch seems unlikely to produce injury to the soft tissue unless the muscle is overstretched or body positioning is incorrect.

Coaches should take care to avoid prescribing prolonged stretches to experienced athletes who have completed very intense training sessions. Such sessions will normally cause damage to the muscle fibres, which will result in inflammation of these fibres, leading to delayed onset of muscle soreness (DOMS – which will be explored further in Chapter 9). Stretching in such situations may cause this damage (and therefore muscle soreness) to get worse.

Each stretch performed will have a defined beginning and end point. This end point (the position at which the stretch should be finished, or held in a static stretch) is the position at which the athlete feels a definite stretching sensation, but no sharp pains or cramps. If the athlete feels either of these symptoms, it means they have overstretched and the position should immediately be released. When stretching, the athlete should always exhale as they manoeuvre into the stretch.

There are a number of static stretches that can be performed for individual muscle groups, each of which has a number of variations. Those detailed below are considered to be easy, effective and safe methods of static stretching of the major muscle groups used in the majority of sports, although many variations of these can be performed.

Back (Torso)

Lower Back

The athlete lies flat on their back and brings their knees to their chest, with the feet as close to the buttocks as possible. The knees should be drawn towards the chest, as far as possible, by pulling with the arms behind the knees (this avoids hyperflexion of the knee joint). From this position, the athlete exhales and pulls their knees towards their chest, raising the hips off the floor.

Figure 380: Lower-back static stretch

Abdominals and Trunk Stabilisers

The athlete lies on their stomach, with elbows directly below the shoulders and palms flat on the floor (Figure 381). Keeping the hands still and the pelvis in contact with the floor, the athlete straightens the arms until they can go no further (Figure 382). They hold this position, then return to the floor.

Now they reach the left arm around to their left side, keeping the pelvis in the same position and arms bent. Again, the arms are straightened so the body twists to the left and are held at the point where the athlete can not straighten their arm further without moving the pelvis (Figure 383). At this point, the athlete turns their head as far to the left as they can, to stretch the front neck muscles. From here, they return to the start position and repeat to the right.

Figure 381: Start position

Figure 382: Trunk-extended position

Figure 383: Trunk extended and rotated

Upper Back

Begin by kneeling, so there is a 90° angle at the knees and the trunk is upright. Raise both arms straight up in the air, as high as possible (Figure 384). From here, lean forward as far as possible, so the trunk and shoulders are fully extended and the palms of your hands are flat on the floor (Figure 385). From this position, exhale and sit back on your ankles, keeping your hands in the same position on the ground (Figure 386). The stretch should be felt throughout the shoulders and the muscles of the upper back.

Figure 384: Kneeling in the start position

Figure 385: Fall in to the trunk position

Figure 386: Sitting back on to the ankles

Gluteals and Abductors

The athlete sits on the floor with the legs extended and hands slightly behind them, supporting the torso. From here, they cross the left foot over the right leg and slide the heel towards the buttocks as far as possible (keeping the foot flat on the floor). Now, they rotate the trunk to the left as far as possible (looking over the left shoulder), and place the right elbow on the outside of the left knee (Figure 387). From here, the athlete exhales and looks over the left shoulder while rotating the trunk and gently pushing on the left knee with the right elbow, pushing the leg towards the right. They hold this position, then return to the start position and repeat on the other side.

Figure 387: Gluteal and abductor stretch

Hamstring and Hip Flexor Combination Stretches

This sub-routine stretches the hamstring and gluteals, and the hip flexors, including iliopsoas, quadriceps and abdominals.

Phase 1

The athlete kneels on their left knee, with trunk upright. They extend their right leg so the bend at the knee is greater than 90° (but the knee is not straight – this allows the belly of the muscle, rather than the ends, to be stretched). The athlete now points the toes of the right foot towards the floor and turns the foot slightly inwards at the ankle. Keeping their head up and trunk straight at all times (a rounding of the back will change the stretch from a hamstring stretch into a back stretch), the athlete bends forward from the waist (about the lower pelvis), bringing the head as close to the knee as is comfortably possible (Figure 388). The athlete holds this position before returning to the start position.

Phase 2

The athlete returns to the start position (kneeling on the left knee), and raises their left arm straight above their head (or right arm if the left leg is forward). They maintain an upright position, extending the trunk while keeping the left knee anchored to the floor. From here, the pelvis is pushed forward (with no pelvic tilt) to a comfortable end position, then held (see Figure 389).

The athlete then returns to the start position of Phase 1 and extends the right leg further in front. This sequence is repeated 2–3 times for each leg.

The athletes have to make sure the knees and, especially, the feet do not roll inward – the coach should watch for any movement from the centre line. In some individuals, placing a towel or mat under the left knee prevents any soreness to the patella. In Phase 2, the coach should watch for any tilting movements of the pelvis. Ensure the extended knee is kept bent in a wide angle and the hip and trunk are extended in order to stretch the iliopsoas (major hip flexor).

Figure 388: Hamstring stretch   **Figure 389: Hip flexor stretch**

Hamstring and Groin Complex

This stretches the adductors in the groin and the hamstrings at the back of the leg. The athlete sits on the floor, with the legs out straight in front of them. From this position, they bend their left leg out to the side, and place the sole of the left foot against the inner surface of the right thigh (Figure 390). Keeping the head up (this helps to avoid curvature in the lumbar spine), the athlete reaches down the right leg with both hands until a comfortable end position is reached. They hold this position for the appropriate count (15–30 seconds) and then relax.

The legs should then be shaken off and the stretch repeated with the end point pushed a little further down the leg. This should be repeated three times for each leg. The head should be kept up and back straight throughout the movement. The coach should ensure the athlete avoids any bouncing or excessive reaching along the extended leg. If possible, the athlete should pull the toes of the extended leg towards the body, as this allows an athlete to obtain further stretch to the calf muscles.

Figure 390: Hamstring and groin complex stretch

Quadriceps and Hip Flexor Stretch

The athlete kneels on their right knee, with the left foot flat on the floor in front of the knee. Leaning forward, so that there is a diagonal line formed between the right thigh and shoulders, they should keep the back as flat as possible. Keeping the knee and foot positions as they are, the athlete bends the lower part of the right leg up, and catches the toes (or as much of the foot as possible) with the left hand. They pull the lower leg up (towards the buttocks) and across (towards the left) until the end point of the stretch (comfortable stretching sensation) is reached. The stretch should then be repeated with the leg positions reversed.

Figure 391: Quadriceps and hip flexor stretch

Quadriceps

The athlete stands on the left leg, holding on to a wall or other support. Bending the right knee and grasping the ankle from behind with the left hand, the athlete slightly bends the standing (left) leg and pulls the ankle of the bent leg towards the buttocks, keeping the knees together and the pelvis in a neutral position. This should be repeated twice for each leg.

Figure 392: Standing quadriceps stretch – second phase

The next phase of the stretch involves standing on the left leg holding on to a wall or other support. The right knee is bent and grasped at the ankle from behind with the right hand. The stretching action is then repeated.

The coach should make sure the athlete does not allow the knee to drift outward. Athletes should also try to avoid leaning forward or tilting the pelvis, which will increase the lumbar curve in the spine. The spine should be kept as normally straight as possible and, as the leg is pulled back, the abdominals should be contracted to ensure the stretch is lengthened through the knee.

Groin

The athlete lowers themselves into a deep squat position, with feet flat on the floor and wider than shoulder-width apart. Their toes should be turned slightly outwards and the buttocks should be as close to the ankles as possible. From here, the athlete places the palms of their hands flat on the ground, inside the knees, with the elbows resting against the thighs. They exhale and lean forward slightly, pushing outwards with the elbows until a comfortable end point is reached. Putting the elbows against the inside of the knees and clasping the hands together between the legs can also achieve this effect. Keeping the hands together and pulling them upwards and towards the body will increase the stretch on the inner thigh. Using the elbows to provide manual resistance (by pushing them outwards), this can be easily utilised as a proprioceptive neuromuscular facilitation (PNF) stretch (see page 223).

Figure 393: Groin stretch

Crucifix

The athlete lies on their back, in the crucifix position, with arms straight out to the sides and legs together. Keeping the hands and shoulders in the same position, the athlete moves the left leg to touch the right hand, and holds this end position. They then relax and repeat to the other side.

Figure 394: Crucifix

Calves

The athlete stands facing a wall (or other similar support) using the arms for stability. They stand with their right leg in a back position, keeping the knee straight, foot flat and at right angles to the wall, with the heel down (Figure 395). This stretches the gastrocnemius. After holding, the athlete repeats the same stretch, but bends their knee. This targets the soleus (smaller, deeper calf muscle) (Figure 396). The opposite forward leg is relaxed and slightly bent. After positioning the feet, the athlete should lean forward, bending the elbows and keeping the hips in line with the shoulders. This should increase dorsiflexion of the rear ankle. The coach should pay particular attention to the heel and hip position making sure the athlete's weight is pushed forward and downward.

Figure 395: The straight-leg gastrocnemius stretch

Figure 396: Bent-leg soleus stretch

Achilles Tendon

Kneeling on both knees, with the buttocks resting on the ankles, the athlete raises their right knee, so the foot comes forward into a position where the instep of the foot is next to the left knee, with the foot remaining flat on the floor. The athlete exhales and leans forward, pushing the knee forward and simultaneously sinking the body weight back onto the ankles (dropping the bottom towards the heel). The foot must be kept flat on the floor at all times if the athlete is to feel a stretching sensation in the Achilles tendon and lower calf muscle.

Figure 397: Achilles tendon stretch

Chest

The athlete stands in a doorway, at an external corner, or uses a partner standing behind them as a foundation to support the arm just inside the elbows, which should be flexed to 90°. The athlete keeps the elbow at shoulder height, with the forearm pointing straight up and held flat against the support (wall/doorway/partner). From here, they exhale and lean forward so the arm is supporting the body weight. This will particularly stretch the sternum (breastbone) and shoulder insertions of the pectoral (chest) muscles, which are vital in many pushing and ripping motions in sports.

Figure 398: Chest stretch front view using a partner

Figure 399: Chest stretch (rear view)

Shoulders

The athlete sits or stands, and moves one arm across in front of their body, keeping the palm facing forward and the arm at shoulder height. They now bend the other hand underneath this arm, at a position slightly above the elbow and, as they exhale, they pull the elbow across the body, while keeping the trunk facing forward. After holding at the appropriate point, they repeat the stretch with their arm rotated so that the palm faces towards the body.

Figure 400: Palm facing away from the body

Figure 401: Palm facing towards the body

Triceps and Latissimus Dorsi (Lats) – Back

The athlete stands with one arm raised overhead, as close to the ear as possible and flexed at the elbow, so the hand is resting behind them, on the opposite shoulder blade. With the other hand, the athlete grasps the outside of the flexed elbow, exhales and pulls the elbow behind the head to an appropriate hold position. The coach must ensure the trunk is kept upright throughout the stretch.

Figure 402: Stretching the lats and triceps

Trapezius (Upper Back) and Neck

The athlete stands with the feet shoulder-width apart and reaches their left hand across their back (with the palm facing away from the body). From here, they reach across the body, so that they can hold their left wrist with their right hand. They keep looking forward and, without raising their right shoulder, tilt their head as if trying to touch their right ear to their right shoulder. This should be held at the appropriate position, then relaxed and repeated with the right hand behind them.

Figure 403: Trapezius stretch

Proprioceptive Neuromuscular Facilitation Stretching (PNF)

This form of stretch typically involves a partner, although there are ways to do PNF stretching without one. While there are a number of different PNF techniques currently in use, a sensible one to use is the contract–relax (CR) method. This involves taking a muscle to a comfortable end-of-range position (assisted by a partner or manual resistance), actively contracting the muscle, then relaxing the muscle. As the muscle is relaxed, the end-of-range position is increased until a newer, comfortable end position is reached. This sequence of contract-relax-stretch should be continued four times per muscle group, with the first 20 second contraction being at 50% maximum, the second at 60%, the third at 75% and the final position should be held by the partner (or whatever manual resistance is being employed), with no active muscular contraction.

For example, a hamstring stretch (see Figure 404). The muscle is first taken to its lengthened end-of-range position. The athlete pushes against the partner's resistance to produce a 50% contraction in the hamstring muscles (50% attempt to move the leg toward the floor during the push phase) as the partner opposes the contraction. This position is held for 20 seconds, at which time the hamstring muscles relax while the partner increases passive pressure to further increase the ROM. The sequence is then repeated three times, as described above.

Figure 404: Hamstring PNF stretch

This type of stretching also helps to develop strength throughout the range of joint motion. However, it should only be used when the coach has experience of the technique and the athlete is able to understand how to communicate when an end position has been reached and is also able to control muscular contractions of differing strengths. PNF stretching can also leave an athlete with some slight delayed onset of muscular soreness (DOMS), caused by micro-traumas that can develop within the muscle fibres. Coaches should therefore take care with the use of PNF within the overall training programme if the techniques are to be used effectively.

Summary

- Flexibility refers to the range of movement possible around a joint. It is a beneficial quality for athletes to have, because the greater the range of movement an athlete has, the more options for performing a skill they will be able to carry out.

- The best ways to improve flexibility are to train strength and skills through a full range of movement and utilise flexibility-training sessions as part of the training programme.

- Static stretching should not be used as part of a warm-up (ie prior to training or playing) as it could be detrimental to the athlete's ability to produce power. Static stretching is ideal for use in cool-downs (following training and playing) and in flexibility-training sessions. Care should be taken not to overstretch at this stage, as this will cause increased muscle fibre damage.

- Static stretches should be taken to a comfortable end-of-range position (where the athlete feels a comfortable stretching sensation but no pain) and held for 20–30 seconds before being released.

Further Reading

Alter, M.J. (2005) *Sport Stretch: 311 Stretches for Sports*. Illinois: Human Kinetics. ISBN: 978-0-880118-23-1.

Pearson, A. (2003) *Dynamic Flexibility: Warming Up on the Move*. A and C Black. ISBN: 978-0-713664-52-2.*

* Available from Coachwise 1st4sport. For a full range of sports education and training equipment, please visit www.1st4sport.com or call 0113-201 5555

Notes page

Chapter 9
Recovery Training for Optimal Performance

Introduction

The goal of any training programme is to maximise fitness and minimise fatigue. For coaches of all levels, whether working with full-time athletes who train every day, semi-professional performers who train together twice a week but undertake their own fitness work, or amateur athletes who train once or twice a week, it is still important to have athletes who are training and performing at optimum capability. Much of the emphasis on training relates to maximising the physical, psychological, technical, tactical and environmental variables that underpin performance. However, the model for ongoing best performance is derived from the following equation:

Optimal Work in Training/Performance + Optimal Recovery from Training/Match + Adaptation to the training stimulus = Optimal Performance

The basis for this equation can be seen in the overcompensation cycle, highlighted in Chapter 1. How many coaches can say they put as much emphasis on their performer's recovery as they do the training? In any environment involving multiple training and playing scenarios, whether with adult athletes, children in schools or competing on a competitive schedule, there is a need to facilitate an active recovery programme into the performers' schedule. Indeed, the US Olympic Committee views recovery as being so important for its athletes that a full-time dedicated facility (The Recovery Centre) was incorporated into the Training Camp facility in Colorado Springs.

The aim of this chapter is to introduce some practical mechanisms coaches may wish to utilise in their routines, in order to achieve optimal recovery.

Short-term Consequences of Training

Assuming the athlete does not train too hard/heavily[28] in a session, the most common consequence of training is muscle soreness. Delayed onset of muscle soreness (DOMS) – also known as induced muscle damage – is experienced. As the latter name suggests, this is caused by microscopic muscle damage and is associated with symptoms such as swelling, soreness and restricted range of motion for up to 48 hours[29]. There is also a significant drop-off in performance capacity – often for up to four days when there is no aided recovery – with athletes typically reporting a lower daily self-rating of wellness the day after a game. This four-day period is also associated with a higher incidence of cough and cold symptoms.

Long-term Consequences of Overtraining/Under-recovery

If an athlete progressively trains when they have not appropriately recovered from a bout of previous training (Figure 405), the athlete is liable to develop symptoms associated with overtraining/under-recovery syndrome. The theory underpinning the appropriate time to train is explained in the overcompensation cycle model section on page 244.

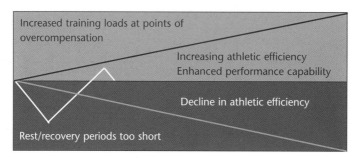

Figure 405: Cumulative effects of training

The symptoms associated with overtraining are multi-faceted and sometimes contradictory. For example, many athletes report an accelerated resting heart rate, while others experience the opposite – a suppressed resting heart rate. One of the most obvious indicators is an unexplained decrease in performance, which is often problematic, as the coach's remedy for this is often to make the performer train harder, making the problem worse. Other common physical indicators include, a sudden loss in body mass and a loss of appetite or change in eating habits. Sleep patterns can also become disrupted, with athletes either not getting sufficient sleep because the athlete experiences disturbed sleep or, conversely, the athlete's sleeping time far exceeds the normal requirement[30].

The coach can also look for signs and symptoms when dealing directly with athletes. Often, overtrained athletes will complain their legs feel tired, heavy or sore, or they do not feel good (although the coach must know the athletes well enough to make sure this is not a sign of them being lazy or simply complaining, as performers sometimes like to do). An athlete's body language can also be observed to indicate cumulative fatigue. A slumped posture about the shoulders, languid facial expression and pale colouring, washed-out eye colouring, bending over to recover from efforts and unexplained bad technique may all be indicators of cumulative fatigue. However, these may be indicators of other psychosocial problems as well, so again, the coach needs to know the athletes well.

Psychological indicators are also important. As mentioned previously, look for low-motivation levels in previously well-motivated athletes, poor concentration, a lack of self-confidence and unexplained levels of aggression. Performers may also experience increases in the number of colds, coughs and other illnesses, due to suppression of the immune system resulting from excessive stress, and/or overuse injuries caused by excessive or maladapted biomechanical loading.

Monitoring Training Status

As generally accepted good practice, athletes have been encouraged to keep training diaries for a number of years now. These are invaluable aids in recording and monitoring training progress and providing data that can be used to set goals. Wellness diaries work on a similar principle. These diaries are simply designed to record the variables closely associated with under-recovery, that is, workload, resting heart rate, body mass, sleep patterns, nutritional status and attitude towards/energy for training. While this seems like a lot of data for a performer to collect on a daily basis, the diaries can range from very detailed records to very simple and easy-to-complete sheets that use Likert scales[31] for straightforwardness. Table 9 shows some example variables and typical Likert scales of response.

Table 9: Example data categories for a wellness diary

Variable	Example Measurement
Workload	*Heavy/moderate/light*
Resting heart rate	*Insert recorded figure (bpm)*
Body mass	*Insert recorded figure (kg)*
Sleep	*No. of hours: excellent/good/average/poor*
Daily nutrition	*Excellent/good/average/poor*
Attitude to training/energy for training	☺ ☻ ☹

For example, feeling tired the day after a game or tournament is understandable, but if an athlete feels lethargic for several days, this may be indicative of a problem. Similarly, while recording body mass will not indicate the body composition of the athlete, a sudden drop in body mass (ie more than 4%) may indicate a potential problem.

Body mass should be recorded after rising and going to the toilet in the morning, but before breakfast. Resting pulse should be taken a couple of minutes after waking (assuming you are not awoken with a start) and prior to rising. Differences of more than 20% above normal are indicative of a potential problem.

Sustained changes in any combination of these areas should be considered as possibly being indicative of a problem by the coach. **A combination of sustained increased resting heart rate and loss of body mass should definitely be investigated by the coach, to ascertain the state of the athlete.**

Post-performance Recovery

As soon as the final whistle goes in a match or training session, the athlete should begin the recovery process. The initial phase becomes the post-event cool-down. This is the hardest part of the session for the coach to enforce, as the interesting part of the day has now been completed and many athletes now want to unwind and enjoy things away from the pitch.

There have been many recommended guidelines on how to structure a cool-down and how long it should last for. As a minimum, athletes need to walk or move lightly for 4–5 minutes after the performance, followed by a period of stretching the major muscles while they are warm. The walking helps to alleviate blood pooling: during exercise, the heart is aided in pumping the blood to the working muscles and back to the heart by the muscular actions in the legs creating a pumping effect. Upon cessation of exercise, this pumping mechanism ceases, often resulting in a volume of blood pooling in the legs. This can cause an athlete to feel dizzy and possibly faint, due to a lack of blood in the head. Blood pooling also prevents the effective removal of metabolic waste products from the muscles that have been working in training.

Static stretching (refer to guidelines in Chapter 8) at this time should be restricted to the major muscles of the body, although this should not necessarily be taken to the end-of-range position, as this may induce further micro-tears to the muscle. The benefits of stretching immediately after performing are that it allows the muscle tension to be decreased and also increases the speed of neural innervations to the muscles, thus allowing the recovery process to be hastened further.

© Eddie Keogh/Action Images/Reuters

Figure 406: England football players gently stretch following a training session during the 2006 World Cup

Too much emphasis should not be placed on stretching at this time, however, as this will have little benefit in the long term and will almost certainly not be carried out with the necessary discipline, due to the athlete's frame of mind. There is a perpetuated myth that cool-down stretches are an ideal time to permanently increase the length of the muscles, as they are being stretched when the muscle is at its most elastic. However, there is much evidence to support an argument against this, due to the small amount of time an athlete will effectively spend stretching in this period. More appropriately, the athlete should undertake flexibility-training sessions during the week to achieve this aim, as discussed in Chapter 8.

Ice Baths and Contrast Bathing

We are all familiar with the energised/bracing feeling we have when we go from a warm environment into a very cold one. This is due to the brain having to recognise and respond to signals from two sources of information (ie the hot and the cold), resulting in the increased feeling of stimulation. Contrast bathing works on a very similar principle (with continuous alteration between the temperature extremes) and can be achieved through the use of either a shower or a spa and plunge pool arrangement.

This treatment also serves to increase blood flow to the worked muscles and is therefore beneficial in removing the metabolic by-products of exercise, thus allowing athletes to recover more quickly from high-intensity training.

The other benefit of this form of regeneration is that it requires a minimum amount of time, using facilities readily available in any sports club, training facility or hotel tour venue. After showering the skin clean, athletes should step into a warm (35–37°C) shower or spa/bath for two minutes or four minutes respectively. Pressure from high water jets and power-shower nozzles has been demonstrated to aid muscle relaxation and considerably reduce DOMS in athletes. The temptation to stay in the warm environment must, however, be avoided, as this can offset the benefits of the treatment and possibly lead to dehydration and neural fatigue. After the appropriate time, the athlete should then enter a cold (10–14°C) shower for 20–30 seconds or bath/plunge pool for 30–60 seconds, before returning to the warm environment. This process should be repeated three times for optimal efficiency. If the training facility does not have cold showers or a plunge pool, the same effect can easily be achieved by filling a portable paddling pool or a wheelie-bin with iced water for the athletes to immerse themselves in.

Similarly, submerging the body in an ice bath for a period of 4–10 minutes, without the contrast effect, has been demonstrated to have an extremely beneficial effect aiding recovery after extremely physical performances. The water should be between 4–10°C for this to have the desired effect and, even if the total body is not submerged for the entire period of time, having the legs, hips and trunk submerged (large muscle groups that perform significant amounts of work during most sports training/competition performances) is often sufficient.

Indeed, it is not recommended that the neck is subjected to this nature of immersion at all: ice packs can be used to work on the shoulders if needed.

Figure 407: Members of Scotland's back line stand in ice tubs to aid recovery, a day after the team's first Rugby World Cup match Finals, 2007

Rehydration

Water is essential to normal body function and elite athletes should be drinking more than four litres of fluid every day, even in temperate climates. This obviously increases in much warmer weather. Research has indicated that 5% dehydration can lead to a performance decrement of up to 20%. During exercise, the major cause of water loss from the body is through sweat. If a coach is unsure how much water a performer can lose during a training session (which will obviously be influenced by environmental conditions), they should weigh their athletes before and after training (remembering to remove wet and sweaty clothing). One kilogram lost equates to one litre of fluid that must be replaced with water as quickly as possible after the performance. However, the athlete must be careful to avoid drinking too much, too quickly to replace fluid lost, as they can rapidly develop *hyponatremia* (an over-dilution of the blood sodium levels) and this causes the athlete to become water intoxicated (eg one international rugby athlete who suffered from this drank six litres in one hour after a game in a warm environment). The condition only rights itself, given a normally functioning kidney, after several unpleasant hours.

Water lost through sweat must be replaced, both during and immediately after matches and training, and athletes should be practised in both. Indeed, during performances, keeping hydrated is more important than supplying fuel to the muscles in any performance lasting less than three hours. Careful consideration should be given to the drink coaches supply to athletes during training. Drinks that are too concentrated will slow the process of water absorption from the gut into the body, and will consequently contribute to any dehydration effect. The drink should be diluted to between 4–6ml of glucose/maltodextrin/electrolyte per 100ml of water. If the coach is unsure of the concentration of a sports drink, remember water is a much better option than a cordial mixed too strongly. Following a game, drinking high-energy drinks containing glucose, sucrose or maltodextrins in concentrations of 6ml:100ml can help to achieve both the rehydration and carbohydrate replenishment needs of the athlete.

It should be realised the body's warning mechanism of dehydration is the feeling of thirst. Please note that feeling thirsty means an athlete is already dehydrated and has not been drinking enough. Prevention is, however, better than cure, and so ongoing monitoring of hydrated status is necessary. A good indicator of athletes' hydration status is their urine: it should be clear and odourless, and passed every couple of hours. Coaches can obtain charts performers can use to monitor their hydration status when passing water.

Figure 408: Rehydration during and after training/competition is vital to ensure performance and adequate recovery

Refuelling

Coaches should also ensure that, during this period immediately following exercise, athletes are not only rehydrated, but the muscle glycogen stores (the muscle carbohydrate energy supply), which become depleted by exercise, are re-stocked. Following intense exercise, there is a window of up to two hours when the body is optimally adjusted to replenish muscular glycogen stores. For this reason, athletes should aim to have one gram of carbohydrate per kilogram body mass (or at least 50g, eg two large bananas) during this time period. The same should be consumed for every subsequent two-hour period, until a full meal is eaten. Proteins should also be consumed at this time, to aid the rebuilding process in the muscles.

Alcohol

Many sports performers have traditionally enjoyed an alcoholic drink after performing. However, alcohol delays the recovery process significantly. Firstly, it promotes dehydration, as it suppresses the secretion of anti-diuretic hormones, resulting in an increased volume of urine production, leaving blood-plasma volume significantly decreased. Secondly, alcohol has a depressive effect on central nervous system activity, dulling the pain sensation from any injuries picked up during a previous game/performance[32]. The depressant effect on the neurological stimulation to the muscle, coupled with the effect of dehydration upon the muscle cells, means that alcohol can retard the recovery process at a significant rate. A general rule for a performer to follow is to drink alcohol in moderation and to not have any alcohol until rehydrated enough to urinate following the performance.

It should be remembered that excess alcohol has secondary effects not conducive to optimal recovery, such as poor or disturbed sleep, impaired immune function through developed fatigue, or maybe even psychological disturbances relating to anxiety from memory loss.

Regeneration the Day after the Game

Swimming Pool Regeneration

The use of water as a healing medium can be traced as far back as 2400 BC in the proto-Indian culture. This is supported by much scientific evidence relating to the physical properties and fluid dynamics of water. When a body is fully or partially immersed in water, it experiences an upward thrust equal to the weight of the water displaced. This means many activities, such as running, can be undertaken in water while not being subject to impact loading caused by ground reactions forces. There is also an accrued psychological benefit, as the feeling of weightlessness associated with suspension in the water can be linked to psychological relaxation strategies, such as visualisation, to enhance the regeneration effect. Hydrostatic pressure is also exerted equally on all surfaces of an immobilised object and this pressure increases with the depth of the water. For example, if an individual is standing in a four-foot deep pool, the pressure of the water at their foot would be roughly four times greater than the pressure at the surface. This pressure would be approximately double that exerted by a standard elastic bandage, and so it not only helps to reduce swelling and fluid gathering at the site of injuries, but also has a massaging effect on the immersed muscles.

Table 10 details an example of a swimming pool regeneration session for use with athletes the day after a performance. This is designed to keep the athletes moving and to stretch all of the major muscles and joints during a 15-min session in a pool without a depth gradient (1.2m is a standard for such pools).

© Action Images/Reuters

Figure 409: Brazilian football players take part in a stretching session in a swimming pool during the Copa America tournament in Venezuela, 2007

Aqua-jogging belts, which fit around the waist and enable the athlete to remain upright and run/walk around in deep water, are ideal for use in regeneration sessions in deeper water, where activities such as jogging, arms-only punching and treading water could all be utilised in an aided capacity. The number of activities that could be introduced into such sessions is limitless. It is often beneficial to use such training sessions for other purposes, such as team-building exercises or fun activities (eg aqua-aerobics or relay-running events) that provide a distraction from the routines of training but also ensure that the performers have a regeneration session in the pool. Such sessions become particularly important during tournaments, or on tour, when the need for pool and regeneration work is great but the sessions need constant variety in order to maintain the athletes' interest.

Table 10: Example of a pool session designed to facilitate recovery between training sessions

Exercise	Duration (seconds)	Notes
Slow walking (backwards and forwards)	60	–
Loose-arms skipping and jumping	60	–
Hip rotators forwards*	60	Hands on head, bring knees up to touch elbows and land foot in front of body. Repeat with other leg. Pelvis to remain neutral throughout. A slow movement to emphasise stretch.
Hip rotators backwards*	60	Pelvis to remain neutral throughout. A slow movement to emphasise stretch.
Jogging (backwards and forwards)	60	–
Straight-leg swings: front–back	2 x 30 each leg	Maintain an upright trunk. Hold partner or poolside for support.
On back, breaststroke legs	60	Arms loose by the side.
Breaststroke, arms only	60	Leg buoy will aid body position in water.
Front crawl at 70% pace	60	–
Backstroke, arms only	60	Full stretch of shoulders and full range of motion.
Backstroke, legs only	60	Straight-leg kick from the hip.
Push and glide	3 reps	Glide through water as far as possible. Feel tension leaving body.
Star float	60	Switch off from session.

*see page 204

Power Naps

Everyone has a daily biorhythm (body clock) regulated by a number of things, including the chemical melatonin. This chemical reinforces the drive to sleep in a human being. Everyone has experienced times during the day when our body clock makes us feel sleepy, and there are many events in an athlete's week, such as a heavy training schedule, or lots of travelling, that can affect this body clock. Power naps (10–15 minutes) are an ideal way to quickly recharge the batteries and reset the body clock of the athlete during such times. They should not last any longer than 15 minutes, however, as this can result in an increased level of melatonin, with the knock-on effect that the athlete's afternoon activities and normal night-time sleep patterns may be disrupted.

Relaxation Techniques

Psychological Relaxation

To try to separate psychological relaxation techniques from other regeneration methods is something of a faux pas, as these techniques are often best employed in conjunction with other active techniques – for example, during stretching routines. However, such techniques are often, as with most skills, initially best learned in isolation and progressively integrated into training as the athlete becomes more adept at the skill. Such techniques are excellent ways of controlling the anxieties and pressures that build up in a performer in the competitive environment. These techniques can either be body to mind (usually used when the symptoms are of a physical nature) or mind to body, which are usually used when the symptoms are manifested cognitively.

Relaxation, as with all mental skills, is something that needs to be practised and worked at. Relaxing in a silent room in your own home is very different from relaxing in the face of competition. The athlete needs to be able to make the transition from one environment to the other if they are to attain immediate activation control in any environment. The most basic body-to-mind technique is known as progressive muscular relaxation. This involves maximally tensing a muscle group and then focusing on maximally relaxing that muscle. This will enable the performer to distinguish between tension and relaxation in a given muscle. They should learn to be able to do this in a relaxed environment, but also progressively, under increased environmental stresses. Ultimately, the aim is to be able to quickly scan the muscles of the body to identify areas of undue tension important for impending performance and to quickly focus on relaxing those individual muscles in the middle of the game. For example, scanning the body for those muscles important in kicking and relaxing those that are tense prior to place kicking in rugby, serving in tennis or taking a free throw in basketball.

Breathing techniques are also beneficial. Athletes should take a deep breath in through the nose, for a slow count of five, and then completely exhale through the mouth, to a slow count of eight. As athletes become familiar with the timing, they should repeat the mantra relax as they inhale and exhale, feeling the tension leaving their body as they do this. Once athletes are able to do this in a quiet environment, they should practise relaxing under conditions/in environments that are progressively more stressful.

Cognitive relaxation techniques normally utilise the skill of imagery. Imagery, or visualisation, is a psychological skill that must be progressively developed from simple beginnings to advanced levels, but it is not purely about the athlete seeing pictures of performances in their heads. It should be a polysensory experience (utilising all the senses), where performers can see what is occurring, hear the noises they would expect to be around them, sense the environment, smell the smells, feel the same sensations/emotions as they would do if they were actually in the place they were picturing. The basic images to visualise are those that invoke a feeling of warmth and heaviness within the body, effortless actions, repetitive and relaxing sounds, etc. Good examples include lying on a beach, in the warm sand, feeling the sun on the back, listening to the repetitive sound of the waves lapping onto the shore.

Most meditation techniques have a basis in such imagery. However, in order for such techniques to be effective, athletes need to be in a comfortable position, in a warm and relaxed environment, and they have to have a passive attitude, which will allow thoughts to flow through the mind freely. Coupled with music and a comfortable environment, such relaxation techniques are ideal ways to end the day before going to bed, allowing the athlete to switch off from the pressures of the day and encourage restful sleep. This is important, as sleepless nights are definitely detrimental to efficient regeneration.

Relaxation Guidelines

Key points for athletes to follow before starting relaxation:

- Get into as comfortable a position as possible. Generally, it helps to loosen any tight clothing and keep your arms and legs slightly bent, not crossed or straight.
- Adjust the lighting in the room so that it is comfortable. Usually, relaxation works best in dark or dimly lit rooms.
- If anything about the relaxation process makes you uncomfortable, either physically or mentally, eliminate that component from your relaxation routine.
- When tensing your muscles, remember to inhale deeply and slowly (4–5 seconds). When you exhale say the word, 'calm' or 'relax' to yourself and relax completely. Over time, you will begin to associate the word you choose with the feeling of relaxation.
- Concentrate on the difference between tension and relaxation. Ensure you spend approximately twice as much time relaxing each muscle group as the time spent tensing them.

The Relaxation Process

- Get yourself into a comfortable position – ie on the floor, a couch, bed, etc and close your eyes.
- Concentrate on your breathing – inhale slowly (for 4–5 seconds) through your nose 20 times. Exhale slowly through the mouth.
- When you exhale, think of your cue word (eg calm or relax).
- Start by contracting your face muscles. Squinting and biting down hard with your teeth will help you to do this. Remember to inhale deeply. Then relax and repeat your cue word to yourself. Repeat this three times.
- Next, contract your neck muscles by making your neck as long as it will go. Remember to inhale deeply when you do this. Hold for 4–5 seconds and then relax, repeating your cue word to yourself. Repeat this three times.
- Contract your shoulder muscles (raise shoulders) on inhalation. Relax by lowering your shoulders on exhalation. Remember to repeat your cue word. Repeat this three times.
- Make two fists on inhaling, relax on exhaling. Repeat this three times.
- Contract your finger muscles (spread the fingers) on inhaling, relax on exhaling. Repeat this three times.
- Contract your stomach muscles on inhaling, relax on exhaling. Repeat this three times.
- Contract your quadriceps muscles on inhaling, relax on exhaling. Repeat this three times.
- Contract your calf muscles (point the toes towards your head) on inhaling, relax on exhaling. Repeat this three times.
- Contract your feet (push the toes forward) on inhaling, relax on exhaling. Repeat this three times.
- Concentrate on breathing again. Inhaling and exhaling 5–7 times.
- Visualise a staircase. Go down each step, one at a time, getting more relaxed the further down the staircase you go.
- When you reach the bottom of the stairs, visualise the most comfortable place for you – specific, detailed, vivid images are important. What are you doing? Who is there? What colours do you see? What do you hear? What do you smell? Take some time to build and enjoy this scene.
- When you are comfortable, visualise yourself being successful (practising shots or during a match).
- Relax in your scene for 2–3 minutes – remember to concentrate on your breathing.

- When you are ready, begin to climb the staircase slowly. When you reach the top, open your eyes slowly.
- With your eyes open, concentrate on your breathing five more times.
- Start to move your limbs slowly.

Stretching-training Sessions

As previously noted, flexibility training (specific sessions built around stretching routines) should be performed at least every other day in an athlete who is training 2–4 times per week. It is during such times that flexibility is permanently increased (although it will be lost if you stop this training), rather than during the warm-up (where dynamic stretches should be performed) and cool down, as commonly thought. The benefits of stretching–training sessions are well documented and include decreased muscular tension, improved body-position awareness, decreased risk of injury problems occurring with antagonistic (opposite) and synergistic (assistor) muscle pairs. If combined with imagery and visualisation training, and relaxing music, these sessions can be very beneficial for relaxation and refocusing. Such sessions (which should last for 20–30 minutes) are most successful if undertaken in a quiet room, with appropriate accompanying music (obviously the choice of the individual) and at the same time every day.

Massage

Many sports performers are realising the benefits of employing a consultant masseur to work on them during a training week. This is because massage can be used for the general relaxation of the musculoskeletal system and is recognised as the best treatment for muscle tension, which develops as either an acute effect from overreaching in a session or a chronic/cumulative side-effect of daily training. Massage also has the distinct advantage over many therapies in that, as well as being a general remedy; the treatment can also be directed into specific, local problem areas, thereby improving recovery. Indeed, with specific injuries, the skilled practitioner can explore the soft tissue more intimately than in any other therapy and problems can be diagnosed and treated very accurately. Massage is a very adaptable regeneration aid, with treatments and techniques uniquely adapted to the specific needs of an athlete at any given time.
For example:

- Fractioning techniques have warming effects beneficial to the pliability of the soft tissues and improve cell metabolism.
- Jostling/shaking techniques have been demonstrated to benefit the peripheral nervous system.
- Deep-tissue fractioning can be used to break down the scar tissue that develops within muscles as a result of repetitive micro-trauma.
- Deep massage has a pumping effect on the blood within the veins and arteries, improving the micro-circulation within the treated muscle.

Other benefits include improved tissue elasticity, pain reduction through the removal of metabolic by-products, the release of endorphins and increased tissue permeability of the muscle-cell membranes to oxygen-saturated fluids. When the massage treatment is applied to a large area of the body, there is a substantial psychological benefit in terms of general relaxation and this is associated with improved sleep patterns and reduced psychological and physical stress.

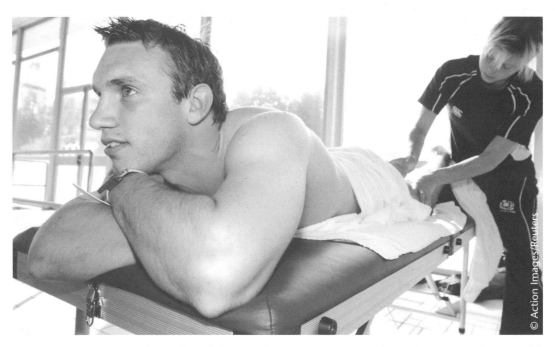

© Action Images/Reuters

Figure 410: Scotland's Mike Blair receives a massage a day after a Rugby World Cup 2007 match

Summary

- Actively promoting the recovery of an athlete following a game or training session is vital in order to ensure they are playing and training with optimal intensity. This principle should apply whether a performer is an amateur, semi-professional or full-time athlete. The heavier the training commitment an athlete of any age has, the more important the recovery strategy becomes.

- The monitoring of training load and the effects of training is a key skill the coach should work with their performer to develop. Wellness diaries are a simple and effective tool for this.

- Nutrition and rehydration are components that underpin the maintenance of an athlete's performance status.

- Swimming pool work, static stretching and massage therapy are all methods a coach can employ to aid the athlete's recovery. Variation in the programme is something the coach should consider in order to keep athletes motivated and interested in the developing programme.

- Psychological relaxation techniques should be learned in isolation and introduced into other practical recovery sessions in order for them to be maximally effective.

Chapter 10
Planning for Peak Performance

Introduction

The coaching process is recognised across sports as comprising the following stages:

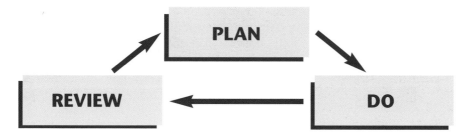

Figure 411: Plan, do, review

Planning is about deciding what objectives you want your athletes to be able to achieve at any particular time. Once you, as the coach, have determined what objectives you wish to achieve, you can begin to identify what methods are best suited to achieving each particular objective.

This is a key concept that is often forgotten at many levels of coaching: **objectives determine methods**.

Periodisation is the organised division of the overall training programme into periods that accomplish a range of differing, yet cumulative, goals. Periodisation of a competitive programme can be for the athlete's career a four-year (quadrennial) plan (eg for Olympic preparation) or an annual plan. According to the theories popularised over the last 20 years, the annual plan is traditionally organised into preparation (pre-season), competition and transition phases (close/off season, active recovery).

Periodisation is the planned variation in training methods on a cyclic or periodic basis. The basic goals are to exploit complimentary training effects at optimal times, manage fatigue and prevent stagnation or overtraining. This involves long-term, intermediate and short-term planning.

Peaking is the manipulation of training variables to maximise potential for attainment of the required performance at the required time.

There are four training cycles used to aid in the planning of the competitive year (Bompa, 1999), as listed below and outlined in more detail in the following sections:

- **Macrocycle**: Usually an annual plan of repeated (yet modified) cycles in the long-term training plan. The end point of the macrocycle is the major competition you are preparing for. The start of the macrocycle is the point at which you begin to train for this major competition. The macrocycle is made up of periods and phases (see below), each of which has a specific emphasis or objective.
- **Mesocycle**: A three to six-week block of training with defined objectives. These will build upon the objectives set in the previous mesocycle and, by achieving these objectives, the athletes will be prepared for the mesocycle that will follow.
- **Microcycle**: Briefer periods of time, usually consisting of one-week training blocks.
- **Training Session**: Individual block of training in pursuit of a training objective.

Many people have argued this method of periodisation does not apply in real life, as things have moved on since the early introduction of the classic periodisation models. This is because many athletes now compete all-year round, with many points in time where they need to be able to maximise competitive potential. Some examples from top-level sport might include a:

- football athlete, who has to play in league, FA Cup, League Cup, European and international matches, all of which are important to the club
- tennis athlete, whose world ranking is based upon performing well in tournaments, with entry to the more exclusive tournaments being limited to athletes of a certain rank
- track and field athlete who has to achieve successive personal bests in home nation championships and British championships to qualify for international events, where the expectation is for another personal best to be performed.

However, while it is easy to say this is absolutely true at the top levels, the same basic principles of planning apply. There are certain times where different emphasis is placed upon the training (remembering the earlier emphasis that strength training and aerobic endurance training interfere with each other). Therefore, train for one, then the other (different mesocycles). Even within an individual microcycle, this will still apply. Some days will have one emphasis, others will have another. So, while on the face of it people may say, 'that doesn't apply to me', the same basic principles will need to be considered and worked through, even if the time frames are different.

The process outlined within this chapter is based upon the manipulation of training variables within time-defined parameters, to achieve the planned objectives. It is a process that can be applied to any stage of an athlete's career, in any sport, even if the athlete is not preparing for target competition(s), it is still important for the coach to plan a progressive programme, based around periods of different training emphasis.

The goal of an effectively planned programme is to maximise training adaptations (general and sports specific) so as to elevate (or in team sports, maintain) performance potential at specific times. This also means the potential for overtraining has to be effectively reduced through the planned programme as well. Variation in the programme comes through manipulation of a number of variables. The role for the coach is to determine how much variation is needed. Too much and the athlete will not be able to adapt to a specific training stimulus (the body will not learn from enough repetition). Too little variation and the body will overlearn the response to the training stimulus and will not be overloaded sufficiently to cause adaptation. Balancing these two considerations is something coaches need to learn to do.

Training variables that can be manipulated:

- **Choice of exercise – Training mode and movement characteristics**
- **Order of exercise:**
  - Keeping the same exercises, the order of exercises can be manipulated t achieve specific objectives
  - Fastest exercises first
  - Exercises involving the largest number of joints first
  - Complexing (strength exercises followed by explosive exercises. The high-force exercises potentiates more motor unit recruitment for the speed exercises)
- **Set configuration**
- **Volume:**
  - Frequency (how often)
  - Number of sets
- **Intensity:**
  - Exercise intensity (some exercises are more intense than others!)
  - How many repetitions
  - Work: rest intervals
    - Within sets
    - Within sessions
    - Within days
    - Between days

The training cycles outlined on the next few pages allow a coach to define the optimal sequence for training emphasis at differing points of the year, so as to maximise potential for competitive performances (a concept known as peaking). The annual plan helps the coach to define the times at which they would like the athlete's performance to peak.

This is achieved by the manipulation of training variables in order to achieve the maximum potential during competitive performances. The number of target competitive peaks in a year depends on the sport, the individual's training age and the individual's competitive schedule. Some sports may require one macrocycle (single peak), for example, to achieve at national or world championships. Others, such as track athletes competing in the indoor and outdoor seasons, may require two macrocycles in an annual plan. These peaks need to be sufficiently far apart to allow the athlete to achieve both.

Conversely, the team-sport performer must try to perform at peak, for a number of successive weeks, over the extended period of a season. This is achieved by manipulation of the training nature, volume and intensity during the training week, following the principles outlined below:

• Recovery should follow performance.

• Heavy training should be built into the early part of the training week.

• Lighter training loads and non-active training (ie classroom-based activities) should feature towards the end of the week/close to competition.

• Recovery and peaking should take place in preparation for the following weekend competition.

However, the basic principles of peaking must also be adopted during preparation and transition periods and phases.

Macrocycle Design

Typically, macrocycles have been split into periods, which coaches will recognise as 'preparation', 'competition' and 'transition/regeneration/off-season'. Each of these phases is then normally sub-divided into phases, as illustrated in Table 12:

Table 12: The relationship between macrocycles, periods and phases

MACROCYCLE				
Preparation Period		Competition Period		Transition Period
General Preparation	Specific Preparation	Competition Preparation	Competition Performance	Transition Period
The general preparation phase (or early pre-season phase) is a time when general fitness is developed by gradually and progressively increasing the volume (rather than the intensity) of training. This general fitness will permit the athlete to undertake and adapt to the more demanding specific training which follows. Training volume should increase in progressive steps to allow time for recovery, adaptation and overcompensation.	Training during this phase is characterised by increases in both volume and intensity. The training becomes more specific to the athlete's chosen sport/position, with conditioning activities emphasising the energy and neuromuscular systems principally used in the sport. Many overuse and overreaching injuries can occur during this time if the coaches do not closely monitor the training status of the athlete.	Where competition modelling takes place (practice matches, events etc). This is where the training is light enough to allow performances to occur, but the emphasis is still on training and development of performance, and trying things out.	Where tapering of training in order to peak performance happens. The success of the macrocycle plan is determined during this phase with competition results the focus (except in a developing athlete, where the competitive performance is usually more important than competitive outcome and so competition is still part of learning).	The emphasis of this phase is on active rest and recovery. The idea is to take a break from the physical and psychological demands of high-intensity competition and training without losing too much of the conditioning that has taken place through the macrocycle. The aim for the athlete is to come back to the next preparation phase fitter than at the start of the previous one, while still having a break from sports-specific training.

As the training age of the athlete increases, so the ratio of the general preparation phase to the specific preparation phase changes. With increasing training age and experience, the specific preparation phase occupies a greater amount of the preparation period.

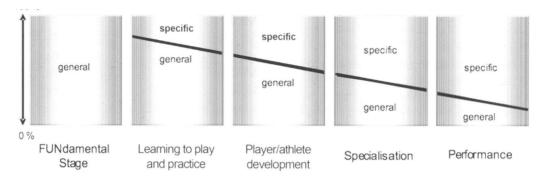

Fig 413: Relative percentages of general and specific preparation periods as the athletes training age increases[*]

In planning, it is very important to always start at the end point and work backwards. There are many examples of top-level coaches whose athletes have got to the period immediately before major events (such as Olympic and Paralympic Games or world cups) and suddenly realised they hadn't done a number of things. Consequently, at times when training should be being tapered (severely lowered volume, maximum intensity), the coaches have asked the athletes to do more, often resulting in poor performances and/or injury. Starting with your final objective and planning backwards is definitely the correct way to plan.

For example: 'If I need to win in August, by July I must have achieved X, Y and Z. This means that, by June, I should have reached U, V and W, so by May I should have done R, S and T'.

While there will be changes as the plan is put into action, at least you will have a structured approach to the objectives and milestones you and your athletes will need to pass along the way.

Training Load

The training load is the combined, interacting effects of the volume, intensity and frequency of training. It is a term used for a particular session and for the cumulative effects of the training programme.

Training Load = Volume + Intensity + Frequency

Volume refers to the work done during training. It is the total of all repetitions, such as, for example, metres or miles for running, kilograms for weight training, the total number of jumps performed, or the total number of minutes played.

[*] Adapted from Thompson, P. (2006) European athletics coaches association conference presentation.

Intensity is the quality of training:

- In speed training it may be the time taken to cover a set distance.
- It may be related to the perceived efforts or heart rates achieved during a training session.
- In plyometric training, it is related to the demands of the nature of the jump (eg depth jumps – jumping down from a height – are much more intense than jumping onto an object).

Intensity	% of athlete's best performance
Supra-maximum	100–105
Maximum	95–100
Sub-maximum	85–94
High	75–84
Medium	65–74
Light	50–64
Low	30–49

- With weight training, intensity is determined by the weight lifted.

If the best an athlete can achieve at this moment in time for any distance, height or weight is 100%, the intensity of training will be a percentage of this best performance.

Frequency simply refers to how many sessions there are within a given time frame (eg a microcycle). This is sometimes referred to as the density of training.

Mesocycle Design

Mesocycles allow for the cumulative effects of training series to be maximally beneficial to the performer, and prevent disturbances to the adaptive training process. The goals for each mesocycle should be cumulative (ie should build on previous goals and contribute to the goals of the following cycle) so the objectives of the overall training plan can be met. Therefore, mesocycles are classified according to their objective (Zatsiorski, 1995).

- **Accumulative**: The objective is to improve basic motor abilities (conditioning) as well as sport technique. Training in this phase is not always sport specific and success is often evaluated according to tests.
- **Transmutative**: The objective is to develop activity-specific fitness and polish specific techniques. Progress is evaluated by performance in simulated competitions.
- **Realisational**: The objective is to put on the best performance attainable within defined parameters of competition.
- **Regenerational**: The objective is to allow the performer a period of active recovery away from sport-specific training and competition stressors, in order to facilitate recovery.

The duration and format of the realisation phases will vary within, as well as between, competitions/games. Tennis players, for example, may have a number of tournaments throughout the year and may frequently play on consecutive days. Typically, the more serious athlete will have a number of discrete accumulative, transmutative, realisational and regenerational mesocycles in the training year. In contrast, team games such as soccer, rugby and hockey will have a much longer, realisational (competition) mesocycle (see Table 13) and may have up to two games a week, but rarely play on consecutive days.

The nature of the competitive phase will determine the periodisation strategy a coach employs. It is important to identify times when training is given priority, competition is given priority and other times when recovery (the importance of which is highlighted in Chapter 9) is prioritised.

Table 13: Generalised example of training plan for a team game

	General Training	Early Pre-season	Late Pre-season	In season	Regeneration
Example Dates	End May to mid-June.	Mid-June to mid-July.	Mid-July to mid-August.	Mid-August to start of May.	First three weeks in May.
Strength and Power					
Objectives	Develop strength base.	Develop power base.	Develop maximal power.	Peaking for the weekend.	Cross training.
Example Methods*	Multi-joint, multi-muscle weight lifting. Sets of 8–10 reps. Combination sets (one rep of 6–7 exercises put together).	Multi-joint, multi-muscle weight lifting. 12–15 sets of five reps. Low-intensity plyometrics.	Multi-joint, multi-muscle weight lifting. 10–14 sets of 3–5 reps. High-intensity, multi-directional plyometrics.	Multi-joint, multi-muscle weight lifting. 8–12 sets of 3–5 reps. Complex training with multi-directional plyometrics.	Multi-joint, multi-muscle weight lifting. 10–15 sets of 10 reps. Eccentric lifts. Upper- and lower-body split routines.
Endurance					
Objectives	Develop base-line endurance.	Develop tolerance for high-intensity activity.	Match-intensity metabolic conditioning (anaerobic endurance).	Peaking for the weekend.	Cross training.
Example Methods**	300–400m intervals. Rowing ergometer.	Lactate generation activities: work:rest ratio of 1:5 Short interval training 50–100m sprints.	Sport-specific practices work:rest ratio of 1:3 to 1:1 Should include all fatiguing elements of the sport (contact, getting off the floor, jumping, running, etc).	Match-intensity drills. 10–50m intervals with sport-specific work periods (eg 30–90 seconds duration) with 1:3 to 1:1 work:rest ratio. Fitness integrated into technical and tactical coaching sessions.	Low-intensity activities that avoid impact loading and sport-specific training demands. Examples: water-based activities and cycling.
Speed and Agility*					
Objectives	Speed technique work.	Develop maximal speed.	Acceleration and agility work.	Peaking for the weekend.	Cross training.
Example Methods***	Technique drills. Stride length. Stride frequency.	Top-speed drills. Gear-change sprints.	Acceleration drills. Resisted and assisted running reaction drills. Sport-specific movement-pattern drills.	Agility drills integrated into warm-ups and technical practices. Complex drills.	Reaction drills. Neuromuscular firing activities. Non-sport-specific practices.

* Refer to Chapters 4 and 5   ** Refer to Chapter 3   *** Refer to Chapter 6

Mesocycles allow the coach to design a programme reflecting the fact that the development of some athletic abilities is considered a prerequisite to others. Training for many sports is multifaceted and requires the development of many training systems. For example, canoeing requires canoeing, running, swimming, weight training and skiing, and specific performance aspects have to be emphasised during certain periods while others are simultaneously stabilised or maintained.

Emphasising one training element over another is part of the practice of conjugative succession of training mesocycles. An old Hungarian saying expresses this in a slightly different manner: 'With one bum you can not sit on two horses!'. This is because the effects of certain types of training can interfere with each other. For example, strength/power training combined with aerobic training can result in no effect at all or a slightly positive effect on aerobic endurance, provided there is little gain in body mass. However, the same combination of training methods (strength/power and aerobic training) can also result in attenuated gains in strength, speed and, particularly, in power. This is because the different types of training target different energy systems and different muscle fibres (Stone and Plisk, 2003). Similarly, performers will not be able to improve their speed if they are fatigued from other training methods. This also applies to plyometric training, not only will tired performers not be able to develop the necessary power to perform these exercises, but they could get injured by the high intensity of the training if they are not sufficiently recovered. Therefore, it is important the coach puts the right training emphasis into the mesocycle at the right time. In the build up to competition, technical and tactical preparation must take up the majority of the coaching time, meaning the mesocycles before this should emphasise the fitness development of the performer. Perhaps 80–90% of physical preparation should be done prior to the competitive phase. The process of manipulating training emphasis in response to desired objectives in a cumulative building process is known as the 'summative sequencing of training cycles'.

Mesocycles allow the coach to investigate the most effective training methods for inducing peak performance, as each stage requires the athlete to achieve a minor performance peak. With the change in emphasis of each session, mesocycles become as motivational to the performer and the coach, as they allow interest to be maintained. The coach should also recognise that competition, playing and training are highly intensive and can not be maintained at a high level throughout the year. Such training has a strong component of stress, both physically and psychologically.

Phases of stressful activities should be interspersed with periods of recovery and regeneration, during which times the athletes are exposed to less pressure. Some of the more traditionally recognised methods used to design mesocycles can be seen below:

- **Traditional wave theory**: Gradual manipulation of training volume and intensity.

- **Step periodisation**: Abrupt changes in volume and intensity, interspersed with periods of regeneration.

- **Skill–strength periodisation**: Educational phase spent perfecting technical/movement skills before embarking on the development of speed, strength etc.

- **Emphasis periodisation** (concentration of loading): Each micro-/mesocycle has a specific emphasis, which acts as a foundation for the following training period.

All theories are emergent from the same starting point, which is the needs analysis of the individual athlete or team. The key dates in the programme structure relate to the competitive objectives of the programme, as determined by the coach and the athlete. However, these theories have predominantly been justified by anecdotal evidence, rather than researched fact, largely due to the logistical problems of undertaking such studies.

Microcycle Design

Microcycles are training blocks of between 4–8 days, although in most game-based sports these are based around seven days. Although general training can be planned for a competitive year (as in Table 13), detailed training planning should only be done 1–3 weeks in advance. This is because training and competition can be interrupted by factors such as injury, suspension etc. This also allows for coaches to evaluate their training methods, look at what is getting results and manipulate subsequent training sessions accordingly.

Training microcycles (and, in the longer term, mesocycles) should all be designed to follow the principles of training[33] and the overcompensation cycle (outlined in Chapter 1). This model is central to the idea of peaking, demonstrating it is only through recovering appropriately from training sessions that the athletic potential of an athlete can actually improve.

When considering the overcompensation model at an individual level, it can be seen that one training stimulus will have different effects upon different individuals, depending upon the training status of those concerned.

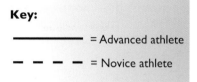

The advanced athlete is hardly fatigued by the training session, therefore recovery is very quick, but there is not much evidence of overcompensation (improvement) occurring. This session may be good immediately before competition for this athlete.

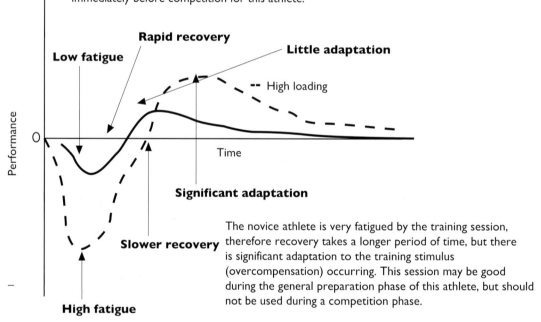

The novice athlete is very fatigued by the training session, therefore recovery takes a longer period of time, but there is significant adaptation to the training stimulus (overcompensation) occurring. This session may be good during the general preparation phase of this athlete, but should not be used during a competition phase.

Figure 413: The overcompensation cycle of a novice and advanced athlete both given the same training stimulus

Similarly, as athletes adapt to a training stimulus, they will get used to that stimulus over time. Therefore, the training needs to be progressively increased (either in terms of volume, intensity or frequency) in order to continuously overload the athlete and continue to cause significant adaptation (improvement – see Figure 414).

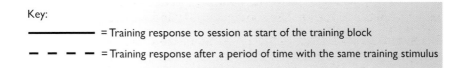

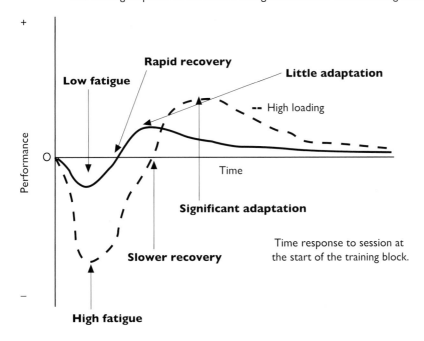

Figure 414: An individual's response to the same training load at different times in a training block

This is a theoretical model and there are no hard and fast rules for how long each individual will take to reach the point of overcompensation after a specific session. This depends on the nature of the training session and the fitness levels of the individual athlete concerned – it can take the neuromuscular system up to 12–36 hours to fully recover from some very intense plyometrics sessions, whereas the aerobic and anaerobic metabolic systems may be recovered within hours from most sessions. What is certain is time to achieve overcompensation can be accelerated by facilitated recovery training/activities. The sooner an athlete recovers from fatigue, the fresher they will be for training and the better the chances of improving. Indeed, the ability of the athlete to recover from heavy training may be a good indicator for coaches to use as a measure of the success of their training programme. It should also be borne in mind that, while the overcompensation model was originally thought of as a physiological model, it also applies to other performance variables, such as psychology. Reduced psychological drive is very much a direct result (not a side-effect) of fatigue.

It is important to realise performers can not progress if they are training at very heavy loads all of the time. Therefore, it is important a coach varies the workload a performer is subjected to between microcycles, as well as within them – this is particularly important in the preparation phases. This enables an athlete to experience progressively increased training loads, interspersed with periods of recovery. In a developmental athlete who is getting used to progressively increased training loads, this sequence of microcycles might look like the sequence demonstrated in Figure 415.

In a more advanced performer, the very heavy training loads may come at the start of the four-week training cycle, when the individual (or team) is able to train with more intensity in a more recovered state. The sequencing of very heavy weeks can be manipulated according to the needs of the programme, although it is recommended that a very heavy training week is always preceded by a medium- to light-intensity training load (Figure 416).

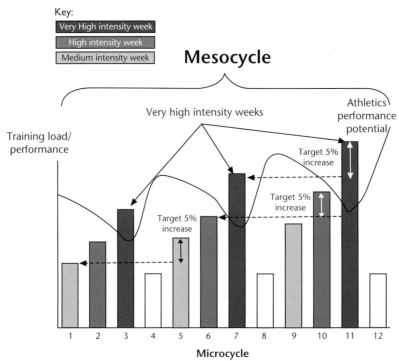

Figure 415: Examples of the manipulation of training loads between weeks in a developmental performer

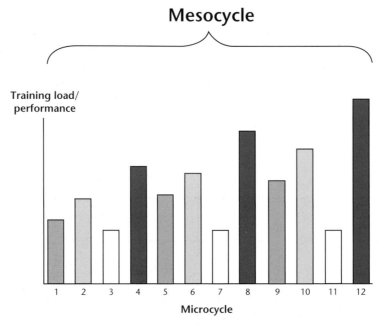

Figure 416: Examples of the manipulation of training loads between weeks in an experienced performer

It is important the training loads incorporate both the volume and the intensity of the work when determining the planning of a group of sessions. Training load = intensity x volume (no. of sessions x no. of sets x no. of reps). For example, in strength training terms, this may mean: kgs lifted x (sets x reps).

When a coach is trying to increase the training background of the athlete (developmental conditioning, or during a preparation period), the manipulation in training load could be achieved by manipulating the intensity at which the athlete lifts, but keeping the volume of work continuous. For example, in a strength-training programme for a developmental judo athlete (17 years old), the following programme might be applied during a preparation phase.

Table 14: Strength-training programme for a developmental judo athlete

Session 1: Objective – strength

Exercise	Sets	Reps per set	Reps per session	Load lifted every set (this varies as a % of estimated 1RM, see Table 17)	Recovery between sets
Squats	3	5	15	Estimated 1RM = 130kg	5 minutes
Bent over row	3	5	15	Estimated 1RM = 80kg	3 minutes
Push press	3	5	15	Estimated 1RM = 60kg	5 minutes
Stiff-leg deadlift	3	5	15	Estimated 1RM = 60kg	3 minutes
Pull-ups	3	10	30	–	2 minutes
Total:	15		90		

Table 15: Strength-speed programme for a developmental judo athlete

Session 2: Objective – strength-speed

Exercise	Sets	Reps per set	Reps per session	Load lifted every set (this varies as a % of estimated 1 RM)	Recovery between sets
Clean pull from thigh	3	5	15	Estimated 1RM = 120kg	4 minutes
Clean	3	5	15	Estimated 1RM = 80kg	6 minutes
Dumb-bell pull-over	3	5	15	Estimated 1RM = 35kg	3 minutes
Dumb-bell shoulder press	3	5	15	Estimated 1RM = 20kg	3 minutes
Barbell roll-outs	3	10	30	–	2 minutes
Total:	15		90		

Table 16: Speed-strength-training programme for a developmental judo athlete

Session 3: Objective – speed-strength

Exercise	Sets	Reps per set	Reps per session	Load lifted every set (this varies as a % of estimated 1RM)	Recovery between sets
Snatch	3	5	15	Estimated 1RM = 70kg	5 minutes
Round the clock lunges with bar behind the neck	3	5	15	Estimated 1RM = 50kg	4 minutes
Split jerk	3	5	15	Estimated 1RM = 60kg	5 minutes
Shrugs	3	5	15	Estimated 1RM = 100kg	3 minutes
Vertical leg shoots	3	10	30	–	2 minutes
Total:	15		90		

Total sets per week = 3 (sessions) x 5 (exercises) x 3 (sets per exercise) = 45 sets

Total reps per week = 270

The volume/load to be lifted will be varied according to whether the week is a very heavy, heavy, medium-heavy or medium training week.

Table 17: Calculating volume load is essential to understanding programme progression

Training Load	Total no. of sets (sessions per week x exercises per session x sets per exercise)	Total no. of reps (total sets x reps per set)	Load lifted every set (this varies as a % of estimated 1RM)	Training Load each week (exercise x sets x reps x kgs lifted)
Medium	45	270	70%	9080
Medium-heavy	45	270	75%	9730
Heavy	45	270	80%	10380
Very heavy	45	270	85%	11030

This indicates that the volume is constant but, on very heavy weeks, the intensity is highest and, on medium weeks, the intensity is lowest.

However, in a training programme where the objective is to be able to develop maximum strength, or when an athlete is tapering volume in order to peak intensity for a given performance, the training volume can not remain constant, as truly maximal loads can only be completed when the athlete is relatively fresh. This means volume must also be reduced and, therefore, the total number of sessions, exercises, sets and reps must be considered.

If we follow this through with our judo athlete (above), after their training age has advanced and they are in a competition preparation phase, or a competition phase involving a taper (when maximum performance is anticipated),now, training load (not intensity) will determine whether a week is characterised as being very heavy, heavy, medium-heavy or medium. This is indicated in Figure 417, where volume is highest and intensity is lowest but, when intensity is really high, the volume (eg total number of reps in a microcycle) is very low, allowing maximum performance (expression of power) in this week.

Another example of an annual plan for an individual athlete, which includes examples of where manipulation of training load is applied, can be seen in Figure 418.

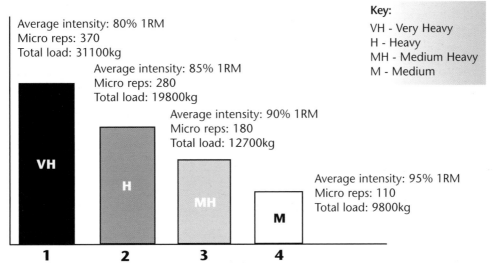

Key:
VH - Very Heavy
H - Heavy
MH - Medium Heavy
M - Medium

Average intensity: 80% 1RM
Micro reps: 370
Total load: 31100kg

Average intensity: 85% 1RM
Micro reps: 280
Total load: 19800kg

Average intensity: 90% 1RM
Micro reps: 180
Total load: 12700kg

Average intensity: 95% 1RM
Micro reps: 110
Total load: 9800kg

VH   H   MH   M

1   2   3   4

Figure 417: Training programme progression through reduction of volume load to maximise training intensity

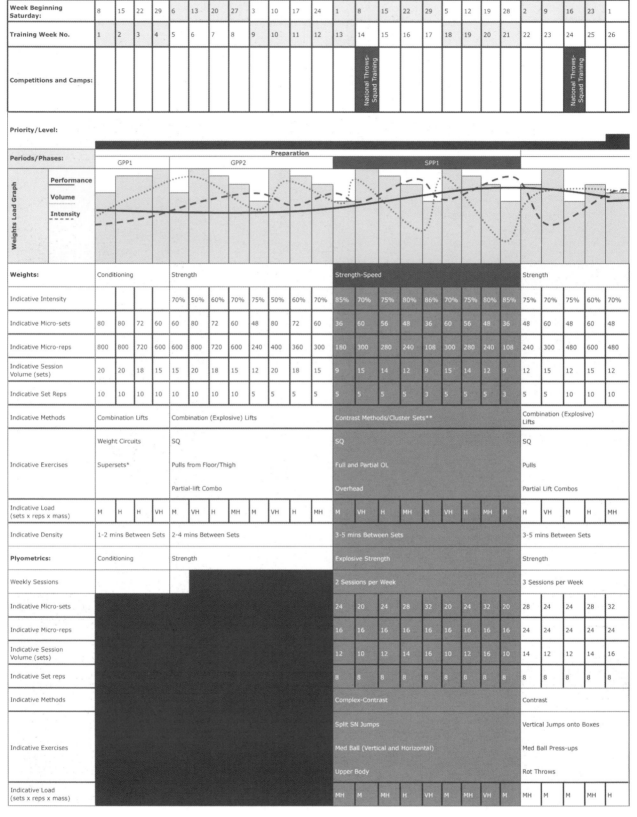

* Supersets: Alternating from one exercise to another.

** Cluster Sets: Having a small break during a set of reps, for example in a five-rep set, performing two reps, having a break then performing the other three reps.

Figure 418: Annual planning for an individual athlete: An example of a hammer thrower aiming to win the Scottish National and GB National championships with training load manipulation during the macrocycle

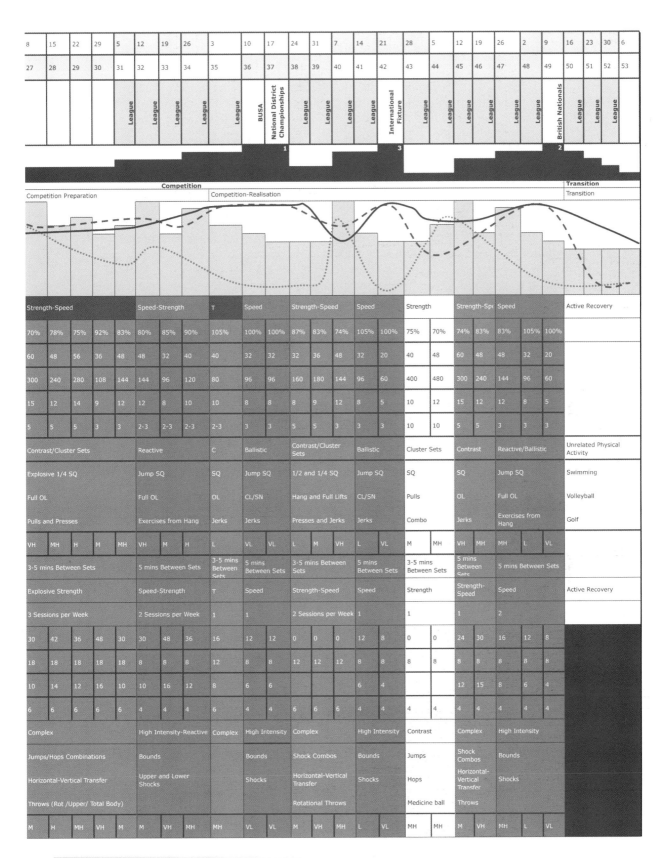

Key:

C = Competition
CL = Clean
GPP1 = General Preparation Phase
GPP2 = General Preparation Phase 2
H = Heavy Training Load
L = Light Training Load
M = Medium Training Load
MH = Medium-Heavy Training Load

OL = Olympic Lift
Rot = Rotational Throws
SN = Snatch
SPP1 = Specific Preparation Phase 1
SQ = Squat
T = Transition
VH = Very Heavy Training Load
VL = Very Light Training Load

The Volume-intensity and Training Mix Debate

Much contemporary debate can be seen to compare what the literature refers to as linear and non-linear periodisation. This debate is about whether a coach should plan in terms of preparation, competition and transition, or whether there should be a different (non-linear) approach. This is really an academic debate, as, in essence, all periodisation is non-linear, due to the constant manipulations of the volume and training load, as described previously. What is clear though is that, whatever it is called, sound planning that is evidentially based and which enables a coach to put in place a series of prerequisite stages (ie if I want to achieve x, I must have done a, b, c, d etc) is essential to achieve real gains in performance.

The consideration given to training load should not just apply to physical conditioning sessions however, but all sessions. If the athlete has a high-volume load (constant volume, high intensity) week in terms of conditioning, then having a high-volume load in terms of technical/tactical aspects of training may severely overload the athlete. Conversely, having a low-volume load for technical/tactical training when the load for physical conditioning is highest, and a low physical-conditioning-volume load when the technical/tactical aspects of training have the highest volume, means the athlete never gets a recovery week and work volumes are always high. Either of these problems may lead to athlete burnout and/or an increased chance of injury.

Practical solutions to this dilemma may include reducing the volume of technical/tactical training but maximising the intensity, when physical conditioning volume loads are high and vice versa. This reduces the overall total training load but enables maximum intensity work all to be done at the same time. Alternatively, the sequences of work can be manipulated to ensure there is always a regular recovery week occurring in the training mix.

Table 18: An illustration of how volume load between different training types can be planned.

	Week 1	Week 2	Week 3	Week 4
Physical conditioning volume load	Heavy	Medium	Very heavy	Light
Technical/tactical volume load	Medium	Very heavy	Heavy	Light
Overall description of physical demand on the athlete	Medium-heavy	Heavy	Very heavy	Light

Unfortunately, illustrating these principles on paper is easy, undertaking them in practice as a coach is very difficult and demanding. This becomes more important the higher up the coaching pathway the coach moves, as more complex demands become based upon the planning principles to ensure a balanced approach to an effective programme.

Remember, with practice, experience and applying scientifically sound principles, an evidence-based approach to practicing the **art** of coaching (it isn't always an exact science) becomes easier!

Tapering

Tapering is the reduction in training volume (though not necessarily intensity) achieved by decreasing the physical and psychological stressors to the body as the competition period gets closer. Intensity should be maintained, as athletes need to be able to cope with the demands of competition and these demands, therefore, need to be maintained within training. However, simply reducing the number of repetitions or total training time the athlete is exposed to can reduce the training load.

In team games, tapering might involve doing very intense and physical training sessions at the start of the week, then doing some very intense (short duration) technical and tactical practices towards the end of the week. This might be followed by some recovery sessions or by replacing physical training sessions with non-physical ones, such as tactical discussions or performance planning. This tapering of the training load should allow the athlete to go into competition feeling fresh and totally prepared for the competition that follows.

The Training Unit

Microcycles are made up of training sessions, which in turn are made up of training units. A training unit is an individual session in pursuit of a specific training objective, within which rest periods are not longer than 30 minutes of a session. There can be a number of training units in a day or indeed within a session (depending on the performance level of the athlete). This is influenced by the *intra-unit* ratio. This is the loading:recovery ratio within an individual training unit. Sessions with larger training loads need to have a small intra-unit ratio. Similarly, a training session immediately before competition may have a large loading:recovery ratio (ie some very small periods of intense activity followed by longer periods of recovery).

Summary

- Training plans can be designed for between 1–4 years at a time, with detailed planning occurring up to four weeks in advance.

- The goals of a training session build into those for the week, month, season and training year.

- Periodisation is the process that involves building a training series into a planned sequence that will allow the athlete to achieve optimal performances at key competitions or matches in the season. Identifying and planning for target competitions for a given performer or squad is the starting point for designing any periodised programme regardless of the level of peformer a coach is working with.

© Action Images/Reuters

Figure 420: Optimum performances are the result of effective planning that incorporates optimal training and optimal recovery and adaptation

The building blocks for a periodised programme are the macrocycle (the competitive objective and the sum total of training for that objective), the mesocycle (blocks of a 4–8-week duration, each with a particular objective), the microcycle (usually a training week) and the training session (each individual session should have a specific objective).

- Undertaking a needs analysis of the individual athlete or team will enable a coach to determine what an athlete or team needs to do in order to achieve peak performance in a target competition.

- When undertaking the planning process, the first things to identify are the needs required to peak at the time of the target competition and to work backwards from that particular point. This enables a series of prerequisite objectives to be identified, against which the best methods to achieve these objectives can be matched.

- The foundation theories underpinning periodisation principles have been predominantly justified by anecdotal evidence, rather than researched fact and, therefore, the theories are there to be challenged by creative and innovative coaches.

References

Bompa, T. (1999) *Periodization: Theory and Methodology of Training*. Illinois: Human Kinetics. ISBN: 978-0-880118-51-4.

Plisk, S. and Stone, M.H. (2003) 'Periodisation strategies', *Strength and Conditioning Journal,* 17: 19–37.

Thompson, P (2006) 'Endurance training in the developing athlete' European Athletics Coaching Conference, Nov 2007, Dublin

Zatsiorsky, V.M. (1995) *Science and Practice of Strength Training*. Illinois: Human Kinetics. ISBN: 978-0-873224-74-1.

Notes

1. *Biceps brachii* – Two-headed muscle located on the upper arm.

2. *Triceps brachii* – Three-headed muscle located on the upper arm.

3. The *quadriceps* group comprises the *rectus femoris, vastus medialis, vastus lateralis* and *vastus intermedius.*

4. The *hamstring* group comprises the *semimembranosis, semitendinosis* and *biceps femoris.*

5. Creatine-phosphate system – energy supply for high-intensity activities lasting 3–10 seconds.

6. Low-intensity exercise is a relative term and depends upon the training state of the individuals concerned.

7. Typically, the point at which the oxygen supply becomes insufficient occurs at intensities somewhere between 70% and 80% of maximum, depending upon the training status of the athlete.

8. Remember that all energy systems work simultaneously.

9. VO_2 max is the maximum ability to consume oxygen for energy production, while breathing air at sea level.

10. Agility – changes of direction with maximal efficiency and minimum disruption to velocity.

11. In some sports, such as tennis, acceleration is the most vital component in this equation. In others, such as rugby union, the strength component is arguably the most vital characteristic.

12. Court surface and its effect on the bounce have implications for the body position when playing shots; something that should be reflected in the training movements used in conditioning, as illustrated in Chapter 4.

13. A threshold value for working anaerobically is usually accepted as four millimoles.

14. Running on a grass park or sandy beach is much harder on the muscles, but great for developing proprioception – internal sense of body position – in the muscles.

15. A similar variation of this exercise can be adopted by the coach, to the same end.

16. SMARTER – specific, measurable, achievable, relevant, time related, exciting, recorded.

17. It is recognised that repeated 180° turns are not part of the game of rugby.

18. Courtesy of Stone, M. (2004) from the sportscotland National Strength and Conditioning Conference. Adapted from Häkkinen and Komi (1985) in the Scandinavian Journal of Sports Science 7(2): 55–64 and 65–76.

19. Kinesiology is the study of joint and muscle actions in movement.

20. Closed-kinetic-chain exercises are when the body has a point in contact with the ground.

21. Countermovements are movements in one direction followed by movement in the opposite direction, thus initiating the all-important plyometrics (ie stretch shortening) reflex response for optimum power development.

22. For more information on this, the coach is recommended to follow the protocols and accreditation procedures recommended by the United Kingdom Strength and Conditioning Association (see Useful Contacts section, page 183).

23. The principles relating to the major steps of the lift are: head up, chest high, shoulder blades pulled back, normally straight back, trunk and gluteal musculature pulled tight and knees moving along the same line as the toes.

24. At certain times, it is important to get the balance right between lifting heavy and lifting explosively.

25. The athlete should be able to see the big toe on the inside of the knee as it is bent into the squat position upon landing.

26. Correct sprinting technique: the body mechanics that result in the best combination of stride length and stride frequency for producing maximum sprinting velocity in a given instance.

27. A reaction ball is a rubber ball with angled, uneven surfaces to produce unpredictable bounce direction.

28. Training too hard is overdoing the intensity rather than the effort. This is known as acute over-reaching and can be associated with an injury to the musculoskeletal system.

29. DOMS is a common phenomenon experienced by many who have been in sport for any great length of time.

30. A serious competitor is recommended to get no more than between seven and nine hours' sleep a night.

31. The Likert scale poses a question and elicits a response on a scale, such as Strongly Agree – Agree – Undecided – Disagree – Strongly Disagree.

32. Pain has a protective purpose in limiting physical activity on any injury site.

33. The principles of training are: progression, overload, specificity, recovery and reversibility.

Bibliography

Alter, M.J. (2005) *Sport Stretch*. Illinois: Human Kinetics. ISBN: 978-0-880118-23-1.

Baechle, T. and Earle, R. (eds) (2000) *Essentials of Strength Training and Conditioning*. Illinois: Human Kinetics. ISBN: 978-0-736000-89-5.

Balyi, I. (2003) 'Windows of training opportunity', paper presented at **sport**scotland at the National Strength and Conditioning Conference, May 2003.

Bean, A. (2003) *The Complete Guide to Sports Nutrition*. London: A and C Black. ISBN: 978-0-713675-58-0.*

Bompa, T. (1999) *Periodization: Theory and Methodology of Training*. Illinois: Human Kinetics. ISBN: 978-0-880118-51-4.

Brewer, C., Favre, M. and Low, L. (2005) 'Weight lifting for sports specific benefits', http://www.coachesinfo.com/category/strength_and_conditioning/

Brewer, C. and Stone, M.H. (2005) 'Coaching the double knee bend', http://www.coachesinfo.com/category/strength_and_conditioning/

Brown, L., Ferrigno, V. and Santana, J. C. (2000) *Training for Speed, Agility and Quickness*. Illinois: Human Kinetics. ISBN: 978-0-736058-73-5.*

Byrd, R., Baker, C., Pierce, K. and Brady, J. (2004) 'Young weightlifters' performance across time', http://www.coachesinfo.com/category/strength_and_conditioning/245

Christmass, M.A., Richmond, S.E., Cable, N.T. and Hartmann, P.E. (1995) 'A metabolic characterisation of singles tennis', in *Science and Racket Sports II* (1998) Lees, A., Maynard, I., Hughes, M. and Reilly, T. (eds). London: E. and F. N. Spon. ISBN: 978-0-419230-30-4.

Chu, D.A. (1996) *Explosive Power and Strength*: *Complex Training for Maximal Results*. Illinois: Human Kinetics. ISBN: 978-0-873226-43-1.

Coachwise 1st4sport (2001) Speed Training Drills video. Leeds: Coachwise 1st4sport.*

Crosland, J. (2005) *Fuelling Performers*. Leeds: Coachwise Business Solutions/The National Coaching Foundation. ISBN: 978-1-902523-23-1.*

Collins, D., Brewer, C. and Martindale, R. (2007) 'Towards a new model for athlete development' sports coach UK Seminar on athlete development', Leeds, January 2007.

Elliott, B., Dawson, B. and Pyke, F. (1985) 'The ergogenics of singles tennis', *Journal of Human Movement Studies* 11: 11–20.

Farrally, M. (2003) *An Introduction to the Structure of the Body*. Leeds: Coachwise Business Solutions/The National Coaching Foundation. ISBN: 978-1-850601-69-0.*

Farrally, M. (2005) *An Introduction to Sports Physiology*. Leeds: Coachwise Business Solutions/The National Coaching Foundation. ISBN: 978-0-947850-96-8.*

Fleck, S.J. and Kraemer, W.J. (1997) *Designing Resistance Training Programmes.* Illinois: Human Kinetics. ISBN: 978-0-873225-08-3.

Galvin, B. and Ledger, P. (1998) *A Guide to Planning Coaching Programmes*. Leeds: Coachwise Solutions/The National Coaching Foundation. ISBN: 978-1-902523-00-2.*

International Tennis Federation (2000). *Rules of Tennis*. London: ITF Ltd.

Meir, R., Colla, P. and Milligan, C. (2001) 'Impact of the 10-meter rule change on professional rugby league: implications for training,' in *Strength and Conditioning Journal 23* (6): 42–6.

Pearson, A. (2003) *Dynamic Flexibility*. A and C Black. ISBN: 978-0-713664-52-2.*

Pearson, A. and Hawkins, D. (2005) *SAQ Youth*. A and C Black. ISBN: 978-0713670-42-4.*
Plisk, S. and Stone, M.H. (2003) 'Periodisation strategies', *Strength and Conditioning Journal* 17: 19–37.

Reilly, T. and Palmer, J. (1995) 'Investigation of exercise intensity in male tennis single/lawn tennis' in *Science and Racket Sports II*, Lees, A., Maynard, I., Hughes, M. and Reilly, T. (eds). London: E. and F. N. Spon. ISBN: 978-0-419230-30-4.

Siff, M. (2003) *Supertraining*. Supertraining Institute. ISBN: 978-1874856-65-8.

Stafford, I. (2004) *Coaching for Long-term Athlete Development*. Leeds: Coachwise Business Solutions/The National Coaching Foundation. ISBN: 978-1-902523-70-9*

Stone, M.H. (1990) 'Muscle conditioning and muscle injuries', *Medicine and Science in Sport and Exercise*. 22 (4): 457–62.

Stone, M.H. (2000) 'Explosive exercise and training', *National Strength and Conditioning Association Journal*, 15 (3): 7–15.

Stone, M.H. (2002) 'How strong is strong enough?', http://www.coachesinfo.com/article/index.php?id=246andstyle=printable

Stone, M.H. (2005) 'The use of weightlifting pulling movements in sports', paper presented at The UK Strength and Conditioning Association Conference, Loughborough, May 2005.

Thompson, C.W. and Floyd, R.T. (eds) (2003) *Manual of Structural Kinesiology*. New York: McGraw-Hill Education. ISBN: 978-0-072558-91-3.

Zatsiorsky, V.M. (1995) *Science and Practice of Strength Training*. Illinois: Human Kinetics. ISBN: 978-0-873224-74-1.

* Available from **Coachwise 1st4sport**. For a full range of sports education and training equipment, please visit www.1st4sport.com or call 0113-201 5555.

Glossary

Acceleration: Time between starting a movement and reaching top speed.

Adipose tissue: Tissue adapted to store lipids (fats) as high-density energy storage.

Aerobic: With oxygen. For example, aerobic endurance – the ability to sustain performance-producing energy using oxygen.

Agility: The ability to change direction or body position with the maximum efficiency.

All-or-nothing principle: Motor units in muscle contraction are either activated or they are not.

Anaerobic: Without oxygen.

Antagonistic muscles: Muscles located so as to oppose a prime mover (agonist) for a given movement.

Ballistic stretches: Forceful, explosive stretching movements that utilise momentum and velocity to increase the range of movement.

Bioenergetics: The process of energy production to fuel work done by the body.

Bracing the trunk musculature: Contracting all muscles in the abdominal wall without drawing in or pushing out. However, it does not imply enormous contraction levels in these muscles.

Burn-out: A negative/damaged physical or psychological state experienced by an athlete who has been overexposed to training and competition stimuli without due recovery. Often associated with injury, overtraining and unexplained underperformance.

Closed-kinetic-chain exercises: Exercises whereby the body has a point in contact with the ground.

Cognitive: Using mental action or acquiring knowledge through thought, experience and the senses.

Complex training: Using heavy resistance training (typically 95% 1RM) to recruit more motor units and then following a rest of 2–3mins, performing an explosive plyometric exercise that is very similar in nature.

Concentric-muscle actions: When one or both myotendinous ends of the muscle (ie the tendon joining muscle to bone) move towards each other and the muscle is shortened during the contraction.

Contrast training: Using a restraint in a number of repetitions of an explosive activity (such as a heavy weight or a bungee cord resistance to a sprint or jump movement) to recruit more motor units than performing the same activity unrestrained, to provoke a more explosive response.

Credit-card rule: The gap left between the heel and the floor upon correct flat foot landing, should allow a credit card to be slipped between.

Dorsiflexion: Pulling the toes towards the knees.

Dynamic stretching: Increasing the range of movement around a joint through movement-based exercises (movement stretching as opposed to static stretching).

Eccentric-muscle action: When the muscle is actively lengthened while contracted. A muscle can only be lengthened by a greater opposing force, as it can not actively lengthen by itself.

Enzymatic reactions: Enzymes are proteins that accelerate the rate of certain biochemical reactions. They are not changed or spent in the reaction. The concentration of specific enzymes involved in the production of ATP influences the bodies ability to perform well in tasks of different intensities.

Extension: Increasing the inner angle of a joint.

Flexion: Decreasing the inner angle of a joint.

Glycolysis: The process of breaking down glycogen or glucose into pyruvate, when it will either be reduced to hydrogen and lactate (fast glycolysis) or, in the presence of oxygen, be taken into the mitochondria to produce ATP (slow or aerobic glycolysis).

Hyperextension: A greater-than-normal extension in a joint or series of joints.

Hyperflexion: A greater-than-normal flexion in a joint.

Intra-unit ratio: The loading:recovery ratio within an individual training unit.

Isometric-muscle actions: *Iso* – same, *metric* – length. A type of contraction whereby the force generated by the muscle is equal to the resistive mass opposing it and so the muscle remains the same length while contracting.

Kinesiology: The study of joint and muscle actions in movement.

Lactate: The end product of fast glycolysis, often mistaken for a toxin but actually a fuel source for slow-twitch muscle fibre and the preferred fuel for cardiac (heart) muscle.

Lactate tolerance: Popular term relating to the ability of the muscle fibres to maintain contractions and enzyme reactions in an acidic environment, caused by a build-up of lactate and hydrogen ions after anaerobic exercise.

Macrocycle: Usually an annual plan of repeated (yet modified) cycles in the long-term training plan (periodisation).

Mesocycle: A 3–6-week block of training within the long-term training plan (periodisation).

Microcycle: Usually these consist of one-week training blocks, within the long-term training plan (periodisation).

Millimoles: A thousandth of a mole. A mole is the standard unit for an amount of a substance expressed as its molecular weight (in grams).

Mitochondria: The powerhouses of the cell. Their major responsibility is to produce energy (ATP), in the presence of oxygen, to power muscle contractions.

Movement time: Time from the beginning of movement to its completion.

Neuromuscular: The system of the body that is made up of the skeletal muscles that perform work and the nerves that innervate these muscles.

Overcompensation cycle: The theoretical model of training–fatigue–recovery that underpins training-programme structure.

Oxidative phosphorylation: A metabolic process within the mitochondria, which removes hydrogen from transport substances to produce ATP in the presence of oxygen.

Peaking: The manipulation of training variables in order to ensure optimal readiness for competitive performance.

Periodisation: A planned training schedule of a year's duration, made up of periods or cycles that are often of differing durations, ie macrocycles, mesocycles, microcycles and training units.

Plyometric: Specialist bounding and rebounding exercises that utilise the stretch–shortening cycle to enable a muscle to reach maximum force production in minimum time.

Postural control: Maintaining control of the spine, pelvic and shoulder girdles in relation to the head, knees and ankles.

Prime movers (agonist): Muscles that are responsible for the initiation of a particular movement.

Pronate: Inward rotation of a joint.

Proprioception: Internal sensory mechanisms that informs the athlete where all the components of the body are, in relation to each other, at any one time.

Range of movement (ROM): The degree of movement available around a joint or a series of joints in the body – the key component of flexibility.

Reaction time: Time taken to detect and respond to a stimulus.

Repetition maximum (RM): The maximum number of repetitions that can be completed with a given load or the given load for a number of repetitions.

Size principle of motor-unit recruitment: Recruitment sequence of Type I, IIa and IIx fibres in response to the resistive load.

Stabiliser muscles: Muscles working in opposition in any given movement often act as stabilising agents.

Static stretching: A form of stretching in which a position is held for a given duration (usually 6–60 seconds).

Stretching: The training method that enables flexibility (range of movement) to be developed.

Stretch–shortening cycle: Reflex concentric muscle contraction caused by the stretch receptor in the muscle fibre detecting the fibre being stretched forcefully.

Synergistic muscles: Muscles that can indirectly assist the prime movers.

Tapering: A reduction in training volume (not intensity) as competition approaches, in order to enable peaking to occur.

Top speed: Maximum running speed in an athlete, reached after about 25m of movement.

Type I fibres: Slow-twitch muscle fibres.

Type IIa fibres: Fast-twitch intermediate fibres able to work aerobically or anaerobically.

Type IIx fibres: Very explosive fast-twitch anaerobic fibres.

Weight lifting: The use of weightlifting movements (and their derivatives) in training for sports performance.

Weightlifting: A recognised Olympic and Paralympic sport, the objective of which is to perform maximally in the snatch and clean-and-jerk lifts.

Work:rest ratio: Designated time interval between periods of work and recovery.

VO$_2$ max: The maximum ability to consume oxygen (for energy production) while breathing air at sea level.

Useful Contacts

sports coach UK

sports coach UK works closely with sport's governing bodies and other partners to provide a comprehensive service for coaches throughout the UK. This includes an extensive programme of workshops, which have proved valuable to coaches from all types of sports and every level of experience.

For further details of workshops in your area, contact the sports coach UK Workshop Booking Centre:

Post:	Workshop Booking Centre
	Coachwise Ltd
	Chelsea Close
	Off Amberley Road
	Leeds, LS12 4HP
Tel:	0845-601 3054
Email:	scukworkshops@sportscoachuk.org
Website:	www.sportscoachuk.org/improve/workshop/search.asp

For more details about other membership services such as insurance, contact the sports coach UK Headquarters:

Post:	sports coach UK
	114 Cardigan Road
	Headingley
	Leeds LS6 3BJ
Tel:	0113-274 4802
Fax:	0113-275 5019
Email:	coaching@sportscoachuk.org
Website:	www.sportscoachuk.org

UK Strength and Conditioning Association

Post:	1 Woodville Terrace
	Lytham
	Lancashire, FY8 5QB
Tel:	0870-116 1566
Fax:	0870-116 1223
Email:	info@uksca.org.uk
Website:	www.uksca.org.uk

Notes page

Notes page

Notes page

Notes page

Notes page

Notes page

Notes page

Notes page

Notes page

Notes page

Notes page

Notes page

Strength and Conditioning Posters

Topics covered:

- Planning
- Overhead Lifts
- The Snatch
- The Clean
- Squats
- Dynamic Flexibility Exercises
- Static Flexibility Exercises
- Supplementary Exercises
- Plyometrics
- Medicine Ball Plyometrics

Key Features:

- Ideal for any gym, hall or training room
- Laminated for durability
- Full colour photographs used throughout to illustrate techniques
- Complex techniques are shown from two different angles so no detail is missed
- 'Know-how' boxes explain key points and unpack scientific theory
- Helpful graphs used to give a visual representation of the effect of training on athletes
- Developed in conjunction with experts from Britain and at the US Olympic Centre
- Coach and athlete-friendly language

A unique set of 10 x A2 posters, compiled by renowned strength and conditioning expert, Clive Brewer, and covering all major strength and conditioning techniques. Each poster is laminated for durability and arrives neatly packaged in a protective storage tube.

How to Order

Both resources are available from Coachwise 1st4sport. Either telephone 0113-201 5555 (9am-5pm) or visit the website at www.1st4sport.com. Alternatively, fax or post the order form below to us, along with your official purchase order if applicable.

Mission Statement

sports coach UK is dedicated to guiding the development and implementation of a coaching system, recognised as a world leader, for all coaches at every level in the UK.

We will work with our partners to achieve this, by promoting:

- professional and ethical values
- inclusive and equitable practice
- agreed national standards of competence as a benchmark at all levels
- a regulated and licensed structure
- recognition, value and appropriate funding and reward
- a culture and structure of innovation, constant renewal and continuous professional development (CPD).

The sports coach UK mission statement is likely to be reviewed in the context of the UK Coaching Framework.